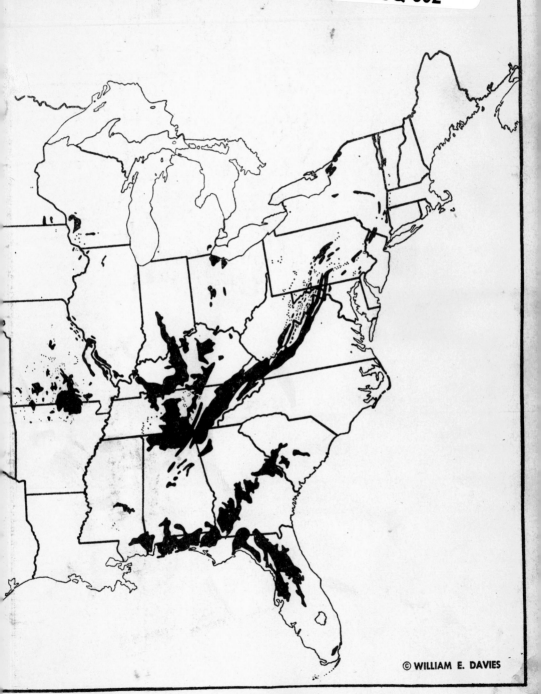

50¢

© WILLIAM E. DAVIES

Exploring American Caves

Exploring American Caves

THEIR HISTORY, GEOLOGY, LORE AND LOCATION: A SPELUNKER'S GUIDE

By FRANKLIN FOLSOM

CROWN PUBLISHERS, INC. • NEW YORK

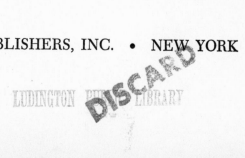

Acknowledgments

So great is my indebtedness to literally hundreds of men and women, living and dead, that it is quite impossible to thank them all adequately. It would be a pleasure to report in detail the unique, courteous and warmly human ways in which help has been offered. The list would range from practical tips given by experienced cavers deep in some cavern to conferences in quiet museums or busy offices, through extended correspondence and long-distance phone calls. And it would fill pages. Space dictates that, except for a few areas of very special indebtedness, my expression of gratitude be limited to a mere nod of recognition to the fact that this book would have been impossible without the unrequited labor of a great many people.

To the National Speleological Society I am indebted for its very existence and for the vast amount of caving and research its members have done and reported in the Society's *Bulletin* and *News*. Specifically I am indebted to the NSS for permission to use and to quote from these publications. This permission has been extended to me by Jerome M. Ludlow, Vice President for Publications, who has in addition been most generously helpful in innumerable ways.

To the Philadelphia Grotto of the NSS I owe thanks for a very special kind of service. At my request the Grotto appointed a committee from among its members—and enlisted the help of other NSS members—to read and check my manuscript with a view to eliminating errors. If errors still persist in the book, the fault lies with my own invincible ignorance and not with the members of the committee. I must add that in no respect are the members of the committee to be held responsible for the material as presented nor for the intrepretations I have placed upon it. A large number of learned and creative suggestions came from committee members, all of whom read at least one chapter and some of whom read the entire

v

manuscript. Working under the very efficient chairmanship of Joseph D. Lawrence, Jr., the following gave help for which I am deeply grateful: M. Girard Bloch, Charles A. Crutchfield, Samuel L. Davis, James A. Fowler, Carl H. Gaum, William S. Hill, George F. Jackson, Norma Jackson, Jerome M. Ludlow, Charles E. Mohr, John Dyas Parker, Ida V. Sawtelle, John L. Spence.

To William E. Davies I owe at least four debts—first for his attention to my communications addressed to him as President of the NSS, second for invaluable information gained from his books and articles about caves, third for his courtesy in allowing me to see a draft copy of his *Abridged Checklist, Bibliography of North American Speleology,* and fourth for permission to base upon a map he prepared the map which appears on the end papers of this book.

To Burton S. Faust, Vice President of the NSS, thanks for permission to consult in my home irreplaceable scrapbooks from the NSS library.

To Albert C. Mueller, Jr., Vice President of the NSS, and his wife Margaret, thanks for personal courtesies and diligent efforts to help me find suitable illustrations for this book.

And thanks to Mrs. Lois B. Cutler, formerly Office Secretary of the NSS, whom I pestered with inquiries.

Before *Celebrated American Caves* was published, Howard N. Sloane, co-editor of the book with Charles E. Mohr, and William Sloane of Rutgers University Press were kind enough to let me read galley proofs. This courtesy made it possible to avoid unnecessary duplication of subject matter which would otherwise have occurred. To the editors and publisher of that unique and valuable book go my thanks.

To Thomas C. Barr, Jr., a speleologist of many talents, I owe thanks for much information, ranging from practical road instructions on how to reach Tennessee caves to data based on first-hand knowledge of the exploration of Higgenbotham Cave (Cumberland Caverns).

My appreciation goes to William J. Stephenson and to his wife, Merle, who gave me my first introduction to caves and cavers in West Virginia, and to the enthusiastic NSS member Robert P. Lipman who at the very outset started me on paths that led to productive research.

A special word of thanks to Dr. George Gaylord Simpson, Curator of Fossil Mammals and Birds, American Museum of Natural History, for telling me the story of jaguars in this country and for directing me to certain of his own scholarly writings about bone caves.

I am further indebted to Roy A. Davis, who generously guided me in Higgenbotham Cave and whose knowledge about the cave he has also made available in correspondence; to Tom Barnes for hospitality on his farm and for information about the early history of Higgenbotham; to Mrs. Jim White for the stories she told me about Jim White and The Kid in Carlsbad Caverns; to Harold Goodro for sending me an account of his descent into Neff's Canyon Cave; to Russell H. Gurnee for his lead to the story about the mysterious medallion and to Jane M. Lape, Curator, Headquarters House, New York State Historical Association, and to Richard Johnson for correspondence and clippings throwing light on this same story; to Raymond Carlson, Editor, *Arizona Highways* for courtesy in connection with information I sought about Colossal Cave; to Julian N. Ticknor, Supervisor, Colossal Cave, Pima County Park, Arizona, for interviewing at my request Frank Schmidt, the only surviving member of the 1922 expedition into the cave; to Phil C. Orr, Director, Western Speleological Institute, for detailed information regarding the activities of the Institute; to John J. Fisher for information about the Underwater Speleological Research Group; to William T. Austin for much information about Floyd Collins' Crystal Cave; to Perry E. Brown, Superintendent, Mammoth Cave National Park, for historical data about Mammoth Cave; to the California Automobile Association for leads to commercial caves I was unable to find elsewhere.

Beyond the writings already mentioned, I owe very specific debts to the work of the following experts: Roger W. Brucker, C. B. Cosgrove, Raymond de Saussure, Malcolm F. Farmer, Dr. M. R. Harrington, Howard W. Hartley, Dr. Frank C. Hibben, George F. Jackson, Joseph D. Lawrence, Jr., Dr. J. C. Merriam, Charles E. Mohr, Brother G. Nicholas, F.S.C., George Olin, John Dyas Parker, Clay Perry.

To the following, thanks for leads to information about caves in their various states: Sam D. Broadhurst, Assistant State Geologist of North Carolina; John J. Broughton, State Geologist of New York;

J. Roy Chapman, Georgia Department of Mines, Mining and Geology; Arthur L. Crawford, Director of the Utah Geological and Mineralogical Survey; Herman Gunter, Director, Florida Geological Survey; Peter Harkins, Director of Publicity and Information Department of Arkansas; Ashley C. Roberts, Director, Montana State Park Commission; E. P. Rothrock, State Geologist of South Dakota; Laurence L. Smith, State Geologist, South Carolina; George A. Thiel, Chairman, Department of Geology and Mineralogy, University of Minnesota; and to Dr. Malcolm Weiss, Department of Geology, Ohio State University, for information about caves in Minnesota.

Thanks to officials and guides of the National Park Service and to owners or managers of the one hundred and forty-four commercial caves listed elsewhere in this book who answered questions in interviews or in detailed personal letters, supplied printed information and extended other courtesies; and to Myron C. Dunlavy, Jr., Secretary of the Pennsylvania Cave Men's Association, for information about the commercial caves of Pennsylvania.

To my wife, Mary Elting Folsom, I owe the greatest personal debt for expert and tireless collaboration.

To Evelyn Singer I am indebted for valuable suggestions about the text.

To Leah Glassoff goes a warm word of appreciation for her willingness to work at her typewriter any hour of the day or night.

And to Herbert Michelman, Administrative Editor of Crown Publishers, thanks for encouragement and for very important suggestions regarding the organization of material in this book.

Table of Contents

Illustrations

Introduction

Men have conquered the surface of the earth from the Antarctic to Alaska, from the Gobi Desert to the jungles of Brazil. They use the air above the earth as a common highway, and even the stratosphere beyond. Men are masters of the Seven Seas, and their science has probed deep ocean waters. But caves, the mysterious world beneath the surface of the earth, are still largely in the realm of the unknown.

Though caves existed long before man, and have been used by man since he appeared on this planet, they are still a frontier—in a sense, the last frontier. Mountain climbers have reached the top of Everest, but their daring counterparts who explore the underground night have yet to reach the end of even the best-known caverns in this country. And for every cave they have partially tamed, perhaps ten more are wholly "wild"—either undiscovered or unexplored.

The adventure into darkness is on—into darkness that is total but hides some of the rarest beauties that ever dazzled disbelieving eyes. Many more than a million Americans each year experience the awe and delight of the eerie underworld. They visit the comparatively small number of caverns that have been prepared for public view. And a growing band of hardy souls is constantly pushing back the subterranean horizon. They are the spelunkers—the cave-crawlers—who get from their unseen sport all the thrills that any aboveground athlete gets from his, with the additional pleasure of going on and on where no human being has ever been before, or perhaps where men have forgotten to go for millenia, and where priceless relics of the human past lie waiting to be discovered.

Along with the spelunkers, scientists venture. Men and women trained in half a dozen different disciplines push further each year into the dark unknown, advancing the new body of knowledge called speleology.

Not only do sciences as disparate as archeology, geology, biology, meteorology and hydrology meet in caves; they also discover there a mutual interdependence. No one science can venture far into the darkness without help from another. Moreover, the sciences often rely on the diverse technologies of surveying, rigging, rock climbing, telephone communication and photography. And integrated with this scientific and technological adventuring across new underground frontiers are the daring and substantial exploits of bold laymen who have been attracted to caves.

All who visit caves—tourists, spelunkers, speleologists—find an added dimension of delight in the legends that issue from them by the thousand, like the elusive bats that live and multiply underground, shunning close scrutiny in the light of day. Folklore is a fascinating part of cave phenomena. So is the bedrock of history that underlies legend and makes caves a part of, not apart from, the central stream of man's development. Caverns, indeed, offer a superb laboratory—where a constant is difficulty—for the study of man's creativity, of his unending ability to go beyond his supposed limits. In caves human beings have a way of taking on heroic stature.

But a rounded view of caves and cavers must also include many small, homely events that have nudged people forward to the major excitements. My own personal experience one spring afternoon in West Virginia may suggest that among the entrances to Cave-America are some quite humble enough to invite the many who do not view themselves as heroes.

I stood, that day, watching a little stream which tumbled swiftly along *toward* a steep hill, then disappeared at the foot of a gray limestone ledge as suddenly as it had emerged from the foot of another ledge three hundred yards away on the other side of the valley. Totally ignoring the ups and downs of the West Virginia mountains, the noisy water traveled *through* them.

The vanishing brook was itself a sufficient wonder to my small party. City folk though we were, we had a little knowledge of the countryside, and we were familiar with orthodox streams that lived out their whole lives aboveground and were sensibly inclined to slip between—or around—big obstacles like mountains. Here, however, was a brook that challenged our conventional ideas of what was right and proper in the landscape. Just ahead of us, beyond the cool shadow at the base of the limestone ledge, lay the answer to our questions: "What kind of underground short cut does this stream take? What is it like inside a mountain? *What is it like in a cave?*"

A cave to be explored lay behind the shadowy point where the brook disappeared, and go into it we felt we must—two sets of middle-aged parents and their ten-year-old children. The kindly farmer who had let us throw down our sleeping bags in his pasture assured us there was no great hazard in the cave. We could all go in safely, even without the equipment that real cave explorers use. Our only approach to professional gear was a collection of "hard hats" such as miners wear and carbide lamps to be carried on the hats—and we weren't even sure we knew how to operate the strange little gadgets. Hilda experimented with the bright red headgear she was supposed to wear, and decided that although she liked the color, she couldn't stand the feel of it. But this first cousin to a space helmet delighted the children. In addition to the lamps, we had plenty of flashlights, and recalling Tom Sawyer's experience in a cave, I saw to it that we also had a supply of candles—just in case.

"Come up to the house when you get out," the farmer requested. "Then I'll know I won't have to go in and look for you. Once some people got lost for a while in there, but there's no need to, if you just follow the stream."

"Where do we go in?" I asked, ashamed of my ignorance. All I could see was a low, dark, ragged slit across the base of the ledge— a slit perhaps knee-high.

The farmer pointed toward the right of the opening. "You crawl in there."

Crawl. That simple word of instruction didn't sound at all simple to the sedate elders in the party. None of us had done any crawling in years, except possibly under beds to retrieve lost toys. Did we crawl head first or feet first? How far? We'd heard the cave might be as much as a mile long.

"After you go about thirty feet, you can stand up and walk. Just look out—pretty soon you'll come to a drop-off. Straight down. Plenty of places to hold onto, though, and you can help each other."

With that, the farmer squatted down on his heels to watch us crawl. The old man took a real interest in his cave, and apparently in us, and he saw our signs of uncertainty.

"Nothing to worry about," he said, shifting the quid of snuff in his mouth. "A couple of spelunkers are in there now. They'll give you a hand if you need it."

At that moment two small yellow lights appeared in the narrow black slit. The spelunkers, a young man and a young woman, were on their way out. Here they came on their bellies, wriggling into the daylight and blinking as they looked around. From neck to toe they were smeared with mud, and their dripping coveralls clung to wet skin.

"Did you fall in or something?" Tommy demanded.

The woman grinned. "We didn't fall—we waded. That's how you get through to the Big Room."

She picked up a small army surplus ammunition case she had pushed ahead of her as she squirmed out of the cave. "Got some good pictures," she announced enthusiastically. "Wonderful cave for pictures." Then she looked at Tommy's camera all rigged up with a flashbulb attachment. "But you'd better leave that here," she added. "You're sure to break it, or get it wet and spoil it unless you have a waterproof carrying case."

With a smile she generously showed us how she carried her own camera and flashbulbs, neatly packed in a Pliofilm wrapping in the ammunition case, which was lined with sponge rubber. "I can drop this twenty feet, and it won't hurt my equipment," she explained. "I can drag it through water and mud, and nothing happens. The case is waterproof, but just to be sure, I use this plastic wrapping, too."

Tommy had looked forward to taking pictures underground. He was disappointed, but realistic. With the help of Bud, his father, he found a place to leave his camera. The cave, after all, was the important thing.

I began fussing with my lamp. I had put gray lumps of carbide into the lower chamber and water in the upper chamber, according to instructions. Now I moved the lever on top and spun the little wheel that was supposed to give off sparks and start the acetylene gas to burning. My luck was no better than it usually is with cigarette lighters. Sparks aplenty came from the flint under the spinning wheel—but not flame.

The young man who had just crawled out of the cave saw my predicament and quietly showed me what to do. He held the palm of his hand over the lamp's reflector. This made a sort of combustion chamber for the gas that issued from the tiny nozzle in the center. After a moment he withdrew his hand, pulling it as he did so across the wheel that made the spark. A surprising little pop meant that the gas had ignited—and there in the center of the reflector was a flame. How could that inch-long sliver of yellow serve me well enough in the darkness ahead?

On went the other lamps, and into the cave we started, some feet first, some head first—each feeling a little individual uncertainty, a sense of anticipation. Sharp rocks dug into elbows and knees as we inched down a steep slope, avoiding the path of the stream. Thirty feet in the direction of total darkness seemed a very long way. But at last Tommy and Rachel were able to stand up. Hilda tried it, too, and banged her head on the rock above us. A flash of understanding, not unmixed with a sense of satisfaction, came to me in the security of my own hard hat. Then a tunnel twice as high as a man opened before us, and along one side of the floor ran our stream. A few steps more and the last gray hint of sunlight was gone.

We were really inside the cave now—a wild cave. Without a guide. Around us we felt cool air, and an immense quiet punctuated by the low splashing of water. The dark pressed in on us from all sides, held back only momentarily and only in tiny areas by the thin beams of our lights.

I led and kept a sharp outlook for the sudden drop about which we had been warned. Every few steps called for a halt. Rachel's light picked out a cricket. Tommy found a daddy longlegs. Hilda bent over something pure white that thrust up out of a mud bank. Examination showed delicate tendrils of some kind of mold sprouting from a stick of wood that must have been washed in by the stream. Hilda, who fought mold in her closets at home with a cold hatred, stood fascinated by the silken threads growing out of the wood.

Bud's light followed along the floor of the cave where the mud seemed almost dry. No question about it—animal tracks. Some animal, maybe a raccoon, had made many trips along here.

Presently the sound of a waterfall began to fill the space, multiplied a dozen times by echoes from unseen walls. The drop-off must be close by. Oldsters and youngsters alike soon shared the delight of feeling for water-worn pockets in the rock, using them as handholds and footholds. A careful scramble, with each one helping the other, landed us at the bottom of the twenty-foot cliff of wet, slippery rock. This was fun—sheer animal, exhilarating fun.

Now a new problem and perplexity. From somewhere—who could tell where?—a second stream appeared and joined the one we had set out to follow into the mountain. (Later, or another time, we would trace it back, up into the sunlight—into what farmer's pasture or onto the far side of what mountain? Today it was downstream for us.) But our brook was much bigger now. Once, then a second time, the walls on either side of it came close together with no bank, not even a muddy one, on which to walk. It was wade or go back. We waded.

The corridor we followed began to widen again, and the two children walked abreast of me. I heard first one and then the other give a gasp of wonder. Their lights had caught our first large glistening stalactites and stalagmites. A cascade of the same lovely stone appeared against one of the cave walls.

Again the passageway grew low and narrow. We stooped and crept along on a ledge above the water. Hanging from the low ceiling were dozens of miniature stalactites—each a hollow tube with a drop of water bulging downward from the end. These straws of stone stood in a perfect row. What secret lay behind this orderly behavior of rock that grew—and grew hollow and downward?

Ahead the pearly rock formations ended, and we saw only the curving sculpture of water on the limestone walls. Abruptly the stream bed grew deep. I was up to my knees, then my hips.

This would be the place where the explorers we had met got soaked up to their necks. No place for children. It would be well over their heads. A great pity, for beyond us must lie the rooms full of mineral splendor we had heard about—much more elaborate and varied in hue than the first stalactites that had left us breathless.

Novices that we were, blundering into an exciting unknown, we had not taken note of the landmarks along our route. As we retraced our steps, we still thought only of the wonders our lights picked out. A cluster of tiny brown bats hung from the ceiling, with now and then a restless movement that revealed the little winged mammals were not dead but only sleeping. Beyond was a pool we had not seen when we came in. A foot-high rim of stone dammed it up on three sides, and a solid sheet of the same stone seemed to pour down into it from the wall.

"I saw a little orange thing like a lizard!" Tommy called from one side of the chamber. "It went into a crack."

Bud examined the wall minutely with his light. "Look—three different kinds of bugs on this one patch of rock—mosquitoes and some sort of fly and spiders."

"We didn't see this place coming in," Rachel announced with pleasure. "Are we going out a new way?"

Long experience has taught me to listen with respect to Rachel's observations. She's usually right. No doubt about it—we were in a passage through which we had not come before. And where was the stream?

Three hours had passed since we entered the cave. It would be getting dark outside very soon. We had better locate our brook and follow it back to the sunlight.

This was easier said than done. For half an hour we were lost. In the end we did hear the sound of water, and the grownups at least gave a sigh of relief. We had wits enough among us then to know that our goal lay upstream.

When at last we wriggled through the narrow opening and sat down blinking in the late afternoon sun, we were as muddy—and as satisfied—a group as had ever taken an outing. Satisfied in one way, but completely tantalized in another. A hundred questions were unanswered. A great part of the cave lay there under the mountain, still to be visited. Where did the stream emerge? Why did bats hang upside down? Where did they fly when they woke up? Why did they go deep into caves, and how did they find their way? How do you keep from getting lost in a cave? How and why did this whole huge cave and its strange formations come into being?

These were things to think over and talk over as we cooked

supper on our little gasoline stove in the farmer's pasture and lay down in sleeping bags and looked up at the stars that night.

A brief trip in a cave had turned two families—adults and children alike—into spelunkers. This would be only the first of many expeditions, only the beginning of a long series of physical and intellectual adventures. There would come a time before too long when we would all have full equipment for comfort—and for safety. And for all of us would come the special pleasure of having our questions multiply every time we found an answer. We had a new hobby of limitless possibilities, and with us, as we enjoyed it, were serious scientists glad to help us in our pursuit of answers, glad to have *our* help at times in their scientific work.

About one thing—and one only—there was no mystery. We would never again wonder why people wanted to crawl about in caves. We knew. And around us we discovered a growing circle of companionable human beings who shared this knowledge.

This book, which grew out of our experiences as spelunkers, sketches briefly some of the amazing variety of things about caves there are to do, understand and enjoy. I wanted to begin it by telling how caves were formed and why. But to do that, I found I had to tell a good deal about the rock in which caves develop. The story of the formation of this very special kind of rock, then, is the beginning.

CHAPTER ONE

The Origin of Caves

I

"That's that, and nothing can ever come of it," we might have said if we could have seen the naked surface of the earth perhaps two billion years ago. But we would have been as wrong as human beings always are when they cling to apparent permanence and close their minds to the inevitability of change.

Although no life existed, the factors that could start the endless chain of evolution were all there. There was energy, for one thing. Some of it existed in the form of heat, both from the sun and from within our primeval earth itself. Energy existed, too, in the form of lightning. A constant exchange of electric charges took place between the earth and the envelope of seething gases and water vapor that surrounded it.

Water vapor condensed into droplets of rain. As these passed down through the atmosphere, they absorbed carbon dioxide. This gas turned raindrops into dilute acid—carbonic acid. Eons ago rain had some of the properties of the charged water we get in soda pop today, and rain still has these properties.

Two different kinds of matter—water and carbon dioxide—had turned into something new and quite unlike the parent stuffs from which they had come. And this new something was to set in motion a kaleidoscopic series of events that has become ever more fascinating down to the present moment.

Carbonic acid acted on a mineral called calcium carbonate that was present in the rock of the earth's surface. (In some places calcium compounds made up as much as twenty per cent of the material in the original rock.) Calcium carbonate and carbonic acid, combining, became a new substance on this earth—calcium bicar-

11

bonate, which readily dissolves in water. The fact that carbonic acid acted on calcium carbonate and produced calcium bicarbonate doomed the earth to incredible changes.

The acidic waters ate away at calcium-bearing rocks, leaving pits and holes. Bits and chunks of non-soluble rock broke away, and water moved them downward as it sought low places on the surface in which to come to rest. Rushing streams used grains of sand and pebbles and even boulders as battering rams against other rocks that were not affected by the dissolving acid. The small rocks pounded away at larger ones, breaking off more bits and being further broken themselves. A colossal process of destruction gathered momentum.

But, at the same time, an equally colossal process of construction began. Certain chemical and physical factors could upset the uneasy equilibrium that existed in water carrying a maximum burden of calcium bicarbonate in solution. When such an upset took place, the solid material, calcium carbonate, precipitated and came to rest on the bottom of ancient lakes and seas. There it formed an ooze. As more and more water flowed into the depressions on the earth's surface, more ooze piled up. Pressure increased on the lower layers of ooze. Most of the water between the particles of calcium carbonate was squeezed out. Finally, the ooze—under tremendous pressure—became a kind of rock that had never existed before. It was limestone.

During untold millenia, acid-laden raindrops and battering rivers gouged away at the higher rock surfaces on the earth and moved great masses of mineral from high places to low places. The bits of quartz that reached the seas in the form of sand became cemented together, by calcium carbonate and other cements, to form another new kind of rock—sandstone. Bits of decomposed feldspar reassembled near the mouths of rivers in the form of clay and then became shale, another new rock.

A vast shifting of weight was taking place on the earth's surface. Rocks that were very dense had already concentrated in the lower areas, and now masses of limestone, sandstone and shale were piling up, creating an imbalance. Finally, something had to give.

In places the earth's hard outer crust cracked under the strain. Enormous blocks of the heavy rock moved downward. Other lighter blocks floated upward on the plastic, doughlike rock (called magma) under the crust. In other places the crust folded, accordion fashion, and new mountain ranges appeared.

Time and again, in response to ever-shifting pressures, parts of the area that is now the North American continent sank, then rose again. Great shallow seas swept in, then out. And always on the floors of the seas, limestone, along with other sedimentary rocks, continued to pile up.

At last what we now know as the continental mass was to rise and shoulder off the water. Certain areas were to buckle and be tossed upward. Limestone beds were to appear far above the level of the sea, and here the inexorable processes of erosion could set to work on them, too. Now rocks which were themselves the products of the decay of earlier rocks began to wear away—both externally and internally. A new complexity had been added to the cycle of events affecting the earth's surface.

It was *inside* the masses of limestone that caves began to appear.

Ever since the beginning, limestone had originated in simple chemical reaction and precipitation. But there were other sources for the rock that gives us caves, and these sources were very much more important than simple chemical action.

II

A wild, haphazard intermingling of molecules of many kinds marked the earth in its formative stage—so goes a theory that is widely held. But at some point, perhaps aided by energy from lightning, various molecules assembled and stayed together in the form of amino acids. These acids are the stuff which makes up proteins—and protein is the essential substance of living matter. In the warm, shallow water near some land mass, life began, and with it began astonishing new changes in the *inanimate* world.

Simple algae were among the early plants, and some of these algae, in the course of the functioning of their organisms, added calcium carbonate to sea water. Under the influence of the sun's energy, the algae took various substances from the water and rearranged them within their simple organisms. Like all plants, the algae used carbon dioxide in their life process. When they removed carbon dioxide from the water, they in effect removed carbonic acid, which was necessary to keep calcium bicarbonate in solution. The solid calcium carbonate then sank to the bottom, increasing the layers of ooze there. Here was a new source of limestone. It was being created by very simple plants. Bacteria, plants that are even simpler, may have helped in a similar way.

Then, as more complicated plant forms evolved, some of them began to use calcium carbonate in their very structures. And water animals, a great variety of them, developed limy structures in their bodies. Some were tiny one-celled creatures whose minute shells dropped to the sea floor in great quantity to increase the size of the beds of ooze. Others were corals that built up whole islands. Snails, oysters, clams, starfish, crinoids, even some sponges added their shells or hard parts to the ever-growing mass of materials that went into the formation of limestone.

Limestone created by animal life—like all limestone—was subject to periodic uplifts from shallow sea floors. Seashells imbedded in limestone made their appearance on mountain peaks.

The nature of limestone varied enormously from place to place, depending on how it was formed and under what conditions. Sometimes it was the snowy white of pure calcium carbonate. Again it was black, tinted with carbon. Orange or brown showed the presence of oxidized iron as a coloring agent. Some limestone could best be described as blue.

Where it was subjected to heat and pressure, limestone became a different and harder rock—marble. Where magnesium carbonate appeared in great quantities along with calcium carbonate, the rock came to be known as dolomite. The limestone family is large and may be increasing, for all we know. At any rate, there is some of it in every state in the union.

Whenever areas of the earth's crust that contained limestone were heaving up, the movement of eroded rock downward toward the sea floor resumed with new vigor and tempo. Swift-moving mountain streams tore away at the landscape with much more gusto than could any slow, sluggish river of the flatter lands. And within the very heart of limestone a special kind of action took place which produced the subject of this book.

III

Very weak carbonic acid dissolved in rain water continued to fall and to eat away with great rapidity—geologically speaking—at limestone. Plants which had emerged from the seas and had taken up life on land provided, when they died and decayed, new sources of the acid that has such a marked affinity for calcium carbonate. Water, trickling down through soil and layers of decayed vegetable matter, absorbed this acid, and when the water reached limestone, a process of destruction or weathering of the stone took place underground— where it would seem that rock stood as a perfect barrier against any effects of weather.

Water bearing the acid seeped along between the layers or bedding planes in which the limestone had been laid down. If the rock had been tilted in a folding action of the earth, the water had an easy downhill channel along these bedding planes through which to seek a lower level. At the time when the limy ooze solidified into stone and was subjected to stresses, cracks or joints appeared at right angles to the bedding planes. Sometimes those vertical cracks were close together, other times far apart. The spaces in the joints were seldom wide—but they were there. Whenever water containing carbonic acid could seep along any of these fissures, solution could go on—and the spaces widened.

Still another route—a minor one—existed for water to follow. Certain kinds of limestone were porous. There were tiny spaces between the bits of solid matter. At the surface of the earth, air filled these holes; deep underground, water filled them; and in between lay a zone—called the vadose zone—in which there was some air and some water. Through the porous rock, vadose water constantly passed downward under the pull of gravity, and as it passed, the work of solution went on. Cavities formed when the dissolved material was carried away.

In the saturated zone, called the phreatic zone, water moved less freely. Still it could move along joints, fractures and bedding planes. (Pressure deep underground—pressure of water on water—can be great.) Seeping or flowing in any direction, even upward, to reach an outlet, phreatic water under pressure often appeared as springs or water holes, even as lakes. And so, in the phreatic zone, cavities developed. In them water took the place of the limestone it had dissolved and carried off to some surface outlet.

Enlarged by solution, the cracks, the joints, the spaces between bedding planes, became caves.

The place in rock at which vadose water and phreatic water met— that is, the water table—was not a fixed and stable one. In rainy seasons it rose, and following droughts it fell. When an uplift in the earth occurred, the cavernous areas of the phreatic zone were often raised above the water table, and the water drained out. Caves were drained in another way, too: the constant carving action of the surface streams sent rivers down to lower and lower levels, and the water table followed the level of the rivers downward. A cave formed in limestone that was once saturated with water could become filled with air instead, merely because the water table had moved down below it, due to the erosive action of a surface stream nearby—or perhaps not so near.

After a cave was filled with air instead of water, it could still grow larger and change its shape. For example, active seepage could dissolve rock in the roof of a chamber, making it higher and higher, creating a dome in the course of time. Often the same rapidly dripping water dissolved out a pit beneath the dome. Well-known Mammoth Cave has examples of these paired domes and pits. (The full story of these sometimes immense cavities is the subject of detailed geological treatises.)

Many caves show evidence of change of another kind. Active streams flowed through them after they were lifted above the water table, and eroded them in the same way that streams erode rocks on the surface. The calcium carbonate, which in the very beginning originated on land, then fell to the sea floor, then was raised perhaps many times above the sea floor, was once again on its way to the sea.

As time passed, gravity itself altered many a cave where masses of limestone with no support now hung over empty chambers. Seepage water weakened the ceilings, particularly along the joints, and as a result chunks of limestone, sometimes enormous in size, fell to the floor. The roofs in many cave rooms became high domes that were stabilized by the natural stresses in the rock. Beneath them lay mounds or hills of rubble piled up on the floor.

Breakdown did not always result in domes. Sometimes it occurred so close to the outside world that the surface rock dropped down, leaving depressions in the landscape, or actual holes leading to cavernous areas below. These are known as sinks or sinkholes.

Not all sinkholes, however, were caused by breakdown. Acidic water, percolating downward from the surface, sometimes dissolved the rock that lay between a cave and the land above. In either case, free-flowing surface water sometimes became another agent that altered the size and shape of sinkholes and of the caverns that lay beyond.

In certain places—parts of West Virginia and Kentucky are notable examples—all the run-off water is carried away by underground drainage through sinkholes. Roads go for miles and miles and never cross a brook or river; yet the streams are there, underground. Topography marked by sinkholes, caverns and underground drainage is known as karst—after the name of the area in Jugoslavia where the phenomenon was first studied.

IV

Caves multiplied and grew and collapsed, not only in limestone (and closely-related dolomite) and in its first cousin, marble, but in another vulnerable rock, gypsum, about which little will be said here because gypsum deposits are small compared with limestone deposits. In gypsum, marble, dolomite and limestone the process of cave formation still goes on.

Likewise, the process of trying to understand exactly how all the many kinds and shapes of caves came into existence is constantly going forward. Theories vary, as they always do when people are digging hard for the truth, and specialists will rightly say that the account I have given does not fully explain this or that cave or type of cave. One theory holds that caves were all created *above* the water table. Another holds that some were created above and some below the water table. Still another holds that most cavern development occurs *at* the water table. For those whose curiosity drives them to read further, there are learned treatises expounding these points of views—and variations on them. But on one point all experts seem to agree: solution by acidic water is the genesis, the birth point in one way or another, of all caves in limestone, dolomite, marble and gypsum. All scientists agree, too, that there is a kind of life cycle of caves, moving on from birth through maturity, even to death, in which something that was a cave becomes something that is not a cave at all, but a new and quite different phenomenon.

Men, becoming ever more curious as they elaborate their knowledge of the world around them, have found and ventured into five thousand of the caves that underlie this country. With ever-increasing skill they constantly seek out the other thirty or forty or fifty thousand caves that may wind around under our feet. At the very moment I am writing this in a camp on the edge of the Grand Canyon in Arizona, three scientists, using special mountaineering techniques, have descended a cliff wall and dangle at the end of a rope on the canyon side below me. There today—or tomorrow—they will gain entrance to one of the large number of caves in the limestone of the area. Of the discoveries these particular scientists have made in four arduous summers in the Grand Canyon, much may be heard in the future. It is enough here merely to document the exciting fact that constant, intensive exploration of caves is going on.

Using the compound of calcium called carbide in their lamps, men and women daily light their way into darkness to study, from deep within the earth's crust, great and spectacular masses of calcium carbonate. And daily they learn more about how both the earth and the life on it have become what they are—and how they continue to become something new.

CHAPTER TWO

Caves—"Living" and "Dead"

Most people feel something of the poet's childlike sense of wonder when they enter a cave. Six million or more Americans have enjoyed the experience of mingled awe, amazement and curiosity in one cave alone—Carlsbad—which is remote from any population center, hidden under the desert in southeastern New Mexico. More millions have ingenuously gasped at the spacious beauties or minute surprises in Mammoth or Luray or Wyandotte or some of the nearly 150 other caves that are operated commercially for the public.

But two, three, even a dozen wide-eyed visits cannot stimulate the complex delight that comes when the nature and cause of the eerie scenery of the nether world are understood. A few facts—even when couched in technical jargon—enrich the pleasure of visiting caves, whether the tour be made on the paved paths of commercial caverns or along muddy crawlways or hazardous traverses in wild ones. And basic to an understanding of the beauties of caves that are well decorated is a knowledge of what water and acid can still do, once they have dissolved a cavity in limestone.

The regimented lines of tiny, fragile tubes on the roofs of caves, the gleaming icicles of stone, the glistening pearly terraces are all evidences of a "living" cave. They are proof that a cavern—once hollowed out of stone by acid-laden water—is now being filled again with stone that is created by water, acid and air acting in partnership. This stage in the career of a cave, when it becomes ornamented with all manner of lovely incrustations, begins only after the passageways and rooms have been drained—but water there still must be, in small quantities at least.

The graceful, bizarre, even airy stone shapes which are the chief delight of the casual visitor have all been slowly deposited out of seepage water. Trickling down through the soil, it carried with it acid formed in decaying organic matter. When the acid-laden water reached beds of limestone, it began a new phase in the age-old cycle of solution. Moving down along joints or tilted bedding planes, the acid combined with calcium carbonate, and the water held calcium bicarbonate in solution until droplets of moisture emerged into cave air. There, one or both of two things happened: If the humidity of the cave was less than 100 per cent, water evaporated, leaving a bit of solid calcium carbonate at the point where the droplet emerged. Or water might leave a deposit because carbon dioxide had escaped from it in the form of gas. (The decrease in the amount of carbon dioxide meant a decrease in the acidity of the water, and hence in the amount of calcium bicarbonate that could be held in solution.) The carbon dioxide escaped from drops of water when they emerged into the cave, just as the same gas fizzes out of soda pop when the bottle cap is removed.

The amount of calcium bicarbonate in each drop of water was infinitesimal, but millions and billions of drops left behind a solid residue of calcium carbonate. Crystals of this mineral formed in two ways—just why is still a matter of some discussion. The more common type is called calcite; a rarer, harder type is known as aragonite. Frequently calcite tended to form in a small circle at the point where water, air and the rock of the cave roof all met. Succeeding drops left their deposit in the same circle, and gradually a hollow tube of stone resembling a *soda straw*—which it is called—grew downward. Often these straws of hollow pendant stone appear in straight lines along the joints down which water has seeped, and just as often they are so fragile that they break at a touch. Here, then is the explanation of the delicate little tubes of stone that so intrigued me when I first saw them.

Fascinating as soda straws are in themselves, they are only the beginning of a variety of quite different forms and shapes that calcite can take when it develops hanging downward from a cave ceiling. All these forms are called *stalactites* (from the Greek word meaning "oozing out in drops"). Often drops of water run down the outside of soda straws, as well as inside them. The result is calcite in the form of icicles, and they, too, often hang in straight rows beneath joints, as icicles hang along the edge of a roof.

Another type of formation also appears beneath joints when there is a fairly even flow of water all along the narrow crack. It resembles a *curtain* or *drape,* and that is just what it is called. When the seepage water creating a curtain or drape carries with it more iron oxide at some periods than at others, the gracefully curving sheet of stone may have alternating bands of white calcite and calcite that is stained a reddish brown. It resembles strips of *bacon* more than anything else in the world and is known by that homely but descriptive title.

A drop of water falls from a stalactite before it has lost all its limy content, and continues to evaporate or to lose carbon dioxide after it has landed. More calcite is deposited, this time on the cave floor. As the drops strike the floor, they splash and spread out, leaving their deposit over a fairly wide area. Succeeding drops build up on this broad base to form *stalagmites* (from the Greek word meaning "a dripping"). Stalagmites are usually broader and much more blunt than the slender stalactites directly above them. Many stalagmites grow under spots where water drips too rapidly to form any stalactites at all.

Occasionally, when the drip falls with exactly the right frequency and force, a stalagmite may rise tall and relatively thin, like a precarious tower made of halves of egg shells piled one on top of the other with the open end down. In many caves a stalagmite of this type is known as a *totem pole.*

Whatever the form calcite takes, its rate of deposit is slow by man's standards—extremely slow—and it varies from cave to cave and from time to time, even from formation to formation in the same cave. Guides in commercial caves are likely to tell tourists that it takes a hundred years for a cubic inch of calcite to accumulate in one of these *dripstone* deposits. The figure is arbitrary, but it does make the important point that stalactites and stalagmites do not hurry into existence. Yet in a great many caves dripstone growing down from ceilings by microscopic stages has met dripstone growing up from the floor by microscopic stages to form massive *columns* or stately *pillars* weighing many tons, or many hundreds of tons.

The forms assumed by calcium carbonate are legion—which, of course, is one reason caves are so endlessly interesting. It grows down along walls, over jagged ledges, covering them with billowing sheaths of snow-white or creamy or tawny stone that reflect the tiny carbide flame in a spelunker's lamp at a thousand different points and angles. This *flowstone,* sometimes called *travertine,* makes the "Frozen Niagaras" that are special features of many a cave.

In at least three caves in this country, flowstone has taken on a special shape that resembles an ancient warrior's shield or an artist's palette. The circular disc of glistening calcite sometimes hangs from a cave ceiling or wall, sometimes is totally detached and held up by a pedestal of dripstone. Mineralogists are still arguing with one another about the exact reasons why calcite happened to take on this unique shape.

In a different form calcite grows around the edges of pools, where it is called *rimstone,* and here it has the odd habit of building upward and inward—squeezing the pools into an ever smaller space and pushing the surface of the water up to an ever higher level. The versatile stone actually constructs dams that keep growing higher and higher. Often a series of these dams and the pools behind them ascend in graceful terraces.

Occasionally calcite may adhere to a bit of foreign matter in a pool and start a process of growth around it. Slight movements in the water keep the stone in motion as it grows, and a little, rounded *cave pearl* results. Sometimes a film of calcite forms around a bubble in a pool, producing an infinitely fragile *calcite bubble* that floats on the surface of the water. Every cave explorer hopes one day to discover this spectacle of stone floating on water, but only a few are so lucky as to succeed.

The catalogue of protean forms that calcite can take is not easily ended. Because some deposits have a knobbly appearance and are tinted orange by an iron oxide, they resemble coral. This *cave coral* is, of course, not true coral, which consists of the limy skeletons of small sea animals. *Cave onyx,* which may be flowstone or dripstone, has likewise been tinted with iron oxide or some other coloring agent. It often turns up in curio stores, cut and polished to reveal its inner coloring. Occasionally calcite is found in a crystalline form that bears the name *dogtooth spar.*

Sometimes calcium carbonate emerges from a cave wall in a soft, claylike, almost liquid form referred to as *rock milk* or *moon milk.* No one has yet come up with a thoroughly convincing explanation for this odd appearance of what seems to be primeval calcareous ooze imbedded in rocks that have been high above the sea floor for ages.

Nor has anyone yet presented a generally accepted explanation for maverick stalactites that are known as *helictites* (from the Greek word meaning "spiral"). Instead of hanging down like an icicle, a helictite may have several branches that curl and twist or grow upwards. The branch of a helictite has even been known to make a corkscrew-like swirl. These stony growths seem to defy the laws of gravity and reason—and the result is a puzzling mineral contortion.

Aragonite crystals produce forms no less interesting but much more regular. Sometimes the long, needle-like crystals radiate out in a cluster from a common source, looking like a delicate flower. The cluster is, indeed, named *anthodite* from the Greek word for "flower." Masses of minute aragonite crystals may cover an area with a white blanket, but woe to anyone who tries to make a ball of this *snow*. The crystals are as penetrating and irritating as prickly-pear spines.

Besides calcium carbonate, another mineral plays an important part in decorating caverns in certain regions. Where the rocks above a cave are of the right kind, gypsum (calcium sulphate) may be carried in by seepage water. In Mammoth Cave and many others this mineral, which is so soft that it can be scratched by a fingernail, emerges from walls and ceilings in curving tongues and leaves that grow outward from the base—not downward from the tip as calcite stalactites do. Gypsum flowers, dead white or sometimes colored with stain, each with its own individuality, decorate whole rooms and corridors or appear here and there as special surprises for the attentive explorer.

Transparent gypsum crystals spring out of certain cave surfaces in long, glittering *needles*. Although they are so fragile that they break at the slightest touch, these needles can reach a length of three feet or more. The floor of the Sewing Room in Higgenbotham Cave in Tennessee resembles a huge pincushion bristling with thousands of glassy, crystal darning needles.

Cave formations (or *speleothems*, as they are more and more frequently called) vary greatly in shape and size, and many of them also take on added interest from their subtle coloring and gradations in shade. Though iron oxide is the commonest tinting agent, calcite may range from transparent Iceland spar through translucent white to cream, buff, orange, blue, even red. In Luray Caverns and in other commercial caves, man has added another shade without any intention of deceiving. There, many speleothems have green areas included in their lush coloring. This green is plant life, which has managed to take up existence in the cave with the aid of electric light.

Speleothems, when they are growing, identify a "living" cave. At first they make splendid the barren cavities that acid-laden water has dissolved out of limestone. Then, if their growth goes on long enough, they block off whole passages. Water, which creates caves, can also fill them—and fill them with a different form of the very substance it removed in order to make the caves in the first place.

But try as it may, water seems to fail much more often than it succeeds in its unconscious effort to stuff with speleothems the underground voids it has carved out. The supply of seepage water may fail as a result of a change in climate, or surface vegetation may drink up all moisture from the soil before it can percolate downward toward a cave. Sometimes seepage water dissolves out for itself channels that bypass the higher levels of caverns, leaving them bone dry, while giving the lower levels a good soaking.

It may seem a small matter, this question of whether or not dripping water enters a cave or part of a cave. But if tiny drops of water cease to exude from the walls, a great change of a new kind overtakes the cave. Calcite speleothems cease to grow, and very soon they cease to "live." When this happens, a cave or cave passage is variously described as *mature* or *dead*. Stalactites cease to glisten. Flowstone becomes dull. Stalagmites lose their lustre. Rimstone around pools that have lost their water becomes soft and flaky. Where the stone once could easily hold the weight of a man, it now may crumble under his step.

The secret of this dramatic change lies in the curious affinity of calcite for water. It must be constantly wetted to retain its lustre and strength. Dehydrated, it slowly but surely turns to dust. A large stalactite may become papery and peel off, layer by layer. What was once a sinuous cascade of calcite of the purest white may end up as a shapeless heap of nondescript dust. Now, until there comes to the climate or land above some change that will once more bring seep-

Eons ago acid-laden water dissolved this cavern passageway. A modern caver, wearing a hard hat and carbide lamp, explores it. *Courtesy: National Speleological Society Photo by Ann Meuer*

This dome, known as the Rock of a Million Layers because so many different strata are exposed in the limestone, has the appearance of an upside down pothole worn out by the swirling water of an underground stream that long ago rushed through Texas Longhorn Cavern with terrific force. *Courtesy: Texas Longhorn Cavern State Park Photo by Mears Studio.*

Portions of many caves still lie completely under water as they did thousands of years ago. In order to see what water-filled passages look like—and what they lead to—explorers must don diving equipment. Here John Fisher opens the valve on his oxygen supply tank, while Ted Sobel and Oscar Huh look after his safety line. Around Fisher's waist are weight belts. Near his right hand is an emergency oxygen tank, and over his left hip hangs a knife which may come in handy. Fisher is about to dive into a water-filled passage of Schofer Cave, Berks County, Pennsylvania. *Courtesy: Underwater Speleological Research Group Photo by D. Nelson*

An underground river of bygone ages, flowing above the water table, scoured out large passages in many cavern systems. This one was discovered by guides in Mammoth Cave, Kentucky, after they had wriggled through previously unexplored crawlways. *Courtesy: National Park Service* *Photo by Ray Scott*

An underground stream, following a zigzag pattern of cracks in the limestone, dug canyons sometimes one hundred feet deep in Niagara Cave, Harmony, Minn. *Courtesy: Niagara Cave* *Photo by S. W. Lock*

Solution of limestone by acid-bearing water often produced strange effects. Here is the Bone Yard in Carlsbad Caverns, New Mexico. *Courtesy: National Park Service*

When cavern ceilings are unstable, fragments of limestone fall to the cave floor. Here in Wyandotte Cave, Indiana, a huge pile of breakdown—one of the largest known—soars up toward a perfectly flat layer of limestone that is now stabilized. Tall stalagmites atop Monument Mountain indicate that an exceedingly long time has passed since any rock has fallen there. Not all ceilings above breakdown are flat. Sometimes they are arched. No matter what the shape of cavities of this type, speleologists call them "domes." *Courtesy: National Speleological Society   Photo by George F. Jackson*

These similar displays of stalactites, columns and flowstone are found on opposite sides of the continent. The photograph above was taken in a limestone cave—Cumberland Caverns, McMinnville, Tennessee. The lower photograph was taken in a cave formed in marble—Crystal Cave, Sequoia National Park, California. (Above) *Courtesy: Cumberland Caverns Photo by Roy Davis* (Below) *Courtesy: National Park Service*

(*Left*) Deep vertical pits were often dissolved out of limestone by acid-bearing water. This one in Mammoth Cave measures 155 feet from the bottom of the pit to the dome above. *Courtesy: National Park Service Photo by Ray Scott* (*Right*) After an underground stream wore out this passage in Niagara Cave, seepage water began the process of decoration. *Courtesy: Niagara Cave Photo by S. W. Lock*

Many thousands of years ago, when water had finished the work of hollowing out this cavern, the walls were bare. Then slowly the work of decoration began. The stone that makes up this fantastic underground scenery was deposited out of slowly dripping water. Here, in Florida Caverns, Marianna, Florida, are stalactites hanging from the ceiling, stalagmites growing up from the floor, and columns formed when stalactites and stalagmites grew until they met. *Courtesy: Florida State News Bureau*

Far beneath the semi-arid land of southeastern New Mexico, slowly dripping water created these delicate forms in Carlsbad Caverns. *Courtesy: Santa Fe Railway*

Icicle-shaped stalactites often begin as hollow tubes of stone that resemble soda straws. Here, in Ohio Caverns, West Liberty, Ohio, pure white stalactites in both the soda straw and icicle form hang side by side. Beneath are thicker, blunter stalagmites. *Courtesy: Ohio Caverns*

There is always some surprise ahead for cavers. Porter Ward of Indianapolis has just found a forty-two-inch-long soda straw stalactite in Boone's Mill Cave, Indiana. Note the heavy rubber pads that protect his knees when he has to crawl through low passageways. *Courtesy: National Speleological Society Photo by Roy Davis*

(*Left*) A stalagmite known as the Giant Totem Pole in Luray Caverns, Luray, Virginia. *Courtesy: Luray Caverns* (*Right and Left below*) Scores of subtle shades of color appear on speleothems in the caves of this country, but only rarely does calcium carbonate occur in pure white form, unstained by some other mineral. These startling deposits are found in Ohio Caverns. *Courtesy: Ohio Caverns*

Fluctuations in the amount of iron oxides carried by seepage water very often created banded effects resembling bacon. *Courtesy: Mercer Caverns, Murphys, California*

Seepage water can drip in such a way as to leave its limy deposit in forms that resemble drapes.   *Courtesy: Bridal Cave, Camdenton, Mo.   Photo by Toennes Studio*

A closeup of drapes in Bridal Cave. Note the bacon-like bands. *Courtesy: Bridal Cave Photo by Toennes Studio*

Large drapes in Carlsbad Caverns. *Courtesy: National Park Service Photo by Kennicott and Grant*

A huge calcite curtain in Mammoth Cave. *Courtesy: National Park Service*
Photo by Kennicott and Grant

Draperies and a "frozen cascade" in the Big Room of Carlsbad Caverns. *Courtesy: Santa Fe Railway*

Flowstone in Indian Caverns, Spruce
Creek, Pennsylvania. *Courtesy: Indian
Caverns*

Pure white flowstone unstained by any
mineral appears in some caves. This is
in Lincoln Caverns, Huntingdon, Pennsylvania. *Courtesy: Lincoln Caverns
Photo by Greene's Studio*

Deep red stains create dramatic effects
on some flowstone and stalactites in Timpanogos Cave, American Fork, Utah.
Courtesy: National Park Service

Soda straw stalactites and helictites in
Wyandotte Cave, Indiana. Note drops of
water on the tips of the soda straws.
*Courtesy: National Speleological Society
Photo by George F. Jackson*

A gnarled, root-like mass of helictites in Great Onyx Cave, in Mammoth Cave National Park, Kentucky. *Courtesy: Great Onyx Cave*

Helictites in Floyd Collins' Crystal Cave, Cave City, Kentucky. *Courtesy: Floyd Collins' Crystal Cave Photo by W. T. Austin*

Helictites in Timpanogos Cave. *Courtesy: National Park Service*

Sloping disks of calcium carbonate are known as shields or palettes. The Bridal Veil is one of these rare speleothems in Grand Caverns, Grottoes, Virginia.   *Courtesy: Grand Caverns*

Calcium carbonate deposited under water takes many forms. Here is a closeup of a grapelike or botryoidal form in Mammoth Cave. *Courtesy: National Park Service   Photo by Ray Scott*

In Carlsbad Caverns, water flooded large areas long after stalactites and stalagmites had formed. While the speleothems were submerged, more calcium carbonate was deposited on them in knobbly forms that resemble coral. These deposits are not true coral. *Courtesy: Santa Fe Railway*

Sometimes, as in Mammoth Cave, calcium carbonate deposited out of a body of water took the form of masses of what appear to be cave pearls. *Courtesy: National Park Service*

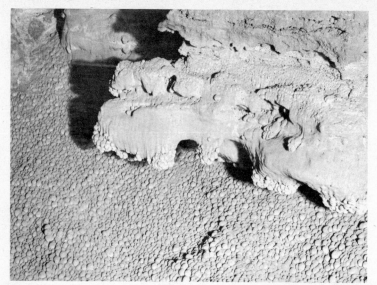

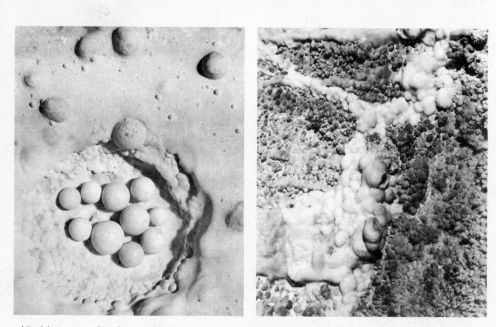

(*Left*) Layer after layer of calcium carbonate, deposited around a nucleus, formed these rounded, unattached cave pearls under water in Carlsbad Caverns. *Courtesy: National Park Service* (*Right*) In one American cave at least, a calcium carbonate deposit has taken the form of a cluster of bubbles. Ranging in size up to an inch in diameter, these bubbles in Mercer Caverns have shells thinner than the shells of birds' eggs. In rare instances calcite bubbles have been found floating in water. *Courtesy: Mercer Caverns Photo by George W. Moore*

age water, the decorations lie dormant—or rather, decaying. Speleothems cease their work of filling voids, and if the cave fills at all, it is only with mud and debris that surface water washes in through the entrance.

Surface water, of course, can bring mud and debris into a very live cave as well as into a dead one, and it can also abruptly terminate the life of a cave by eroding away its roof. More than one cave has ceased to be when a stream, suddenly infused with new life by an uplift in the land, has torn away the rock from around it. The Natural Bridge near Tyrone in Blair County, Pennsylvania, stands as a reminder of one such cave. The Bridge was once part of a cavern ceiling. Big Room Cave in southern Tennessee is only a remnant of what was once the upper level in a cavern system. A surface stream has cut a valley at right angles to the cave, leaving only portions of it intact in hills on opposite sides of the valley. But a lower level of this same cave still persists and has so far defied exploration. All that is known is that a good-sized underground river flows there in the direction once taken by the old upper level—that is, at right angles to the surface stream. The rushing Colorado River has destroyed possibly hundreds or thousands of caves that once serpentined their way in the vast areas of Redwall and Kaibab limestone it has carried off to the sea. At the same time, it has exposed many other caves to the air and, by draining them, made possible their decoration and their entry by plants, animals and men.

Thus caves appear and disappear, or fill up, or are laid bare to the sky. And sometimes "dead" caves come back to life. Water begins to drip once more. Glistening new calcite forms around the papery skeletons of earlier stalactites. Change is endless, and most things that change leave clues of some kind to their past—and to the past of more than themselves. So it certainly is in caves.

CHAPTER THREE

Life in Caves

From the first day when erosion laid bare an opening into a cave, living things had a chance to enter the new underground area. And enter they did. No man knows how many millions of years ago surface water carried the first alga or bacterium or flatworm or fish into the mouth of a cavern. No one can guess very accurately when an air current first wafted a flying insect or the spores of fungi into a cave. No historian was present to record the first time a cricket hopped down into a sinkhole never to return, or the occasion on which the first daddy longlegs flexed the many joints in his limbs and then spraddled his way into the dark heart of a limestone bed. But at many times and many places a variety of living things found themselves in caves—and some of them survived.

Part of this migration underground survived by remaining in the mouths of caves or in the twilight zones just beyond. Mosses, lichens, ferns, and liverworts were among the plants that added cave entrances to their habitats. Some snails and slugs inched as far into caves as there was a hint of daylight. Spiders, flies, mosquitoes, too, ventured into the twilight zone. Fish swam back and forth between the sunlit waters and the sunless streams and lakes underground. Frogs and salamanders, at home both on land and in water, discovered they could also be at home both outside and inside caves. A few birds found that the dark—but not totally dark—cavern mouths were congenial to them. Phoebes nested there, and in some places swallows and an occasional screech owl took up residence, too. At some point after mammals appeared on the earth, these warm-blooded creatures that bore their offspring alive moved into caves. In mid-Pleistocene times, one type of rat—the furry-tailed cave rat, *Neotoma magister*—began to build nests in the twilight zones. Sometimes this versatile creature, which has survived until today, dragged shredded bark into the area of total darkness and wove its nest. Prehistoric bats flew far into black chambers and passages, where they slept or hibernated, hanging upside down. Giant ground sloths found shelter in cave entrances, as did prehistoric bears. Raccoons, mice and other small mammals that were nocturnal in habit all strayed in to sleep out the daylight hours and perhaps to store their food and bear their young.

As time went on, some creatures found they could exist in the twilight zone without returning to sunlight. And others were adaptable to existence deep in caves where light played no role in their lives whatsoever. A common experience—of absolute dark, constant temperature, constant humidity, and dependence on food that came ultimately from the outside—faced all living things in the new environment; and a number of organisms found this stable environment suitable for their survival. Struggling close to the fossil remains of ancient sea animals in cave walls, some of their direct or collateral descendants began to undergo changes that better fitted them for survival in their new abode.

Fresh-water sponges, flatworms, crustaceans of various sorts, spiders, millipedes, springtails, crickets, beetles, snails were among the invertebrates that were so adjusted that they could live and reproduce, generation after generation, in the dark. A few varieties of salamander and tiny fish rounded out the list of true cave-dwellers.

Plants, too, found themselves in a world devoid of life-giving sunlight. This meant that only bacteria and fungi, which could get their nourishment from air and water and minerals and decaying organic matter, had a chance of enduring. No plant that contained chlorophyll—the agent that makes sunlight do essential work in its life process—could reach maturity or reproduce.

From this fact it follows that caves could offer very little of the vegetable food that is the ultimate prop of animal life. In those caves where there were flatworms—simple creatures that almost flowed along in the water, taking on fluid shapes with their flexible bodies—fish and crayfish devoured them. The flatworms, for their part, got food by eating the young of small water lice and the larvae of insects that began life in cave water or were washed in from the outside. Decaying organic matter in the water also gave them nourishment.

Before becoming food for flatworms, the water lice fed on the droppings of bats and other animals that used the cave only as shelter. These, of course, relied on food they obtained outside the cave.

The fish and crayfish that lived deep in a cave and never saw the light of day were part of a long food chain that led ultimately out into the sun. In this respect, cave fauna was no different from other fauna—it depended in the last analysis on sunlight. But in some other respects it was very different.

Since food was scarce there, a cave was no place for large animals that required a lot of forage to keep them nourished. Likewise, cave passages have every odd shape imaginable—some of them are very narrow and low. Only small creatures could have any freedom of motion in search of food. So it is not surprising that all creatures that became permanently adjusted to cave life were small. A good-sized cave fish is only two or three inches long—four inches only very rarely. A cave salamander may be four or five inches long, and is streamlined and sinuous.

Another controlling feature tended to give true cave-dwellers a common characteristic—the steady temperature day and night, winter and summer. No creature in this environment needed a heavy covering to protect it from excesses of heat or cold, or from sudden changes in temperature, for none occurred.

Since the humidity in a very large number of caves is nearly 100 per cent, creatures in such caves did not require the kind of outer covering that would keep their body fluids from evaporating. Likewise, color could play no role in an environment that lacked all light. Pigment, which protects terrestrial animals from sunburn or affords means of identification or concealment, tended to disappear. Even the skin of one kind of salamander that is apparently pink is in reality colorless. The illusion of color comes not from the skin, which is nearly transparent, but from the blood directly under it, which absorbs oxygen through the thin tissues and incidentally eliminates the need for lungs or gills.

Just as color tended to disappear in the underground night, so did eyes which had no possibility of seeing. True cave salamanders are blind. Cave fish, which lost their color and became completely white, also became blind, with only useless, atrophied eyes. But there had to be a substitute for eyes, if sightless creatures were to be reasonably efficient in locating food and avoiding harm. It is known that at least one variety of blind fish has very sensitive papillae on its head and jaws which apparently detect vibrations in the water. A blind cave crayfish has unusually long antennae. A tiny snail that has taken up permanent residence near the headwaters of cave streams has lost not only eye pigmentation but even the eye structures themselves. What compensation it has made for the loss is not yet known.

Creatures which became adjusted to cave-dwelling ranged up the evolutionary scale as far as the amphibians. One of these—the salamander *Typhlomolge rathbuni,* found in Texas—never reached such maturity as did most of its terrestrial cousins. Instead of losing the gills, which are normal equipment for salamanders in the larval stage but which disappear in the adult stage, *Typhlomolge* kept its gills and remained under water. There, a sort of perpetual adolescent, it managed to reproduce. This raises an interesting question: did the cave environment somehow inhibit the full growth and development of its denizens? Certainly some cave creatures display intricate and curious techniques for survival. For example, a cave fly in a limited area of the southeastern part of this country builds a "spider" web to catch mosquitoes, which are merely visitors to the cave.

Although the uniform environment tended to impose common characteristics on them, animals of the same kind tended to vary from cave to cave. Members of the same species that dwelt in neighboring caves often had no means of contact with one another. To animal life—and plant life, too—a cave was likely to be an island in a great sea of stone through which no life could pass. The result was that in an individual cave—or a group of connected caves—some life forms developed which appeared in few if any other places. And in no cave did life burgeon and flourish. Rather, it doggedly persisted.

A great mystery that has by no means been solved surrounds a fact of a different kind. There are sometimes identical species that appear in widely separated areas.

A theory with highly dramatic implications attempts to explain the wide dispersion of one species of the white blind fish *Typhlichthys.* It appears in caves that make a great arc from the Mammoth Cave country in Kentucky up into Indiana, then westward through Missouri, ending in northeastern Oklahoma. How could tiny two-inch fish that live only in underground water populate caves spread

over such an enormous area? Even if they were washed out of
one cave into a large river like the Ohio or the Mississippi, how
could they swim upstream to reach caves that have no known
connection with these rivers? Even if they could achieve this most
unlikely feat and become widely diffused, how could they remain
undifferentiated in widely separated caves over a long period of
time?

The answer that has been tentatively offered is breathtaking in
its implications: it is that a continuous cavern system, an interconnecting maze of tubes in the phreatic zone, exists all the way from
Kentucky *under* the Ohio River into Indiana and Illinois, *under*
the Mississippi River into Missouri, Arkansas and on into Oklahoma. The same Mississippian limestone is continuous throughout
this area. Enough organic matter does seep down into phreatic
water to supply small fish with subsistence.

Possibly—just possibly—further study of this one small cave fish
may result in proof that a vast part of the central and southern states
lies above one incredibly vast cavern system. A two-inch-long fish
that is blind may lead us one day to a water supply of unimaginable
magnitude.

Another variety of blind fish may lead us also to an understanding
of the nature of the dread disease cancer. Scientists in the laboratories of the American Museum of Natural History have studied
generation after generation of cave fish in the hope of discovering
what triggers an evolutionary change, such as the disappearance
of eyes. The possibility of important findings about the endocrine
systems of these blind fish so interested the American Cancer
Society that it has financed researches in this area. Thus the patient,
and seemingly impractical, studies of tiny and by no means abundant creatures that come from deep within caves may lead to
astonishing practical results for mankind.

Similarly the study of a cave snail only a tenth of an inch long
has produced information that may be of future import. This small
mollusk lives *only* in the headwaters of streams that originate
underground. It has lived in such places for untold generations.
This means that where it dwells there is a water supply that has
never failed, no matter what droughts have parched the land above.

Man searches unendingly for reliable sources of water, and a snail indicates one such source.

A snail so small that it may be mistaken for a bit of gravel, a shrimp so transparent that it can be recognized better by its shadow in a flashlight beam than by its own bodily form, a fish that darts under a ledge at the slightest disturbance of the water, a sala-mander that slithers out of sight into a tiny crevice—all these are likely to escape the attention of any casual cave visitor. It is the specialist who knows how to locate them and has the patience to do so. For most of us cave life may appear to consist of very few creatures indeed, and the largest of them will be small mammals—rats and bats. To find even these beasts, sharp eyes are often necessary. Rats particularly may escape notice because they do not live in colonies. But somewhere in or just beyond the twilight zone, the watchful caver may see two bright eyes peering at him from a ledge. Nearby can be found what appears to be a bundle of excelsior in the middle of a dry cave floor or tucked away in a crevice. This will be the rat's nest, made of carefully shredded cedar bark. Possibly this ever-curious creature will pop up out of the hole that leads to the warm interior of his nest, and give his visitor a good looking-over at very close range. And possibly inspection of his nest will reveal that it is not made from bark fibers after all, but from rope which some caver has left and which the rat has neatly unraveled.

Near his nest someplace, he has a storehouse of nuts and seeds brought in from the area around the cave entrance, and there may also be a more or less orderly arrangement of other objects that have no apparent use to him. If untidy cavers have been around, his collection may include flashlight bulbs, cigarette packages, tinfoil. One caving party missed a loaf of bread from the lunch supplies, only to discover it later near a nest, piled neatly slice upon slice, with the wrapper as a crowning glory on top of the rat's architectural achievement. A rat has even been known to rummage among a photographer's gear while he was in act of trying to get a picture of it.

Neotoma magister is not limited to a cave environment. He forages and also lives aboveground. Many species of bats likewise make use of caves, but can and do live elsewhere. From prehistoric times, these small, winged mammals have darted in and out of caves all over the world, as fossils of extinct species imbedded in flowstone prove. Possibly they have survived because of the security that caves have offered against predators. Whatever the reason, a bat's bodily structure is a fascinating elaboration on what most of us tend to think is normal in the realm of warm-blooded creatures that bear their young alive. Alone among mammals bats can really fly. Their wings are made up of membranes enclosing the arm bones and greatly elongated finger bones, which act as reinforcements.

Perhaps because bats are nocturnal in habit, a wealth of thoroughly unreliable legend has grown up about them, and men have made of the harmless, even beneficial, little beasts a means of expressing their unreasoned fears. Bats were standard paraphernalia for witches; the female half of humanity stood in terror that bats would become entangled in their hair. Phrases crept into the language expressing man's revulsion or ignorance—"bats in the belfry"; "batty"; "blind as a bat."

The facts are a good deal different from the nightmarish fancies that linger on to the present day, and one of the astonishing facts is that very little was known about bats until the present generation. The few who studied them at all knew that the cave-dwelling bats in the United States were for the most part insect eaters—not only harmless, but exceedingly useful to mankind; that they left on cave floors fantastically deep layers of nitrate-rich guano, excellent for fertilizer; that they always hung upside down while sleeping and that they never got tangled in ladies' hair. A few of the more common varieties were even known by name to some laymen. There was the little pipistrelle or Pygmy bat, with its yellowish fur and pinkish wing membranes. It led a solitary existence, always hanging alone and never in groups. In damp cave air the pipistrelle often glistened and appeared to be itself a snow-white speleothem. On its soft hair, droplets of moisture condensed and reflected back the rays of cavers' lights. In contrast to the solitary pipistrelle were the brown or blackish-brown bats which hung in clusters. A total of perhaps two dozen species, large and small, dwelt in hundreds of caves throughout the country. In the Southwest, literally tens of millions belonging to the variety known as the Mexican Free-tailed swarmed nightly out of cavern mouths in dense clouds. Scientists were well aware that bats were not blind—but that the eyes were not the organs that guided the creatures in their flight through darkness. (An eighteenth-century Italian experimenter had actually blinded some specimens, and found that they could still avoid striking obstacles while in flight.) How, then, *did* bats navigate in confined spaces and in total darkness? The answer, and much other data that had surprising practical implications for mankind, had to wait until almost yesterday to be discovered by speleologists.

These pioneering scientists have increasingly taken up the challenge offered by cave life—with its special clues to the central fact of change and evolution. However, the most dramatic discoveries so far made are preliminaries to the study of change. It has been sufficiently exciting to find out what cave life is really like and in what extraordinary ways cave creatures function. Some of the most startling stories revolve about bats, and these will be related later on in this book. But first must come the story of the considerable information that caves can yield about other mammals—some of which have long been extinct.

CHAPTER FOUR

Mammals Enter Caves

When mammals appeared, the earth had undergone most—but not all—of the great changes that have given it its present appearance. And by the time mammals had become the dominant form of animal life, the caves we know had taken on most of their present characteristics.

In place after place, mammals wandering the surface of the earth found cave entrances, and used them for shelter and left traces of their visits. Time and again animals fell into sinkholes and could not get out—and left their bones as mute evidence of their entrapment. Often these bones became incrusted with calcite or impregnated with other minerals which preserved their original shape, protecting them against the agents of decay.

Sometimes damp clay surrounding bones was enough to keep them in a perfect state of preservation for thousands of years. That happened in Cherokee Cave, the mouth of which lies near the corner of 13th and Cherokee Streets in the heart of the city of St. Louis, Missouri. But this is getting ahead of the story.

About three hundred million years ago, a shallow sea covered the area where St. Louis now spreads its skin of asphalt, concrete and brick over the terrain. For many millions of years limestone piled up on the sea floor, and then the land rose and the waters flowed off to the south. Perhaps a million years ago, fresh water laden with carbonic acid began to eat away at the limestone. Quite probably solution had started long before that, below the water table, and it may have continued after the limestone found itself above the water table. At any rate, corrasion followed solution— that is, an underground stream tore away at the limestone and scoured out a tunnel that was something like twenty to twenty-five feet in diameter.

Then one day the roof over the mouth of the cave collapsed and formed a dam. This meant that water which had heretofore passed through in the form of a stream now lingered as a lake. And so the gritty clay which the underground stream carried fell to the floor of the cave, instead of being tumbled along to the Mississippi River—only six city blocks away. Eventually more than fifteen feet of sediment accumulated in one massive layer on the cave floor.

After accomplishing this great labor of deposition, the stream found another—no doubt more direct—channel to the nearby Mississippi, and the cave dried up—relatively speaking—except for seepage water which dripped from the roof and walls. Flowstone spread out on top of the sediment which had been left. Stalagmites reared up here and there, and a few stalactites hung down from the roof.

No one yet knows how long this period of decoration lasted. But it was followed by many extraordinarily wet years. At certain seasons the cave floor was covered by an underground lake, and clay in fine, thin layers piled up on top of the flowstone.

Meanwhile, aboveground, animals roamed the land. Among them were bands of a species of piglike peccary that has long been extinct and is known to scientists as *Platygonus compressus*. These creatures looked very fierce with their boarlike tusks, but their diet was strictly vegetarian, and they used their tusks only for digging up roots. Whole bands of them foraged on the land above the cave. Once— perhaps several times—something happened to frighten a band. The peccaries stampeded in a frenzy, as animals often do, and tumbled to death in a sinkhole or fissure which had once opened from the surface into Cherokee Cave, but which was now clogged at the bottom with debris. From time to time after that, rain water collected in this deep hole, forming a small pond or lake, and the peccary bodies decomposed, leaving a heap of bones.

Then one day when the hole was filled with water, the plug of debris in the bottom suddenly gave way. A great flood rushed down into the cave, strewing bones as it went and leaving them on top of the layers of sediment that had previously piled up there. The newly opened sinkhole or fissure was now a channel through which more surface water flowed, bearing more sediment—the loose, granular kind of clay that comes directly from the surrounding surface earth. This latest deposit covered the peccary bones and almost completely filled the large, more or less tubular, cavern passageway. Nothing bigger than a rodent could now make its way between the surface of the deposit and the ceiling, and in places there was no space at all.

There matters rested for thousands of years, until the 1820's when St. Louis had become a vigorous settlement and a gateway to the frontier. A German named Gottfried Duden, who was in search of a new home for some of his oppressed countrymen, came to St. Louis and found there what he considered a singular asset: Caves lay within the city limits—ready-made refrigerators for the beer which some of his compatriots from the Rhineland could brew with profit in this thirsty, bustling town.

Germans did settle in St. Louis and they did use the caverns as storage vaults for beer. One of them, Adam Lemp, cleared out the entrance to Cherokee Cave, removed tons of clay and bones from the passageway and carted them off—who knows where? With the coming of refrigeration, the Lemp brewery ceased to use the cave as a storage place, but in the 1890's a young member of the family with money to spend had it fitted out with an underground swimming pool and a stage for theatricals. To make the barren room look more realistic, he had artificial cave scenery installed. (Shades of Alexander Pope, who had had an artificial grotto constructed in his garden more than a century earlier!) The Lemps soon lost interest in their cave-within-a-cave, and when Prohibition came, they sold their brewery to a shoe manufacturer. Cherokee Cave now lay idle and forgotten beneath the busy streets of St. Louis.

Finally, in 1946, Lee Hess, who owned a quaint old mansion that had been built near the brewery-turned-shoe-factory, decided he would look into the possibilities of opening the cave as a commercial attraction. He had workmen break down the artificial wall that marked the end of the area where beer had once been stored. There ahead lay enormous masses of clay, obviously filling a big passageway. The workmen dug into it and began uncovering bones.

Hess wondered if the bones might be of interest, and so he sent some to the American Museum of Natural History in New York. Dr. George Gaylord Simpson, Curator of Fossil Mammals and

Birds, whose accounts of this cave form the source of what I have written about it, was indeed interested. He went to St. Louis with an assistant and began excavation—while he lived among the bric-a-brac in the old mansion above.

A week's digging in this incredibly rich bone mine yielded thousands of ribs, vertebrae, fragments of skulls. In due course Dr. Simpson pieced together as much of the story of the peccaries and of the cave itself as he is likely to—given the fact that scientists are not usually invited to uproot great business buildings or apartment houses in a hunt for a prehistoric sinkhole or fissure. A huge city now stands between researchers and the ancient deathtrap, no doubt long since filled in and deep under some street or structure. Dr. Simpson doesn't know exactly where the peccaries fell, nor exactly why, nor why only peccaries and very few other animals perished there. But a little bit of the animal past is clearer for his labors in Cherokee Cave.

On another occasion Dr. Simpson made a discovery of a very different kind in a cave in eastern Tennessee. The cave was a large one—Craighead Caverns—and it yielded up only a few bones, but these were sufficiently puzzling to provoke a piece of detective work that has added a colorful page to the rich history of America's mammals.

Craighead has been a much traveled cave, but caves have a way of holding back their secrets from prying eyes. Prehistoric Indians brought the first human traffic there, although they did not go far into the region of total darkness. Even if they had managed to make the discovery which astonished Dr. Simpson, they might not have been surprised at it—and this very fact gives a curious twist to the story, as we shall see.

Apparently the first private owner of the cave was a Cherokee Indian who was known by the surname of Craighead, and to him it owes its name. Perhaps during the time of Craighead's ownership, or perhaps later, after the Cherokees were herded off to Oklahoma, saltpetre-miners worked the cave and explored its large rooms, looking for petre-dirt to dig up. Other men came there to watch cock fights out of the view of censorious neighbors. Young men and women held dances in the spacious privacy offered by one of the chambers. For a while the cave was commercialized and visited by many tourists. Then a mushroom farmer put it to use. All in all, Craighead Caverns was a well-known place. But, luckily for the scientist who came later, none of this human activity disturbed a little cluster of bones that lay in one side passage. No careless boot marred a pair of curious footprints that had been left in damp clay.

In 1939 the cave was again being commercialized, and two employees—Jack Kyker and Clarence Hicks—grew enthusiastic about the place, much of which had not yet been explored. On their days off, they went farther and farther into the unknown, trying to probe to the end of every niche and cranny. In one of these crannies—a narrow fissure open at the bottom but closed at the top—several hundred feet from the entrance, they found some bones. In another place, more than a thousand feet beyond the bone pile, they found—high on some breakdown in a room that sloped up and finally pinched off—a big, curious animal track in wet clay.

Scientists at the American Museum of Natural History studied the bones and found they belonged to a jaguar—the same big spotted cat that lives in Central America today. Now here was a remarkable fact—a jaguar in Tennessee! No member of this species of big cat had ever been reported that far to the north. Dr. Simpson went out from the Museum to have a look, and there, close by the spot where the original bones had been found, he located more. These, too, proved to be part of a jaguar, and with them were the broken bones of a newborn elk. The bones were fossils, but they were only old in the terms man uses to describe the sped-up pace of history since white immigrants arrived on this continent. A geologist who thinks in units of millions of years—or at least hundreds of thousands—would not call them old by his standards.

There could be no doubt at all that at least one jaguar had lived in Tennessee—and in fairly recent times. This unexpected fact was a great general mystery, but there was a particular mystery about this one jaguar that also called for solution. How did he get to the very tight spot where he died? And what about the baby elk?

Dr. Simpson studied the cave structure and came up hesitantly with a guess: the jaguar had ambled into the cave with the small elk between his jaws, and walked too far and lost his way. In the total darkness he fell through a hole in the floor on an upper level—still carrying his food supply with him—and landed in a fissure up which he tried unsuccessfully to climb. The wall bears scars that might possibly be claw marks. In the end, he died of starvation after he had consumed the meat of the small elk.

With nothing more, apparently, that could be learned about the jaguar, Dr. Simpson turned to examine the mysterious footprint that had been made on top of the breakdown, close to the ceiling of a room deeper in the cave. There, no doubt about it, was the print of a large paw—seemingly with one toe missing. It was as fresh as if it had been made the day before. Almost no dust had settled on the paw print, which might have been in the damp clay for centuries. But that was not surprising because there was little dust to settle in the pure cave air.

However, Dr. Simpson is no man to stick his neck out. Before he would let himself believe that here, indeed, was the footprint of a jaguar, he had a cast made which he later compared with paw marks of a live jaguar supplied by the New York Zoological Society. After carefully eliminating the possibility of a hoax, he could only come to the conclusion that the footprint had been made not just by some big cat with a missing toe, but by a jaguar in the process of leaping.

How did this jaguar track turn up so far from the cave entrance? Was it made by the same beast who had died elsewhere in the cave, leaving his bones in the fissure a thousand feet closer to the entrance? Or had two different jaguars been lost in the cave? It was anybody's guess. But there could be no doubt of one thing. Craighead Caverns had produced evidence that jaguars once roamed far beyond what had long been regarded as the limits of their range.

This discovery prompted Dr. Simpson to take a second look at many other specimens. He found that in place after place, in widely separated parts of the country, big cat bones which had been carelessly identified were really jaguar bones.

Jaguars once ranged over most of the United States! This bit of news might never have been known but for the discovery of a skeleton and a footprint in a cave in Tennessee. But the story is not quite ended. Sebastian Cabot, the son of the famous Venetian navigator, John Cabot, drew a map of the eastern seaboard of North America in 1544, and on it he placed as a symbolic decoration a large spotted cat. Could Cabot have seen jaguars along the coast?

Thomas Jefferson heard stories about cats that he felt sure could only have been jaguars. The question as to exactly when and why this mighty race of cats disappeared is intriguing. Did Indians kill off jaguars just as white men later killed off the buffalo? Or were non-human factors responsible for the extinction of this species throughout most of the United States?

Mammalian life in the past certainly did undergo great changes without any intervention by man. A sweeping picture of these changes has come from a cave in a ridge near Cumberland, Maryland. This cave had two entrances—one which went in horizontally through the side of the ridge, and another straight down through the top. This latter was a sinkhole leading to the main level through a fissure dissolved out between beds of Helderberg limestone that had been tilted almost vertically. This limestone had been laid down in the Devonian age, when fish were the dominant form of life in the world—long before reptiles emerged from the water or birds took to the air. But the cave did not take on special interest until mammals appeared and became the rulers of the animal world.

Although the cave grew during long ages, its tunnel never seems to have exceeded two hundred feet in length. At some time before the last great Ice Age, sometime during the Pleistocene era, the two openings appeared in the ridge which offered a convenient trail between highlands and lowlands. In those days the coastal plain down to the east of the cave was watered with tropical rains, and a dense forest grew there. The Alleghenies to the west had less tropical vegetation because of the much higher altitude. But both areas supported an animal population, many forms of which have long since disappeared from our part of the world, or from the world as a whole. Animals from both the dense forest of the lowlands and the more open woods of the highlands wandered up and down the ridge in which lay the cave, with its treacherous sinkhole opening. Elands and tapirs and peccaries were small enough to make their way through the undergrowth. They could cross Wills Creek Valley below the cave and climb up the ridge. Big cats, preying on these and other animals, could also live in and around the forest, and they, too, reached the ridge.

At one time or another some of these animals that strayed up out of the forest onto the ridge fell into the sinkhole. Foxes, skunks, porcupines and other animals from the higher woodlands likewise strayed downward toward Wills Creek—and some of them fell to death in the cave.

After a long period the climate grew cooler with the last glacial advance. Semitropical grasslands replaced the tropical forest, and conifers replaced the deciduous trees of the uplands. Animals that were adapted to the new climate fell into the cave.

As the region grew still colder, new cold-weather animals, such as the lemming mouse, ended their lives in the sinkhole. The vast glacier that was moving south, bringing an arctic climate with it, never reached Maryland, and thus never filled or destroyed the cave. When the glacier retreated, the climate grew warmer, and animals familiar to us today appeared at the edge of the sinkhole and fell in.

The bodies of all these animals lodged in crevices near the top of the fissure that led down to the main level of the cave. Then the flesh decomposed, and the bones fell piece by piece from ledge to ledge until they reached the bottom. There they lay in an incredible jumble, many of them broken. Thousands of them piled up—ribs, jaws, legs—from forty-five different kinds of mammal, twenty-eight of which are now extinct. Water dripped over the bones, impregnating them with mineral so that they retained their shape and were solid.

For perhaps fifty centuries the place remained hidden and undisturbed. Relatively few modern animals added their skeletons to the heap, for the reason that the ridge became less and less the natural travel route between lowland and highland that it once had been. Erosion by Wills Creek had lowered the valley floor and rendered the ridge more and more inaccessible. If Indians entered the cave, no record of their visit was ever found, but pioneer white hunters did know of it and used it for shelter at least. They even left old flintlock guns there on the main level, and either forgot to come back for them or could not. At any rate, they saw nothing of special interest in the large heap of bones, nor did workmen when, in 1900, they set about sytematically destroying the cave as they quarried for limestone on the site.

Not until the Western Maryland Railway decided to make a cut through the hill, did anyone take an interest in the bones that still remained. An amateur naturalist from Cumberland one day saw quantities of the bones being removed by men at work in the cut. He sent word to J. W. Gidley of the United States National Museum, who came to the site and saved what he could. Off and on for four years Gidley collected bones from the small portion of the cave that had not been destroyed, first by the quarry and then by the railroad. Fifteen years later another man from the National Museum, C. Lewis Gazin, resumed work for a time.

An ardent young speleologist who taught science in a Catholic high school in Cumberland, Brother G. Nicholas, knew of the collections made by Gidley and Gazin, and of the reports they had published. He was curious about the Cumberland Bone Cave, and one day in 1950 he took a look at the place. To prevent accidents, the railroad had sealed the entrance to what remained of the cave. Brother Nicholas tried for several days to reopen it, but did not succeed. While he was at work, however, his trained speleological eye noticed something high on one side of the cut that interested him greatly. There, exposed to the weather, were the remains of calcite speleothems—stalactites and flowstone. A wall of the cave exactly coincided with the point where the vertical cut had been made. There was more than a good chance that some evidence of a cave passage would appear on the opposite wall of the cut at about the same level. Brother Nicholas searched the rock and found the opening he expected. It was small, very small, but it led into a hitherto unexcavated portion of the cave. The room he entered was cramped—scarcely twenty feet long and ten feet wide, with two feet of space between the ceiling and the debris on the floor. Still, it took only a glance to see that the debris contained fossil bones.

Brother Nicholas began to dig—but he had troubles. The opening through which he had entered was so small, and the ceiling so low, that he could not shovel out the dirt. He had to make a new entrance under a thin wall of limestone that stood between part of the old quarry and the railroad cut. Now he could shovel debris from one part of the cave to another. But progress was slow. He had to sift every shovelful of dirt so that he would not miss any bones or bone fragments, and the dust was stifling. By the end of 1950 he had dug down two feet, and that only in some parts of the room. He continued with helpers to dig at intervals for another year. The work was exceedingly arduous. The room was tiny, the ventilation poor, and the dust very thick. The diggers had to wear respirators in order to breathe and goggles in order to see. Nevertheless, excavation went on until it seemed likely that the stone above, which was already weakened by quarrying and by blasting for the railroad cut, might collapse.

The railroad, which had destroyed so much of the bone deposit, then came to the rescue and removed the dangerous stone, leaving what was once a cave open to light and fresh air. Work could go on with much greater ease and safety. By the summer of 1953, Brother Nicholas had a large number of bones—enough to merit careful study. He then began cleaning and cataloguing his finds. After that, using his own collection and the older collection in the National Museum, he started a new piece of scientific detective work.

Many a paleontologist would have been satisfied with discovering new species of extinct mammals. Brother Nicholas, however, went on to make his collection give up something more significant. From the bits of bone and teeth he determined how each animal must have lived—whether on plants or meat, and on what kind of plant or meat. Using data gleaned from the geologic history of the Cumberland area, he determined where this food could have grown—and when. In time he had enough data to piece together a whole panoramic picture of changing climates and changing plant and animal life, and of the interrelationship of animals to one another and to their total environment. All this from a heap of broken bones in a cave that had almost been destroyed!

Other caves—and some of these have been destroyed by quarrying operations, too—have produced similarly important deposits of fossilized bones. The biggest is Port Kennedy Bone Cave in Montgomery County, Pennsylvania, which was worked for over thirty years and yielded more than forty-five tons of bones.

No man can say when or where or by which caver the next significant find of Pleistocene bones will be made. But there can be no doubt that more discoveries are waiting for the alert spelunker or speleologist.

CHAPTER FIVE

Caves—a Clue to Human History

While animals now extinct were falling into bone caves, other ancient mammals foraged in the rain-drenched forests and around the marshes and lakes in what is now the semi-arid state of New Mexico. Hunters armed only with stone-pointed spears brought down camels, mammoths and mastodons. Sometimes they chased one of the huge beasts into a swamp, where it made a safe, stationary target; sometimes they drove their prey over a bluff as the handiest way of getting meat. Game was plentiful in New Mexico, and in the face of a bluff in the Sandia Mountains, one band of hunters found something else that they liked—a cave consisting of a tunnel ten feet in diameter where they could take shelter from the rains. There, perhaps twenty-five or thirty thousand years ago, they set up camp.

The naked—or almost naked—men and women built fires for warmth, and they may have roasted chunks of camel and mammoth meat over the flames. At any rate, they split the animals' bones with sharp-edged stones in order to get at the nourishing marrow. After sucking out this delicacy, they tossed the cracked bones aside on the cave floor, to be covered later by other garbage and ashes and dust. Since the ivory tusks of the prehistoric elephants made good tools, the hunters brought some of these into the cave, too. And being careless, just as people are today, they lost some of their pointed stone spearheads in the rubbish that littered their dwelling place.

Time passed, and these first occupants of the New Mexico cave moved on or were killed by rival hunters. The cave lay vacant for a long while. The rains continued, and seepage water left a deposit of an iron compound—yellow ochre—on the floor. Gradually the deposit hardened.

Then about ten thousand years ago, when the cave was again dry, a new group of hunters discovered that it made a convenient shelter. They, too, using only spears as weapons, killed camels and mammoths just as their predecessors had done. They also ate horses —a species that disappeared from the Western Hemisphere long before the Spanish arrived with the ancestors of our present horses. And they had still another delicacy that earlier men had apparently overlooked, although the creature was surely somewhere about, lumbering slowly, almost waiting to be killed—the giant ground sloth.

The newcomers were no more tidy than the first tenants in the cave, and were just as careless with their tools. They, too, lost spear points in the debris. These points were very different from those of the first inhabitants—more finely wrought, with very tiny chips removed to make cutting edges, and with a distinctive groove running down the center of each side. Because points fashioned in this style were first found near Folsom, New Mexico, they are called Folsom points, and the men who used them, Folsom Men.*

In time Folsom Men moved out, and the cave remained empty for several thousand years. Another wet period came, and this time a calcite crust of flowstone formed over the layers of debris.

Then, within the last few hundred years, Pueblo Indians made some use of the cave and left behind them proof of their great advances in skills. The Pueblos had learned the art of farming, and they knew how to make beautiful pots of baked clay in which to store and to cook corn and beans and dried squash. Broken pottery littered the floor of Sandia Cave, as it was soon to be called. But

---

* To anticipate queries which the author knows from experience are bound to come, he hastens to add that he had nothing to do with discovering Folsom points or naming them or having them named. He is not related to Folsom Man, to the best of his knowledge. Rather, he is descended from an immigrant who arrived in this country only a little over three hundred years ago—instead of more than ten thousand years ago—and the immigrant's name was not even Folsom. His name was John Smith, which he changed when he found himself surrounded by too many other Smiths, choosing—and misspelling—the name of the English village from which he had come.

at last a section of the limestone bluff up which so many different people had climbed to shelter fell away, leaving the entrance less convenient to reach than it had been for thousands of years.

Apparently none of the early Spanish settlers, or the early American pioneers who followed them, ever entered the cave. It was not "discovered" until one spring day in 1936 when a group of Boy Scouts found their way in. Their reports of the place reached Kenneth Davis, a student at the University of New Mexico in nearby Albuquerque. He set out for a weekend of exploring, located the small opening that betrayed the tunnel in the face of the bluff, and scrambled up to it. Pottery fragments on the dusty floor roused his interest. He took a cigar box full of them to the energetic archeologist, Dr. Frank C. Hibben, at the University. The potsherds in themselves were not unusual, but Dr. Hibben went, in a more or less routine way, to check up on the cave where Davis had found them—and a lucky thing he did. The longer he looked amid the suffocating dust of the place, the more excited he became.

During four summers, with a crew of helpers, Dr. Hibben dug down through the layer of Pueblo debris, then through the hard calcite crust, then through the layer of Folsom Man debris with its bones of extinct mammals. The find of Folsom material, together with these animals, was important enough. Up to this time Folsom Man was believed to be the oldest human being on the American continents, and any new evidence about him was welcome.

But beneath the layer of yellow ochre, Dr. Hibben unearthed more spear points not at all like those worked by Folsom craftsmen, and more bones, some of them cracked and still bearing the marks of the stones that broke them. Here was evidence of a man many thousands of years older than Folsom Man. Sandia Man he is called, after the name of the cave.

How old was Sandia Man? No one could be quite sure, but Dr. Hibben made an estimate of twenty to twenty-five thousand years. Subsequent laboratory tests indicated that organic matter in the Sandia Man layer was at least seventeen thousand years old—perhaps twenty thousand. These tests in themselves were a demonstration of the expanding range of sciences that speleologists can call on to help them unravel the mysteries held by caves: It was nuclear physics that produced the date, by analyzing the ratio of radioactive carbon atoms to non-radioactive carbon atoms in the organic material.

The theory is that all living things contain a certain proportion of radioactive carbon—carbon 14, it is called. But after a plant or animal dies, this proportion constantly decreases as carbon 14 turns into ordinary nitrogen through the steady loss of electrons. The rate at which this change takes place is known. In the first 5,568 years—give or take 30 years—half of the carbon 14 in a piece of organic matter disappears. Then, in the next 5,568 years ±30, half of the remaining carbon 14 disappears, and so on. By analyzing the amount of carbon 14 that remains in old material, and comparing it with the amount in living material, it is possible to know fairly accurately how much time has passed since that material ceased to live.

With nuclear physics, as with all sciences, refinements continue to be made. By the fall of 1955, new Geiger-counter tests of Sandia material indicated an age of twenty-five to thirty thousand years. The organic matter tested was ivory from the prehistoric elephant tusks which Dr. Hibben found in association with Sandia Man's spear points. It is possible, of course, that those ancient hunters salvaged ivory that had been lying around for some thousands of years, but since they ate the meat of the huge creatures, it is fairly reasonable to suppose that they lugged into the cave the tusks of a fresh kill.

Whether the date of Sandia Man goes back twenty or thirty thousand years, Sandia Cave has supplied evidence that man has been on this continent an exceedingly long time. Here, as has happened in many places around the world, excellent data on ancient human life had been preserved underground—and there are thousands of American caves undiscovered and unexplored. Possibly one of them contains the bones of Sandia Man or Folsom Man himself. These have not yet been discovered. So far we know these early men only by their artifacts. Perhaps—not perhaps, certainly—caves still hide many clues to the history of human beings in our hemisphere.

Dr. M. R. Harrington filled in one historical gap when he excavated the floor of a small cave in a gypsum formation in Nevada. On top he found relics of the Paiute Indians who had somehow managed to survive in the area after a drought had made the great

Nevada-Utah Basin almost uninhabitable. Below that were remains of Pueblo Indians who had spread far and wide, drawing strength from the corn they raised when the Basin was not yet withered to a desert. And below the Pueblo debris lay remains of clever makers of baskets upon whose culture the Pueblos had built. But still lower lay the first evidence discovered that man and the giant ground sloth had lived at the same time, when moisture was abundant.

Dung of the ground sloth covered the floor of the cave, but Dr. Harrington didn't know at first what it was. Packages of the ancient excreta went out through the mails to eminent museums in various parts of the country. Only when the huge droppings were positively identified by paleontologists was he sure of the significance of his find, for he had also discovered man-made spear points and wooden spear shafts lying among the dung. To clinch matters, he had proof that a ground sloth had been there *after* man had built fires and left tools in the cave. A ground sloth skull lay *on top of* breakdown that had fallen and covered a whole layer of sloth dung and human relics.

Ventana Cave in southwestern Arizona recently yielded a story of human occupation at various times during the last ten thousand years. However, Ventana is not a true solution cave—that is, it was not formed by the action of water on soluble limestone, dolomite, marble or gypsum—and hence it has no place in this book. It is one of the shallow shelters in a volcanic formation which, like many small openings in rocks of various kinds, have been called caves. Similarly it would be tempting to tell of the archeological finds in the great sandstone niches in Mesa Verde National Park and elsewhere. It is enough to indicate here what an explorer who has an archeological bent may expect to find in the deeper and much more elaborate solution caves. And when such a caver finds evidence of human habitation, may he have the modesty and self-control to leave the place and its contents just as he found them! Then fully qualified scientists can use their delicate techniques in an effort to expand the horizon of man's knowledge about himself.

In the fall of 1947, a group of spelunkers who had heard such advice received interesting news one day. They were invited by Jeff Higginbotham, a farmer in Tazewell County, Virginia, to be the first to explore a cave he had just discovered on his land. The spelunkers, all students at Virginia Polytechnic Institute in nearby Blacksburg and all members of the National Speleological Society, put on their muddy coveralls and hard hats and went off in high hope. A new cave was always exciting.

For years Jeff Higginbotham—and obviously his predecessors on the land—had plowed around a large boulder that lay in the middle of a field. This year, however, was different. The plow accidentally caught on the boulder and pulled it to one side. Since it was so easily moved, Higginbotham hitched his team to the big rock and dragged it out of the field. To his amazement, he saw that it had covered a hole—and that the hole led down into the earth. Hoping that he might have laid bare a cave of some possible value, Higginbotham called in the nearest group of spelunkers about whom he had heard.

The students lowered themselves by ropes down a fifteen-foot shaft into the darkness below. At first they encountered only mud, but soon they spied a bone, then another bone, sticking out of the muck. A little more search revealed a human skull. Here, in fact, was a great heap of human bones. Few cave explorers had ever come upon such a find. The excited spelunkers—among them Albert C. Mueller, later to become a vice-president of the National Speleological Society—agreed to leave everything as they found it, so that experts could unravel whatever mystery surrounded the place.

Back at college after the expedition, the students discussed their discovery with a scientist on the faculty, and under his enthusiastic direction they set about exhuming the bones. They dug up thirty skeletons—all Indian, as proved by jewelry found together with the bones, but all dumped unceremoniously into the cave in a most un-Indian-like fashion. One, at least, of the skeletons revealed evidence of violent death. There was an arrow imbedded in a vertebra. But he and his companions had not been victims of a massacre at the hands of white men, for not a bullet mark could be seen on the bones. Here teacher and students reached an impasse. The cave offered no evidence to explain why warriors and women and children had been buried there without any of the formalities that were usually so important to Indians in disposing of the dead. Nor was it known to be the custom of victors to bury their victims, even by so easy a method as dumping them in a hole and then rolling a rock over the entrance.

At this point a local legend revealed a possible explanation. When white men first entered the area, they heard that at some time in the past there had been a big battle between two rival bands of Cherokees and Shawnees, and one of them—to conceal its losses—had hidden its dead. One day scientists with more evidence before them may come up with a more precise explanation for this astounding assemblage of human remains. Fortunately for archeology, a great quantity of bones was left unexcavated in the cave for later scholars to examine. The initial care of the student spelunkers who did not disturb what they found—or take skulls and bones back to their dormitories as souvenirs—and the later care shown when part of the deposit was left intact for future study were models of good sense which may one day result in greater understanding of America's Indian history.

Other caves that have preserved evidence of Indian life offer glimpses, sometimes illuminating and sometimes merely tantalizing, of the ways of early man. Wyandotte Cave in southern Indiana is perhaps richest among the well-known caverns both for the solid facts discovered there and for the mysteries it holds that have so far defied scientific investigation, although they have been well described by George F. Jackson in his book, *Wyandotte Cave.*

Visitors to the cave in the mid-nineteenth century often noticed that a large chunk of the huge stalagmite known as the Pillar of the Constitution had been broken away. The best guess then was that saltpetre-miners who had worked the cave during the war of 1812 had been guilty of this act of vandalism. But in 1877 a geologist found near the marred stalagmite several rounded stones that greatly interested him because they were not native to the area. They were like many other such rocks that had been carried south by the great glaciers of the Ice Age, but how did they get *inside*—far inside—a limestone cavern?

The rocks showed bruises and wear of the kind they would show if they had been used as hammers. Professor John Collett, the geologist, concluded that primitive human beings who used rocks as hammers must have brought them into the cave at some distant point in the past. A year later Dr. H. C. Hovey, an alert student of caves, pondered the evidence and agreed that Indians must have mined out the base of the Pillar of the Constitution.

In 1896 W. S. Blatchley did some serious excavating near the Pillar, and what he found was amazing. Under a half-inch layer of bat guano lay fourteen inches of ashes mixed with chips of stalagmite. Human beings had built a great many fires here during a very long period of time. Beneath the ashes was an inch of charcoal, more evidence of man-made fire. Then came three more inches of ashes. Then twenty-eight inches of broken chunks of stalagmite. Then a half-inch of charcoal, and finally four more inches of stalagmitic material.

Nor was this all the evidence that primitive man had engaged in mining. Blatchley dug up more stones—foreign to the cave—which could have served as hammers, and deer horns which Indians in a great many places used as wedges. Later diggers found more hammer stones near the Pillar.

There was no doubt that prehistoric men had mined calcite far inside the dry upper level of Wyandotte. But why did they do this mining—and when?

No one has so far been able to turn up evidence that any Indians who ever lived near Wyandotte used calcite for anything. A good guess might be that the relatively soft glossy mineral was mined so that it could be fashioned into ornaments. But no calcite ornaments have been found in the area—and very few exist anywhere. At this point mineralogists enter with the explanation that even if ornaments had been made of calcite in the distant past, they might not now exist because of the tendency of calcite to decompose.

The two questions—*why* the stalagmitic material was dug out and *when*—may, then, be closely related. It is well known that Indians of the Mound Builder culture, which spread up the Mississippi and Ohio River valleys over a thousand years ago, did a great deal of mining. They dug copper in the Great Lakes area, and they hacked out sheets of mica in the Appalachians. Both of these minerals they fashioned into beautiful ornaments. Possibly they did the same with calcite, but we just don't know about it because calcite can and does turn to shapeless flakes and dust.

Two bits of evidence, however, suggest that the miners may have lived long before the Mound Builders. One is that the hammers used were merely rounded rocks, and not rocks to which handles were attached. Mound Builders knew how to make and use hammers with handles. The second piece of evidence is at once more definite and more puzzling. It turned up in the mid-nineteenth century and greatly interested Dr. Hovey when he studied the cave in 1878.

In 1850 explorers widened a small hole in an otherwise solid wall of flowstone. Fairly careful estimates of the growth rate of the flowstone indicated that two or three thousand years might have passed since that hole was large enough for a human being to crawl through.

Yet on the other side of the flowstone wall discoverers found moccasin tracks! Obviously the footprints had been made when the clay floor of the room was damp. The sharp-edged heels of modern shoes left almost no trace in the clay. So moccasined feet must have passed this way long, long ago.

But the mystery has only begun. The tracks all point in one direction—*deeper into the cave*. Was there another entrance to Wyandotte at some distant time? Diligent search has so far failed to locate any such entrance. Did the calcite-miners leave these footprints, or did a later people?

Large-scale evidence exists that many pre-white men visited a quite separate part of the cave—a passage on a level one hundred feet below the spot where the big calcite digging lies. The fact is that Wyandotte was a rich source of a material on which primitive hunters depended for their livelihood. It contained large quantities of flint imbedded in the limestone walls—flint for knives and spearheads and arrowheads. And where it appeared, we can still see proof that it was mined. Chunks of artificially broken stone lie on the cave floor, along with charred wood, and remnants of torches made of strips of hickory bark bound together with grapevine thongs. Smoke blackens the walls in places where flint nodules have been cracked off or gouged out.

Flint was mined in Wyandotte—of that there is no doubt—and men quite sensibly took it out into sunlight to do the delicate work of shaping it into tools and weapons. The sites of several workshops where flint points were made have been found in the general area. But were the flint-miners the same people who hacked away, in the smoky light of fires, at the Pillar of the Constitution until they had removed 240 cubic feet of its base?

The calcite-miners could reach their goal in the cave without ever passing a flint deposit. Little if any mining of calcite took place on the level where flint is found. Two different sets of people from two different cultures, at two widely separated times, could have been involved. Since remarkably little scientific digging has yet been done in this cave, there is a very good chance that archeologists may yet piece together a full story of those early explorers who lacked all standard spelunking equipment, but who penetrated the deep recesses in one of this country's really extensive cavern systems.

When an archeologist digs in a cave—even with the most refined techniques—he does not, in an automatic way, remove puzzles from the long lists which have kept scientists wondering. As like as not, a dig may merely increase the roster of things we know we don't know. Take, for example, the caves in the limestone bluffs of the Hueco Mountains in the western tip of Texas along the New Mexico border. A 1925 expedition from the Peabody Museum at Harvard, led by Mr. and Mrs. C. B. Cosgrove, located forty-one shallow caves in the area and reported that there were doubtless more. The Cosgroves and their helpers excavated thirteen of them, using the greatest care to salvage every bit of the considerable Indian remains perfectly preserved there by the dry desert air. From the layman's point of view, the most interesting discovery was a wealth of colored paintings, which still remain to be seen on the walls. These American caves contained primitive art quite as interesting in its stylized way as the famous pictures left by prehistoric "cave men" in the Pyrenees. Beautifully colored ceremonial objects made of wood also turned up in abundance. Fabrics showing a great variety of weaving techniques remained intact—bags, mats, baskets, fur cloth, cordage, braided bands. There were elaborate snares for catching small animals, a wealth of arrow points and spear points, and shafts carefully and cunningly constructed.

Religious objects of many kinds abounded, along with personal decorations—hair ornaments, beads—some fashioned from transparent gypsum, some made of seashells brought all the way from California. Tanned buckskin remained well preserved, and wooden tools—fire drills and sticks used by southwestern farming Indians for planting corn. There were bone awls, stone hammers, mortars and pestles for grinding up small seeds and coloring matter, corn-grinding tools (manos and metates). Corn cobs ranged from the small primitive ears up to large ears that resemble the corn we know today.

The quantity of material discovered was tremendous, and it made possible a complete picture of how Indians in the now dry and desolate Hueco Mountains once lived—and how they evolved a continuously higher and higher form of culture. Burials in the caves gave added information.

Scholars, working with these and similar materials gathered all over the Southwest, have been able to put together an even larger picture of pre-Columbian Indians in the area, from the days when their highest achievement was the making of baskets, down to fairly recent times when Pueblo Indians became masters of the advanced art of pottery. It has even been possible to trace trade routes that interlaced the Southwest, running between various caves and shelters and between farming communities aboveground. The shells from California provided one clue to the considerable trading back and forth. Pottery offered another; each village had its own distinctive designs and shapes and often its own methods of firing pots. Thus, with only a fragment to look at, an expert can usually tell where a pot was made, perhaps many miles from the ruins in which an archeologist, working with a sieve, strained the shard out of the dust and dirt.

Indian sandals have yielded still another clue to the vast interchange among Southwestern tribes. So much footgear has been dug up by various expeditions that scholars now know where, and even approximately when, a sandal was woven out of yucca or some other fiber by a prehistoric shoemaker.

More than twelve hundred *worn-out* sandals were found by the Cosgroves in one of the Hueco caves. But their various designs showed that they came from many widely separated Indian settlements. Here was proof that people had trudged mile after mile to converge on a small group of shelters in a remote mountainside. But why had they journeyed? One might expect traders to exchange worn-out footgear for new, but why should this mass of castoff sandals have been saved? Quite clearly the sandal cave had not been used for dwelling purposes. It contained none of the household goods which were abundant in nearby caves. Archeologists could give only one guess. The cave must have been some kind of shrine, and pilgrims who had come long distances left their worn-out footgear there as part of a religious rite.

But what fear or hope—what compelling belief—had drawn large numbers of human beings to this hole in a limestone bluff? Perhaps more digging in the area may one day turn up evidence of the world-view of a people who obviously attached great significance to one particular cavity twenty-seven feet wide, fifteen feet high and ninety feet long. Whether or not the mystery of the sandals is ever solved, the Hueco caves have richly documented the fact, known from many other sources, too, that the Indians of the Southwest had a long history and gradually evolved a most complex way of life.

How little we know about some phases of this life became apparent only recently as a result of exploration in caves of the Grand Canyon by the Western Speleological Institute. There, in a cave in the Redwall limestone near Yaki Point on the South Rim, Malcolm F. Farmer and Raymond de Saussure found a large number of animal-shaped objects that on first sight resemble the woven toy horses sold in Mexican markets today. But these cave miniatures were usually much smaller than the modern toys, and they had been made of split twigs bound together. Many of the figurines were in the large outer chamber of the cave, but some lay farther along in the area of total darkness. Finally, the speleologists discovered in the cave materials for making more figurines. The little objects had apparently been constructed on the spot and left there—but why were they left, and when, and by whom?

Split-twig figurines were not unknown to scientists. Others had been found in the Grand Canyon area and always in caves. It seems possible that they served some ceremonial purpose—as prayers for good hunting or effigies of some other sort. (Two seem to have been made with spears stuck in their ribs.) But no known legend or practice of any of the Indians who have lived in the area in historic times throws any light on them, and no clear evidence helps to date them. Here is a cave puzzle as unique in its way as that of the sandals in Ceremonial Cave in the Huecos. As the tempo and intensity of exploration increase—which they have been doing

in recent years—some enterprising speleologist may find the keys to
these perplexing products of the energy of early Americans, who
probed in their own ways to solve the riddle of survival in a very
baffling world.

The search for solutions to problems is no special characteristic
of modern Americans of European origin. Indians often used magic
formulae in an effort to resolve the difficulties which beset them—
a practice we moderns have by no means dropped. The Wintun
Indians, who lived on the western side of the Sacramento Valley
in California, near a cave which they called Samwel and which
still bears that name (sometimes spelled Samuel), thought they
had found a good nostrum in the water of an underground pool. An
old legend taught them that people who ventured into the cave
and drank this water would have good luck. On top of the legend
was a story, which persisted down to recent times, of three young
women who went to the pool and drank from it, but with no
perceptible results. Then an old woman of the tribe, who knew
about such things, assured them that if they returned to the cave
and drank from a second pool, the good luck they sought would
surely be theirs. The maidens went back in search of the second
pool. But on the brink of a deep pit one of the three, So-Se-Ne by
name, slipped and fell. As she plummeted into the darkness which
the light from their torches could not pierce, her companions heard
So-Se-Ne strike something. They heard her body strike a second
time—and then all was silence.

This story was told and retold among the Wintun Indians for
perhaps two hundred years, and at last it came to the ears of
scientists interested in what caves had to offer. Among them was
Dr. J. C. Merriam, a paleontologist primarily concerned with locating prehistoric animal fossils. But Dr. Merriam, together with other
members of an expedition that went out to dig in California caves,
decided it might be worthwhile to look in Samwel for any evidence
that would prove or disprove the story about So-Se-Ne.

A vigorous hunt yielded no evidence of the pit, let alone of the
Indian maiden, and the researchers moved out of the cave—all
except a stubborn member of the group named Furlong, who
wanted to have one more try. He stayed behind. Dr. Merriam
hadn't been back in his base camp very long when word came from

Furlong that he had discovered a series of chambers which had been overlooked. In one of them was a pit that might be ninety feet deep. Would Merriam please return with a rope ladder?

Dr. Merriam obliged as best he could, but the ladder he brought was not long enough. Using odds and ends of rope, and sticks picked up nearby, he and Furlong improvised an extension to the ladder and lowered it into the pit. Then they drew lots to see who should go down first. Furlong won. Before long he shouted from the depths, ". . . big cat!" Merriam feared for his companion's safety—or sanity—and was both relieved and professionally interested when word came up out of the pit that Furlong's cat was only a skeleton.

When Merriam himself descended, he found not only the big cat bones but also the skeletons of many other animals, all ancient. They were deeply incrusted with dripstone, and some of them belonged to mammals that were entirely new to science. These were find enough, but alongside them lay something of greater interest—the delicate bones of a slender young woman, and these bore only a thin coating of mineral. They were very recent by paleontological standards. Moreover, they lay at the bottom of a pit, and above them a rock jutted out. This could well have been the place where, according to the Wintun legend, So-Se-Ne struck and then tumbled on down to death. Here was very good evidence—perhaps even proof—that the old story was based on fact.

As Dr. Merriam proceeded to examine the prehistoric animal bones, he found one tiny thing that excited him greatly—the fragment of a human tooth. Could it be that man and these very ancient animals had lived in California at the same time? If so, Merriam had made a find of potentially great significance to science. It might push far back the date of human habitation of America. However, Merriam did not let himself be carried away. He considered all possibilities, and one of these was that the fragment might have come from one of So-Se-Ne's teeth. A check showed that such was the case. Science would have to look elsewhere for a link between these ancient animals and man.

But how, then, did the tooth fragment come to lie some distance from So-Se-Ne's body? The exact words of the Wintun story came to Merriam's mind again. "She struck and struck again—and all was still." He had found a jutting rock in the wall of the pit where her head could have hit as she fell. The force of the impact must have sent the broken tooth flying across the room from the spot where her body landed. So-Se-Ne must have met death just as Wintun story-tellers had been claiming for generations.

Let cynics complain that no physical anthropologist ever examined the slender bones to determine whether they belonged, in fact, to a boy or a girl. The story is too good to spoil. And the interest which Furlong and Merriam took in it paid off in ways which they could not have expected—as often happens with science and with human curiosity in general. They found the bones of hitherto unknown prehistoric animals well preserved in stone, among them a goatlike animal and another with oxlike horns.

But was it possible that these creatures had strayed through dark galleries until they, like the Indian girl, slipped and fell into the pit? The positions in which the bones lay indicated no such thing. Then there must have been, long ago, some easy passage from the pit to the outside world. Search revealed a possible route through which the animals might have come in, but the former entrance—if such it was—had been sealed for a very long time. There was nothing to do but dig, and so Merriam's party set to work, shoveling away both inside the cave and at a spot outside where they calculated the ancient opening might have been. Their reward came, not too unexpectedly, when tools broke through the earth fill, and one of the underground laborers crawled cheerfully through the hole.

A mystery—two, in fact—had been solved because an Indian legend led white men to a cave. Indians themselves have led white men to other caves, just as they led them into the heart of the continent by way of trails they had laid out and had sometimes worn very deep. Caves—which are still a new frontier in one sense—were in another sense part of an older frontier where white men literally followed in the footsteps of Indians.

CHAPTER SIX

Mines, Money and Mayhem

When white men first stepped ashore on the Caribbean islands and along the eastern seaboard, Indians were most hospitable and became enthusiastic tutors to the newcomers in their land. Realization that the white men were not just visitors but invaders was by no means universal or immediate. A hundred and eighty years after Columbus landed, the Spaniard Friar Berreda was still greeted warmly in a Choctaw village in the westernmost part of Florida just south of where the Georgia-Alabama line now runs.

The Choctaws not only allowed Friar Berreda to preach to them; they also showed him the sights—one of which was a cave nearby that had a room large enough to hold two hundred people.

Friar Berreda was apparently an itinerant missionary and did not linger long or return soon. Nineteen years passed before he came back to minister to his converts—if, indeed, he had any. He found the Choctaw village gone, for reasons he does not report. But he remembered the ample cave and the shelter it could give, and on the night of June 12, 1693, he camped there and enjoyed the brook which he noted "gushes from the living rock."

Friar Berreda's visit to the Choctaws' cave (which is now part of Florida Caverns State Park near Marianna, Florida) is the earliest to be recorded. And it shows the classic pattern: White men were heirs to the knowledge of this land which Indians had gained.

North of Florida, the hardy explorers and fishermen and traders who visited the eastern coast, and then the colonists who set up precarious housekeeping at Plymouth and Jamestown, had nothing to say about caves in the New World. The reason for this was simple. There were almost no limestone caves of any size close to the Atlantic seaboard.

Some shallow caves that had been hollowed out of various kinds of rock by the pounding action of waves did appear on the more rugged portions of the coast, and men who had the kind of business best conducted out of the bright glare of sunlight did find and use some of these sea caves. Legends have it that this or that sea cave still holds pirate treasure. The name of Captain Kidd is linked with more than one grotto, and the searches for treasure in them have been legion.

Possibly—just possibly—some day a major find may be made in some hollowed-out cranny near the sea by some ingenious and persistent person with modern electronic equipment. At least one such find of some value has been made, but it was in the beach sands of Cape Cod and not in a cave: in 1945 Edgar Rowe Snow, using an electronic treasure detector and following clues he found pricked with a pin in an old book, turned up a copper chest full of rare coins dating back as far as 1694.

Very early in American history the search for wealth, if not for treasure, in caves began. While settlers still hadn't moved beyond the coastal plains and low hills near the Atlantic, explorers were learning as much as they could about the vast Mississippi Valley. One of these was a Frenchman, Jacques Renault, who in the year 1716 camped somewhere near the present site of St. Louis. There he listened carefully to stories told by friendly Indians, probably Osages. The Indians spoke of a cave to the west that was the home of one of their gods, and they mentioned rocks of a kind that greatly interested Renault because he felt sure they contained valuable copper and lead.

The Frenchman, following directions given by the Indians, ascended the Meramec River, beyond the point reached by De Soto 177 years before. The cave was exactly where he had been told it would be—and Renault was the first white man to enter what is now widely known as Meramec Caverns.

Back East where settlement was still confined to a fairly narrow strip of land, cave exploration revealed no such spectacular underground systems of tunnels as Meramec—for the reason that there were none to find in the inhabited area. Still there were small caves, and hunters and farmers often located them, and at least once an early spelunker entered a New England cave in the face of very real danger. It all happened before the American Revolution, and a man who was destined to be a hero of the Revolution was also hero of this adventure. Israel Putnam was his name. Clay Perry has retold the story in his *New England's Buried Treasure.*

Putnam and the other farmers in the neighborhood of Pomfret, Connecticut, had grown weary of the raids that a certain she-wolf was making on their flocks. It was bad enough when a wolf had an occasional meal off a sheep or a lamb, but the wolf in question had developed a frenzied love of killing for its own sake, and on one foray she destroyed seventy-five of Putnam's sheep. He was no man to take such an attack as a preordained act of God.

Organizing his neighbors, all of whom were also sufferers at the jaws of the wolf, he led a party that was determined to track her to her lair and destroy her. The identity of the wolf was known. She had a crippled paw and left an unmistakable track. Putnam and his men found her trail and followed it for hour after tedious hour. Finally it led to an opening on a limestone ledge on a hill. The hole was not much larger than a man needed for entry, but Putnam determined to continue the chase. After loading his musket with buckshot and lighting a birchbark torch, he headed into the unknown to face the wolf. But before he got down on his belly and started his crawl, he made spelunking history by becoming the first cave-explorer in this country known to have used a safety rope. His method of attaching it was unorthodox by today's standards, although it had a certain logic. He tied the rope around his ankles so that when he signaled with a vigorous kick, he could be pulled out feet first through the narrow opening.

Inside the cave his smoky torch revealed a space only slightly broader and higher than the opening. The whole thing was only about forty feet deep, but off its narrow main channel ran small side channels—a good place for a wolf, but a poor place for a man to meet one.

The blaze from the torch soon reflected back from two shining objects that could only be eyes. The wolf at bay in the far end of the forty-foot passage growled, and her growls were loud enough to be heard at the entrance. The farmers and Putnam's servant, fearing for his life, hauled away without ceremony on the safety line. Putnam came out through the opening feet first, as he had planned, but swearing furiously, his shirt over his head and his body badly scratched.

With the aid of a good swig of hard cider, he regained his composure and squirmed back into the cave. This time he managed to take uncertain aim in the gloomy cramped quarters. He fired. Again his aides pulled him out. Determined to see if he had hit his mark, he crawled in once more, and when he was dragged out through the opening again, he had the dead wolf by the ears.

Like Putnam's wolf, bandits, outlaws, Tories, fled to caves before and during the Revolution to escape well-deserved justice. And patriots who served their country heroically also found shelter in caves. In New Jersey, which was infested with Tories, the brave farmer Thomas Hart signed the Declaration of Independence, but having done so, found that if he wanted to live, he had better hide. He went to a small cave in the Sourland Mountains near Hopewell known only to him and to a few of his trusted neighbors. There for months he stayed in safety, if not in comfort, and his friends brought him food.

Caves were numerous around Schoharie, New York, and in one of them an interesting friendship developed that was a strange contrast to the violence of the Revolutionary War in the area. This cave was known to the Mohawks who had lived nearby for centuries— they called it Otsgaragee, "The Cave of Many Galleries"—but by the 1770's the Indians seldom visited it. They had little use for it as a shelter, since they had become village-dwellers, living as much from farming as from hunting. And now they sent fewer and fewer hunting parties to the area near the cave. Instead, they stayed closer to their homes and cornfields and orchards, and when they traveled, it was to the west where they sought furs from other Indians to trade with the British, with whom they had a strong alliance.

At the same time, white men who had no love of the distant British King moved into the Schoharie Valley, and with them came traders. These settlers were German Protestants who had fled Germany to escape feudal oppression and to practice their own religion. For the most part the Germans obtained their lands by peaceful treaties and by purchase from the Indians, and there was little hard feeling between the white farmers and their copper-skinned neighbors. However, the Mohawks did object when traders

from Schoharie and other new white settlements began to do business in the Indian towns. The Mohawks had made arrangements
with the British to have control of all the trade in their area. And
behind the white traders always seemed to come more settlers.

Perhaps this situation led some Mohawks to make threats against
a trader named Jonathan Schmul. Or perhaps it was the coming
of the Revolution itself, in which the Mohawks sided with the
British, who promised them permanent protection of their lands
against settlers—and who paid them handsomely for the scalps of
rebellious colonists. At any rate, one day Jonathan Schmul crawled
into Otsgaragee, "The Cave of Many Galleries," whose location he
may have learned from some old Mohawk. That day Schmul wanted
a hide-out, for a party of young warriors was after him, apparently
determined to rid their country of white traders and apparently
either ignorant of the cave or sure that Schmul would never enter it.

It seems clear that no other white men had ever found the place,
and so Schmul was safe there from both the forgetful Indians and
the unsuspecting Tories. He decided to make the cave his secret
home. However, he trusted the leader of the little German community at Schoharie, Rev. John Peter Resig, and soon afterward
revealed to him the place where he hid when raiding parties of
Mohawks and Tories were in the neighborhood.

"Since you are a minister," said Schmul, who was of the Jewish
faith, "and can keep the confessional, I'll tell you where I live. Ten
miles West is a creek named after the German, Kobel. There I found
a cave when the Indians were after me. That's my home. But be
silent about this. If war breaks out, then flee to this cave and you
will be safe."

Later Schmul offered haven there to at least one other person, a
sick woman whom Pastor Resig visited in the candlelight. Before
the war was over, the pastor had occasion to make good use of the
cave himself as a hiding place, but he was no man to stay away
while his parishioners were under attack. Once, he left the cave to
take part in a bloody battle against the Tories and Indians, using
as his weapon an Indian battle axe.

Virgil H. Clymer, who has dug up most of the known facts, does
not report what finally became of Jonathan Schmul, and Pastor
Resig kept Schmul's secret, confiding it only to a diary he wrote in

German which was published some time later in Germany. The Mohawks—taking with them whatever memory they had of the place—moved to Canada after the Revolution. The cave was completely forgotten for three generations. But events were to take place which would bring Otsgaragee, like many a forgotten thing, once more very much to the attention of man. Today the hide-out of the Jewish trader and the Protestant minister is known to hundreds of thousands, who have walked its corridors or gone boating on its underground river, as the largest cave in all New York State and New England—Howe Caverns.

As frontiersmen began to close the gap between the known areas east of the Appalachians and those along the Mississippi River, they entered a region that was rich in caves. Whether Daniel Boone was actually directed by Indians to any caves is not known, but he had much quieter relationships with the tribes that used Kentucky as a hunting ground than some accounts of his life would have us believe. At any rate, he did visit or camp in many a cave, as his signature on the walls testifies to this day. Squire Boone, Daniel's brother, knew caves in Kentucky and also in Indiana, where he found one so much to his liking that he asked to be buried there—and he was.

Legend has it—and legend is worth listening to when it parallels what could very well have been the truth—that sometime late in the eighteenth century, as the frontier began to reach Indiana, a nameless pioneer nursed a nameless wounded Indian back to health. To show his gratitude, the patient led the pioneer to Wyandotte Cave, not far from the spot where the Blue River enters the Ohio. Thus began white man's acquaintanceship with this great cave which Indians had known and used for many centuries.

Farther down the Ohio, Cave-in-Rock (now a state park in southern Illinois) achieved a kind of fame on the frontier long before Wyandotte did. This limestone cavity in the actual riverbank, facing directly on the water, was the seat of a highly organized piracy operation that would be the envy of modern racketeers if they knew about it. From the cave mouth, in a high bluff, all the flatboats which plied the river after the American Revolution could be easily observed. The cavern itself provided ideal living quarters for pirates and their families. (Many of them were steady-going family men who kept their wives and children with them.) The cave even had a secret rear exit, and a small side chamber perfect for committing murders—and on occasion used for that purpose—out of sight of the kiddies and other possibly talkative witnesses.

The early pirates of Cave-in-Rock sent their wives and children out on the river bank to hail in the crews of flatboats. The usual pretext was that the women and children needed transportation to a safe port down the river because their menfolk had been killed by Indians. Once the flatboats had beached to perform their errand of mercy, the pirates took care of the crews and appropriated the valuable cargoes, which they proceeded to float down to market in New Orleans.

This method of accumulating wealth was far too crude for one Samuel Mason, a gentleman who had acquired some finesse as an officer in the Continental Army during the Revolution. He wanted no scandal of any kind associated with Cave-in-Rock. It was to be a respectable "Liquor Vault and Place of Entertainment," and he advertised his roadhouse on the bluff near the cave so that thirsty crews would come ashore. And come they did. In their cups they told of their cargoes, and Mason laid his plans. When the cargoes were good, these plans usually included posting near a ticklish stretch of river below the cave a pilot who was one of Mason's gang. The pilot's job was to steer the flatboat to a place where it could be easily boarded and any troublesome crew-members disposed of.

Mason's business prospered, but not all his associates were scrupulous about keeping suspicion away from his headquarters, and he finally had to move on.

Successors took over the cave for brief periods, and two of these, the Harpe brothers, committed enough senseless murders, before, during and after their occupancy, to win them some kind of award for special achievement in the annals of depravity.

The pirates put their cavern to a practical use, and this question of practicality was uppermost in the minds of most frontiersmen and early settlers who found themselves possessed of a cave. Few of them actually needed underground shelter—at least for any length of time. They knew very well how to build lean-tos or cabins for protection from wind and rain. They had weapons that were superior to those of the Indians, who resented trespassers, and it was the exception rather than the rule that white men had to hide from war parties when they were away from the blockhouses they built as a routine defense measure.

However, the very weapons that gave pioneers their advantage over Indians, and that provided them with the meat which was the main item in their diet, set in motion a search that brought them to caves as a matter of greatest importance.

Gunpowder was essential on the frontier, and it was exceedingly difficult to get because of the great distance from the powder factories of the East or of Europe. During the Revolution the Continental Army had felt the pinch when the British supply was cut off, and a new source had to be found. It was part of folk-knowledge that saltpetre for making gunpowder could be got from manure piles and even from the earth under cabin floors. Something about that particular kind of earth, when it was soaked in water and when the water was boiled with ashes, produced saltpetre. A great scraping of earth from the dark places under old buildings went on as part of America's effort to achieve its freedom.

The frontiersmen had very few manure piles and no old buildings to scrape under, but some ingenious soul experimented with the dirt from a cave floor—and it worked. Saltpetre (also called nitre) could be leached out of it. Moreover, this nitrate-bearing earth covered the dark, ancient cave floors in vast quantities. The frontiersman was thus freed for new exploits, and he could more nearly achieve his dream of complete self-reliance and independence from the eastern civilization he usually disliked.

By 1799 Mammoth Cave in Kentucky was already known as a source of nitre. (This was the year in which, according to legend, a hunter named Houchins chased a bear into the mouth of the cavern, thus discovering it.) A few years later Wyandotte Cave in Indiana was producing saltpetre, and thoughtful men began to speculate about the mysterious source of the precious nitrate in cave earth. By 1806 one scientist had urged that the government consider the importance of saltpetre caves in the event of a national emergency. Such an emergency came very soon.

When England made its effort in 1812 to recover the American colonies it had lost, the British Navy cut off all foreign sources of nitre from the United States. Large amounts had been imported

from India and Spain for use at least along the eastern seaboard.
American soldiers now faced a powerful enemy with empty guns in
their hands.

It was at this time that Wyandotte and Mammoth and other caves
played what may have been a decisive role. In fact, without them
the United States might very well have lost the War of 1812. Saltpetre-mining at Mammoth Cave became a mammoth undertaking.
One Archibald Miller, acting as agent for the owners of the cave,
set large numbers of slaves to work digging out earth from the floor
and carrying it in bags to collection points in the roomier passageways. Some of it was brought from as far as five miles inside the
cave, and all of it was dug under the light of smoky torches or crude
lamps. Oxen, drawing carts through the poorly lit tunnels, then
hauled the earth to wooden leaching vats—still in the cave. Water
for the leaching came down from the entrance in a wooden pipe
made up of logs with the centers bored out by a huge hand-turned
auger.

After passing over the earth in the vats, the water flowed ultimately into a reservoir, from which it was again pumped by hand
through other wooden pipes to the surface. This nitrate-bearing
water, which the thirsty slaves ironically nicknamed "beer," was then
run through wood ashes and boiled. A day and a night after it had
cooled in wooden troughs, crystals of nitre could be removed and
sacked for shipment by muleback or cart to the United States Army
supply center far to the north in Philadelphia, or possibly by flatboat
to New Orleans. Three to five hundred pounds of saltpetre a day
resulted from this arduous hand labor in Mammoth alone. That
made a lot of gunpowder—and the people of the United States were
able to win the war.

As usually happens where munitions are concerned, there was
profit as well as patriotism involved in the saltpetre-mining. One
index of this was the soaring real estate value of Mammoth Cave in
1812. On a single day, July 9 of that year, the property was bought
and sold twice, according to Margaret M. Bridwell who has published a learned history of the cave. The first sale price was $116.67.
Before the day was over, the price had jumped to $3,000. Six weeks
later a half-interest in Mammoth was sold for $10,000—a nearly two-
hundredfold increase in the value of the site of a war industry.

An unexpected by-product of the mining operation soon laid the basis for another kind of profit to be made from the cave. Visitors began to come, sometimes from great distances, to behold Mammoth's now much-talked-of wonders. Sight-seeing continued after the end of the war, when peace terminated the digging and leaching of cave earth. By 1816, stagecoaches connected Mammoth with stagecoach routes that had spread out over Kentucky. A new phase in the history of Mammoth—and indeed of caves all over the country —had begun. Out of a widespread search for petre-dirt came a spurt of interest in caves as a source of pleasure. A new and peaceful industry—the commercial operation of caves as tourist attractions—was one result of the War of 1812. And commercialization in turn led to still more interest in caves and their exploration.

CHAPTER SEVEN

Caves Go Commercial

Large-scale saltpetre-mining in caves ended as abruptly as it had begun. By the year 1815, the Negro miners entered Mammoth not to dig petre-dirt, but to escort visitors through the passages with which they had become so familiar. In that year a slave boy, Stephen Bishop, was born somewhere in the vicinity of the cave, and as he grew up, he fell heir to all the knowledge of Mammoth which the miners had gained. At some point now unknown, young Stephen was allowed or ordered by his master to accompany sight-seers. Nothing could have pleased the boy more. But in the beginning the tourist business did not prosper. The value of the cave had sunk by 1828 to an estimated $400. Then, in 1837, three important things happened: Bishop's master, Franklin Gorin, became owner of Mammoth; Gorin placed Bishop in the cave as the first "official" guide; and a vast new underground area was discovered when Bishop crossed a hazard known as the Bottomless Pit, which had stopped all previous explorers. Probably due as much to the skill of this guide as to any other one thing, popular interest in the cave quickly increased.

Bishop explored far beyond the Bottomless Pit, and he was sought after by geologists and celebrities who wished to study or visit Mammoth. No small part of Bishop's fame apparently rested on the extraordinary intellectual interest he showed in the cave and in the fields of learning that it led him to. He achieved an education under his own initiative, for laws and customs in the South forbade the teaching of slaves. Once he had mastered reading and writing in English, he went on to study the languages he found so important to the scientists who visited the cave—Latin and Greek. His knowl-

71

edge of geology was considerable, as geologists he led through the cave readily testified.

Only a handful of specially favored slaves pretended they liked being held in bondage, and Stephen Bishop, though favored, was not one of these. His reading led him to discover what seemed a means of escape. He saved the tips he got from parties he guided, planning to buy his freedom and move to the one place in the world

Stephen Bishop, the Guide—Mammoth Cave.

Stephen Bishop, the slave who was the first explorer and guide in Mammoth Cave, Kentucky. A self-educated man, Bishop learned a great deal about geology and other cave sciences.

From Horace C. Hovey's *Celebrated American Caverns* (1882)

he knew where Negroes were themselves the rulers—Liberia. But before he could set out on this difficult, circuitous route to liberation, and before freedom came by the more direct route of emancipation, Stephen Bishop died in 1859 at the age of thirty-seven.

Living though he did under the extraordinary handicaps of slavery, Bishop forecast the experience of other cave-explorers right up to the present day. What began as a physical adventure into the unknown became an intellectual adventure. Hundreds of people who start out as spelunkers go on to develop serious scientific interests. They are all in a very real sense indebted to Stephen Bishop for helping men of imagination more than a century ago to realize the fascination of the vast underground world.

All of the early guides in Mammoth were Negroes, and until freedom came, they were slaves. The brothers Matt and Nick Bransford, in the eyes of many, shared honors with Stephen Bishop. Matt's son Henry became a guide and so did his sons, Matt and Louis, and his

Matt Bransford, who began guiding in Mammoth Cave as a slave in 1837 and continued there until 1886. His grandson, Louis, the last Negro guide in the cave, worked there until 1942, a year after Mammoth Cave National Park was fully established.

From Horace C. Hovey's *Celebrated American Caverns* (1882)

grandson, Elzie Bransford. Ed Hawkins was another early guide, and later Edward Bishop, a descendant of Stephen Bishop, continued the work of exploring and opened up a beautiful new area known as Violet City.

The Negro guide William Garvin, in 1870, discovered a now-famous passage called the Corkscrew. Shrewd detective work rather than daring, or trial and error, led him into the section of the cave he opened up. He had long observed the movements of bats, and using their flight paths as clues, he was able to find the passage through which no man had ever gone before. Garvin's talents extended beyond his ability to reason out where more cave must lie. He added greatly to the excitements of a guided tour by furnishing sound effects—he was an accomplished ventriloquist, as hundreds of visitors who had been frightened by ghostly voices coming from inaccessible nooks were to discover.

White guides and explorers made their contribution to Mammoth, too. And, as with their Negro predecessors, the habit of "cavin'" descended from father to son. Some of the men who lead parties today are descendants of the early white guides. In 1938, a hundred and one years after Stephen Bishop crossed the Bottomless Pit on a cedar pole, four guides—Carl Hanson, with his son Pete, and Leo and Claude Hunt—spent their day off on a postman's holiday. They went exploring, and entered a huge virgin area of Mammoth now called the New Discovery. Each of the guide-explorers has based himself on the knowledge already gained. But no man to this day can say he has covered all of Mammoth Cave.

Immediately after Bishop's exploits in 1837, it became amply clear that as a commercial cave Mammoth could be a source of wealth to its owners. When Bishop had been an official guide for only two years, his master, Franklin Gorin, was able to sell the property for $10,000—twice what he had paid for it. Bishop himself remained at the cave. The buyer was a young Kentucky physician, John Croghan. Though Dr. Croghan had grown up in Louisville, he first heard of the cave while he was a medical student in Scotland. The reports so fascinated him that he went to Mammoth promptly after he returned to the United States in 1839. Almost as promptly he bought the cave and set about expanding its facilities for tourists. Because he was a physician as well as an entrepreneur, Dr. Croghan decided that Mammoth was the place for a medical experiment which has gained him a macabre kind of fame. He reasoned that the purity of the air in the cave should be good for sufferers from tuberculosis. So he built underground rooms, roofless because there was no rain to keep out, and then used them as a sanitarium for lung cases. The pure air that the doctor prescribed was there—but the sunlight that the patients needed was not. All of them languished, as did the flowers and trees they tried to grow around their hospital-huts, and one—probably two—of them died as a result of the experiment.

Dr. Croghan's business judgment apparently exceeded his medical skill. When he died in 1849, his heirs found that public curiosity about Mammoth was as immense as the cavern itself. Thousands came from all over the world to view its wonders. The Emperor of Brazil, the Grand Duke of Russia, famous personages from the theater world, all suffered through the stagecoach ride and enjoyed the luxury of the hotel that had been built near the entrance. They were fascinated not only by the cave itself, but by the stunts that went with a conducted tour. In places where the feeble light of lanterns was insufficient to reveal some special beauty or some yawning pit, the guides skillfully tossed burning flares onto distant ledges —a trick that tour leaders still perform with pride.

In the days before the Mammoth Cave Railroad began to run between Glasgow Junction and the cave, the place attracted one visitor who was quite as famous in his way as the other celebrities were in theirs. Thinking that the large sums collected at the hotel and at the entrance gate would be on the stagecoach known as the *John A. Bell*, on the afternoon of September 3, 1880, Jesse James— with a companion—spurred his horse from behind a clump of trees and ordered the passengers out of the coach. He relieved them of a total of $831, a gold watch and some diamond rings, but the receipts from the hotel, alas for Jesse James, had gone to the bank by another route.

The presence of highwaymen did nothing but add zest to the pastime of cave visiting. And the success of Mammoth stirred up interest in many quarters. Other caves were turned into underground showplaces. The now famous Wyandotte Cave in Indiana began its career just as Mammoth had—it served as a saltpetre mine during the War of 1812. Since it was closer to the frontier, where gunpowder was a daily necessity, the mining continued for some years after the end of the war. A Dr. Samuel Adams owned Wyandotte, and he found that it contained not only nitrous earth but also crystals that were stock-in-trade of the medical profession in those days— Epsom salts. His successor, Henry P. Rothrock, had no more interest in Epsom salts than the average layman, but he was to discover that the stuff was even worse medicine than he had thought. A law was passed which forced him to fence in the entrance to his cave in order to save wandering cattle from the purgative effects of the salty crystals.

Rothrock took a somewhat dim view of his cavern in general. He had a farm and a sawmill on the land above it, and the visitors who came—and then wanted to spend the night at his house—often were a nuisance. However, tourists persisted. The Rothrock family finally built a hotel for them, and hired guides. In 1850 a party of explorers made a discovery that increased Wyandotte's fame and assured it a place in the ranks of successful commercialized caverns. A thousand feet from the entrance, the explorers noticed that a strong draft blew from under a large stone. They succeeded in moving the stone and entered a vast, hitherto unknown portion of the cave. The subsequent discovery that prehistoric man had covered the hole and sealed it off only added interest to the "New Cave." A year later, explorers drilled through a calcite curtain and opened up still another large area, which contained the famous Indian moccasin prints pointing inward, away from the entrance.

By the 1870's twenty miles, more or less, of cavern passageways were being traveled by gentlemen clad in rough old clothes and by ladies who were advised to wear "gymnastic dress." Guides had discovered that Bengal lights, made in the same way as fireworks, produced a blue glare that added interest to such places as the vast room in which there is an underground mountain of breakdown 175 feet high. Burning strips of magnesium ribbon gave full though brief views of the vast speleothem known as the Pillar of the Constitution. Flickering candles lighted tourists through tight crawlways and over steep climbs.

In 1883 the perennial search for ways to make money from caves took a novel turn in Wyandotte. Two characters who were plotting to make a fortune over the winter leased a portion of the cave. There they laid out on the dry floor all the onion sets they could buy up—which seems to have been most of those available on the local market. The idea was that the onions would be well preserved in the dry cool air, and that the gentlemen could charge any price they wished when spring came. Unfortunately for their get-rich-quick scheme, the sets did not behave the way other vegetables were known to in the cave. They sprouted, then wasted away. The would-be monopolists lost their shirts, but the papery outer wrappings of the onions remain to this day as odorless reminders of a smelly operation.

Wyandotte and Mammoth were vast and fascinating, but remote

Slippery Hill, a steep mud bank on the tourist route in Wyandotte Cave. According to Horace C. Hovey, author of the first general book about caves in the United States, this was "a place of merry difficulties . . . about which many a racy story is told."

From Horace C. Hovey's *Celebrated American Caverns* (1882)

from centers of population in their early days. Back closer to the big cities of the eastern seaboard, at least one cave admitted paying customers even before the War of 1812. Let Horace C. Hovey, the first great authority on America's caves, give his report on its discovery:

"The story goes, that Mr. Bernard Weyer was greatly annoyed by a ground-hog (*Archtomys monax*), and set a trap for the creature. The bait was taken, and so was the trap, which had been dragged into a fissure in the rocks. Not to be outwitted by such a beast, Mr. Weyer pursued the lawless depredator with spade and pick, and presently found what he was *not* looking for—[a] splendid cavern . . ."

Weyer's Cave, now known as Grand Caverns, lies near the small Virginia town called Grottoes. It is still open to visitors, and its early popularity, together with the success of Mammoth Cave, made newspaper readers all over the East alert to possible exciting experiences underground.

Maybe a New York State farmer, Lester Howe, had read some of these accounts—maybe he had not. But he did show very considerable initiative as soon as he found that he had a cave of his own. When Howe settled in the Schoharie region of New York, he heard old-timers make passing reference to a mysterious place on his farm known as Blowing Rock. None of the neighbors had ever investigated the rock to see why it blew out a stream of cool air, and there were no special tales about it. The rock just blew, and that was that.

For a while Howe's cattle took greater interest in the Blowing Rock than either he or his neighbors did. In fact, they made practical use of its cool air on hot days. Unaware of this, Howe began to wonder why his cows gathered at the same spot in the pasture whenever the thermometer soared, and one warm day in May, 1842, he decided to do some detective work. His curiosity led him to the Blowing Rock. Pushing aside some brush through which an air current poured, he saw a crevice in a limestone ledge. This was the source of the breeze.

Howe had no idea that Blowing Rock was the entrance to Otsgaragee—the long-forgotten cave known and used by the Mohawk Indians, then by the peddler, Schmul, and by the pastor, Resig. (Nor did anyone else guess the identity of the cave until much later.) Howe's interest was uncomplicated by any romantic feeling for history. He simply looked in. There was only darkness ahead, darkness that his sun-dazzled eyes could not fathom—and who knew what else lurked there? Howe fetched a lantern and, just to be on the safe side, a ball of tape. He hitched the tape at the entrance and unrolled it as he ventured into the black hole. There would be no getting lost for Lester Howe in whatever dark maze awaited him, even if his lantern failed. The tape would guide him back to daylight.

Before long he found the going slow. Wet rocks, tilting at all angles, lay in his way. Then an underground lake stopped him completely. In a few days he was back at the cave with some lumber, which he lugged over the slippery breakdown and built into a raft at the edge of the lake. His dim lantern revealed no opposite shore, but—undaunted—he launched his clumsy craft. For what must have seemed the longest eighth of a mile he ever traveled, he splashed ahead through darkness until he reached a landing place.

Then came a series of discoveries in quick succession. He beheld beautiful flowstone formations, stalactites, stalagmites—weird and unlikely rock-shapes for which nothing in his experience had prepared him. And the cave was large, very large. It was not to be completely explored in a day—or even in many days. Howe had to come back and back again. But before he had reached its limits, he bragged about the cave under his farm. The news spread rapidly and was soon in the papers. Howe, besieged with sight-seers and scientists, was so busy guiding them that he never did have time to finish probing all the leads in his cavern.

As fast as he collected fifty-cent pieces from the curious who came in droves by horse-drawn coach from Albany and points much farther away, Howe bought equipment to make trips through his cave even more alluring. He acquired rubber boots which his customers wore in the places where they had to wade. He accumulated a supply of special cone-shaped lanterns. He built up a wardrobe of sturdy trousers and jackets for men to wear instead of the holiday clothes in which they usually arrived. And for the ladies he furnished garments that were daring indeed for the mid-nineteenth century: box-legged trousers that reached the tops of high-buttoned shoes and, to cover the pants, a modest long-tailed tunic that came down to the knees.

The novelty of the gear, as well as the underground scenery and the underground boat ride which Howe offered, attracted more and more people. To the oil lanterns which tourists continued to carry, he added gas lamps which illumined strategic points in the cave. Apparently the pipe that conducted gas to these lamps was found by stumbling visitors to have a usefulness Howe had never intended. They grasped it as a handhold and wrenched it so that the lamps were constantly out of order.

Such minor problems only led to further improvements, for Howe was eager to ride a rising tide of interest. Commercially operated caves had definitely become a colorful corner of the whole exuberant American scene. A hundred years ago—before the days of television and movies—natural wonders had precious little competition as a source of entertainment, and cave-owners, with Howe in the lead, were by no means above embellishing the work of nature to make it even more sensational.

Howe piped cool cave air into the dining room of the hotel he now maintained near the cavern entrance, and his biggest venture of all was a miniature railroad installed in one of his underground passages. Expenses constantly mounted, and although the cavern was popular and accessible, the crowds of paying customers did not keep pace with the costliness of improvements. Howe finally had to relinquish his beloved property. It was a bitter experience to see other men take over what he had discovered and developed. Equally galling was the fact that among the beneficiaries of his failure were neighbors who had known about the Blowing Rock but had never bothered to investigate it.

Disappointed though Howe was, he now had "cavin' " in his blood. In between spells of trying to re-establish himself as a farmer in the area, he roamed the hills looking for crevices in limestone ledges. He was determined to make another discovery that would rival or outshine the cavern which bore his name but which he no longer owned.

The story goes that he did find a crevice leading to a cave of such extraordinary beauty that he called it the Garden of Eden. But experience in the world of business had made him extremely cautious. This time he gave no announcement to the world as he had done earlier. He kept the location of his cave a secret, and more than that, after crawling and walking and climbing great distances to assure himself that it was indeed spectacular, he sealed up the entrance.

Howe died before he ever opened his Garden of Eden to the

One of the features of Howe Caverns, from the earliest days to the present, has been an underground boat ride. Nineteenth-century cave artists made their sketches for pictures like this with the aid of twenty to fifty lamps, supplemented by magnesium flares.

From Horace C. Hovey's *Celebrated American Caverns* (1882)

public, and with him died the knowledge of its whereabouts, but interest in it by no means disappeared. Perhaps a dozen times since then some caver has found what he thought might be the Garden of Eden. Not one of these caves, however, quite measured up to the great expectations Howe had led people to have.

A group of spelunkers did create a flurry of excitement when they came upon a passageway in a cave that had been blasted shut long ago. By removing broken stone they managed to force an entrance. Attractive chambers lay beyond. All things pointed to the possibility that here might be the Garden of Eden which Howe claimed he had closed. Then came a new mystery. Within the sealed area the spelunkers found two curiously shaped and intricately decorated brass pots or lamps. Officials at the state museum in Albany were amazed when they studied the two objects. So were other experts. The lamps, of oriental design, had been made nearly two thousand years ago. What could explain their presence in the lost chamber of a cave in New York State?

Finally someone remembered that in his early expansive days Howe had collected curiosities. At that time America's famed clipper ships and whalers ranged far and wide, bringing back souvenirs from all over the world. Quite possibly some sea captain had picked up the two lamps in an eastern bazaar, and Howe had obtained them in turn. They were suitable for burning whale oil, and in the days before kerosene was readily available, most people—including cavers—used whale oil lights, when they didn't use candles. It was not fantastic at all to guess that Howe had explored the ancient mysteries of many a limestone cavern with the aid of these ancient lamps. Perhaps more is to be learned about the lamps. And perhaps speleologists, who are ever devising more and more refined methods of research—including the historical—may one day discover what is unmistakably the real Garden of Eden.

While Howe Caverns was a mecca for the curious of the northeastern states, visitors continued to flock to Weyer's Cave in the Shenandoah Valley of Virginia. If Weyer and his successors could make a living out of tourists, others in the valley could do likewise—so reasoned Andrew and William Campbell, brothers, and their friend Benton Stebbins. All they needed was a good cave. Accordingly they set out in 1878 to locate one. For a starting place there was property they owned a few miles east of New Market on what was propitiously called Cave Hill—because of a sinkhole and small cave known to be there.

Seriously and, possibly, systematically the Campbells and Stebbins went to work, tramping over every inch of their land and over adjoining land, too. Every day for a month they tramped and searched, and neighbors began to think them touched in the head. They had no special taste for being martyrs, so it hurt when old friends made rough jokes at their expense, calling them "phantom chasers" or "cave rats" and implying that they didn't know the difference between a rabbit's den and a mare's nest. At the end of the month the three of them were about ready to admit defeat and return to the normal pursuits of their fellows.

They decided, however, on one more try. On a hot August day they began what they expected to be their last attempt. To avoid acquaintances who might heap more ridicule on them, they kept away from the main road that led up over Massanutten Mountain. Instead, they skirted pastures and clung to woods, and before long they found a sink filled with a growth of weeds, briars and sumac. At the bottom of the depression they could see a limestone ledge. Sinks and limestone ledges were the natural habitats of caves, so the men shoved their way down through the brush to investigate.

No cave entrance was apparent here, but William's hand, resting on the ledge, felt something strange. The rock seemed cool—much cooler than you would expect on such a hot day. He moved his hand down the face of the rock. The coolness increased. No question—a draft of air was coming out through a crevice at the very base of the ledge.

Now the men set to work with a will to make an entrance. After about five hours of sweating and heaving and digging, they had a hole large enough for Andrew Campbell to crawl through. With the end of a safety rope held in one hand and a candle in the other, Andrew backed in. Soon he came to a room at least fifteen feet wide but not very long—a disappointing discovery after so much labor. Nevertheless he surveyed the small chamber carefully. Along one wall the dim flicker of his candle revealed a narrow opening. This must be an entrance to something, and he tried it. It was an entrance indeed—to Luray Caverns, perhaps the most beautiful in the United States.

The three men who had set out on purpose to find a cave had succeeded. Now it remained only to buy the land above and around the place, do a little construction to prepare it for tourists—and the money would roll in. But when potential wealth is involved, the ways of men are seldom simple. Before long the Campbells and Stebbins found themselves involved in litigation. They had not revealed why they wanted the land when they bought it. Since it had been put up at sale to raise funds with which to meet the previous owner's debts, and since it brought only enough to pay ten cents on the dollar of money owed, there was trouble ahead. The man whose debt had been so meagerly repaid claimed he had been cheated. The property was quite valuable enough to have given him full return. He pressed his claim, and in the end the three discoverers of Luray Caverns found themselves without a cave.

In the hands of experienced business men, Luray became something of the successful rival to Weyer's Cave that the Campbells and Stebbins had dreamed. Its fame spread, and among those who heard of it was a retired Congregational minister, T. C. Northcott, who had grown up in Springfield, Illinois, where he had known Abraham Lincoln.

Northcott had curiously taken a great interest in a phase of engineering that was in its very infancy at the turn of the century—ventilation and air-conditioning. He reasoned, as had Dr. Croghan, that the pure air of a cave would surely be good for victims of lung trouble. But when Northcott bought Luray, he did not repeat the Mammoth Cave experiment of taking sufferers down underground. His engineering bent led him to quite another solution. He pumped air from the entrance up to a building in which he housed the patients.

Here was the first modern air-conditioning system—if we exclude the simpler experiment made by Howe many years before. Northcott had expected the sanitarium to be the center of his business operation. But in time the cavern itself proved by far the more profitable part of his enterprise. Limair, the sanitarium, became his air-conditioned home, from which he directed the operation of the cave between 1905 and 1941 when he died, aged ninety-seven. The pure cave air that Rev. Northcott breathed during thirty-six summers certainly did him no harm.

A hundred and fifty thousand people a year walk through Luray, which has been kept in a perfect state of preservation, on carefully constructed paths, and look at the almost incredible concentration of varicolored speleothems—and marvel. Unlike Mammoth, and to some extent Wyandotte, where vastness itself is a feature and where there are long undecorated corridors, Luray is notable for the number of stalactites, stalagmites and curtains closely crowded together.

Weyer's Cave and Luray were by no means the only caverns of the Shenandoah Valley which attracted visitors. Many wild caves, some small and some large, were known to local people and often to enthusiasts who came long distances to explore independently as well as to take guided tours in the commercial caverns. One cave known as Endless Caverns, three miles south of New Market, was discovered a year after Luray, and for a while it was informally commercialized, then closed down until its present period of operation began. Another, now called Melrose, near Lacey Springs, was used for a long time as shelter by Indians, then by white settlers fleeing from the wrath of the Indians whose lands they were taking away. By 1824 an owner of Melrose had cut a flight of stairs into the solid rock at the entrance, apparently to accommodate paying visitors. During the seesaw Civil War campaigns up and down the Shenandoah Valley, soldiers from both armies took shelter in Melrose, but never ventured as far in as the Indians had gone. Here, at least, the Confederates had the last word: They scratched out names which many Union soldiers had laboriously lettered on calcite columns and walls, and replaced them with names from south of the Mason-Dixon line. With much of the evidence of its military occupation still intact, Civil War archeology has become a feature of this now commercialized cave.

During the latter part of the nineteenth century, the interest stirred up by Virginia caves spilled over into other states, often increasing an interest that already existed. Many caves were explored but never commercialized—and some big ones are still wild. For instance, Nickajack Cave, which lies under Georgia, Alabama and Tennessee at the point where the three states meet, was known by 1882 to be twelve miles long, but it has never measured up as a tourist attraction. Possibly a description of it recently circulated by J. Roy Chapman of the Georgia Department of Mines, Mining and Geology may suggest why. Says Mr. Chapman, who actually is an ardent cave fancier, Nickajack is "a large and long cave, whose most distant passages can be reached only by a half-mile boat trip upstream along an underground river that is sometimes 20 feet deep. A long journey on foot then brings the weary explorer to a place where he must crawl flat on his stomach for 170 feet. (This is extremely tiresome.)"

Many caves in West Virginia—not quite so large or tiresome-sounding as Nickajack—became well known when they were mined for saltpetre by Confederate troops during the Civil War. After the war they continued to draw small enthusiastic exploring parties, but they had to wait many years before tourist travel was sufficient to merit developing even a small number of them commercially.

One cave, however, which was commercialized shortly after the Civil War, had no long history of exploration. A man broke into it quite unexpectedly in 1871 while quarrying limestone east of Hamburg, Pennsylvania. There were no stories of a colorful past to be told about it—not even any evidence that either Indian or white had ever entered it. Here was a really new cavern, which was promptly named Crystal. Within a few months it was prepared for visitors and launched on a commercial career that has lasted more than eighty years.

Farther west, in Centre County, in the year 1870 a strait-laced farmer, George Long, bought the property around what had long been known as Penn's Cave. No sooner had he become owner than he began to frown on the obvious enjoyment visitors got from the cavern and from picnicking near it. His sons, however, took a different view after they visited Mammoth Cave in Kentucky. They realized that their cave had a feature which Mammoth did not possess: starting from its magnificent natural entrance, tourist parties could look at its beauties during the course of a boat trip along an underground part of a stream called Penn's Creek. And so, after George Long's death, the sons ordered a boat to replace the rafts that early explorers had used, built a hotel, and invited the public. Penn's Cave has been a show place from that day to this.

Every cave boasts its special features. Penn's has its boat ride and in addition an unusual stock of folklore, thanks to Henry W. Shoe-maker, Chairman of the Pennsylvania State Historical Commission, who has preserved it. Other caverns boast of their size or of special displays of anthodites or gypsum flowers, of vast unexplored areas or enormous columns or dainty miniature stalactites above reflecting pools. Commercial caves—except for the ease with which they can be negotiated—are almost as varied as caves can be. And one thing about them had become very clear long before the turn of the century. People liked them and were willing to pay out good money for a chance to see them.

Once there were pools of water that built up these rimstone formations in Carlsbad Caverns. *Courtesy: National Park Service*

Oddities are endless in caves. These "fried eggs" in Luray Caverns are said to be the bases of small stalagmites that were broken off during construction of trails. Tourists, who are not allowed to touch most speleothems, are encouraged to touch these, and they keep the yellowish yolks well polished. *Courtesy: Luray Caverns*

A veritable shower of water pours down steadily into this pool in Ozark Caverns near Camdenton, Missouri. Elsewhere in this cave are stalactites from which single drops of water fall every few seconds with metronome-like regularity. *Courtesy: Ozark Caverns*

Peggy Mueller looks at calcite in the shape of lily pads that have formed in quiet water in Poor Farm Cave, Hillsboro, West Virginia. *Courtesy: National Speleological Society   Photo by Albert C. Mueller, Jr.*

Anthodites (cave flowers) are a rare form of aragonite crystals. *Courtesy: Skyline Caverns, Front Royal, Virginia*

Aragonite crystals. *Courtesy: Mercer Caverns   Photo by George W. Moore*

Some caves have beautiful displays of speleothems called gypsum flowers. Unlike calcite formations, gypsum flowers are not caused by dripping water, but grow outward from their bases on walls or ceilings. A guide throws light on one cluster of the flowers in Mammoth Cave. *Courtesy: National Park Service Photo by Ray Scott*

About five per cent of Carlsbad Caverns is still "alive"—that is, seepage water still builds speleothems and collects in pools such as this. *Courtesy: National Park Service*

Gypsum flowers in Great Onyx
Cave. *Courtesy: Great Onyx Cave*

Courtesy: National Park Service   Courtesy: National Park Service

(*Left*) A twenty-two-inch spiral of gypsum growing out of a wall in Mammoth Cave.
(*Right*) Gypsum speleothems sometimes look like spun glass or sheep's wool—or snowballs. This fluffy white mineral greeted explorers in a new section of Mammoth Cave
in 1938.

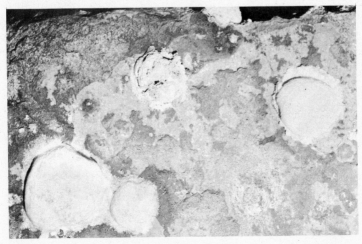

Gypsum snowballs in Mammoth Cave.   *Courtesy: National Park
Service   Photo by Ray Scott*

Gypsum flowers in Floyd Collins' Crystal Cave. *Courtesy: Floyd Collins' Crystal Cave Photo by W. T. Austin*

A gypsum growth, shaped like a ram's horn, one inch in diameter, in Mammoth Cave *Courtesy: National Park Service*

Gypsum flowers take many forms. Here is a cluster in the Crystal Palace section of the Great Extension in Cumberland Caverns (formerly Higgenbotham Cave). *Courtesy: Cumberland Caverns Photo by Thomas C. Barr, Jr.*

As long as seepage water passes over flowstone, even in the thinnest of films, the stone glistens under light and is said to live. *Courtesy: Lincoln Caverns Photo by Greene's Studio*

This is what calcite looks like when water stops dripping or flowing over it. Speleothems such as these have lost their luster and are gradually crumbling in dry Colossal Cave near Tucson, Arizona. This vast cavern, interesting for its size, is also remembered for the part it played in a fabulous train robbery. *Courtesy: Pima County Parks and Recreation Department*

A biologist seeks blind fish and crayfish in an underground stream in Kentucky. *Courtesy National Speleological Society*

Photo by Charles E. Mohr

The White Cave crayfish (*Cambarus ayersii*) of the Ozarks closely resembles other cave-dwelling crayfish that are found eastward and southward as far as Florida. *Courtesy: National Speleological Society*

Photo by Charles E. Mohr

The larva of the Ozark Blind Cave salamander. As it matures, the gills disappear and eyelids develop and fuse together. *Courtesy: National Speleological Society   Photo by Charles E. Mohr*

Blind fish from the Echo River in Mammoth Cave. *Courtesy: National Park Service*

Using an aspirator, Bernard L. Smeltzer collects tiny insects by sucking them off a cave wall. *Courtesy: National Speleological Society*
Photo by Charles E. Mohr

A party in Starr Chapel Cave, Bath County, Virginia, of which the author was a member, watched for more than an hour while Charles E. Mohr took pictures of this cave rat (*Neotoma magister*). Very different from the house rat, he was as curious about his human visitors as they were about him, and he made frequent trips out of his snug cedar bark nest to check up on the general situation. Here he is curled up in his nest with part of his furry tail sticking out of the opening as he eats a piece of bread from Mohr's lunch. *Courtesy: National Speleological Society Photo by Charles E. Mohr*

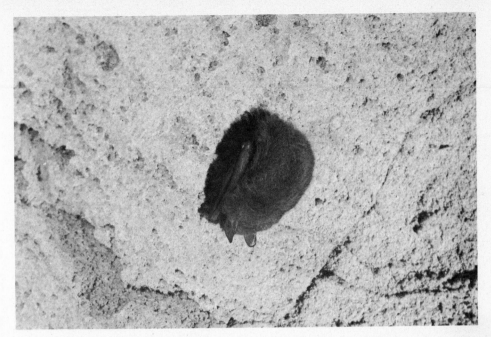

Little Brown bats (*Myotis lucifugus*) are the most widespread of the bats that winter in caves. They often spend six to eight months in hibernation. Usually they roost in colonies. This is a close-up of an individual bat in Mammoth Cave. *Courtesy: National Park Service Photo by Ray Scott*

Bats hang upside down while they sleep or hibernate. These Little Sooty bats (*Myotis sodalis*) have found rough places to which to cling along cracks called joints in the ceiling of a passage in Mammoth Cave. No one has yet discovered where this species of bat spends the summer. *Courtesy: National Park Service*

Photo by Claude W. Hibbard

One of the finds that archeologists made in Ceremonial Cave in the Hueco Mountains, Texas, was this burial of an Indian. Scientists urge cavers to report all finds like this but to disturb nothing, because any amateur investigation may destroy evidence that is essential in dating the remains. *Courtesy: The Peabody Museum of Archeology and Ethnology*

The entrance to Ceremonial Cave where pre-Columbian Indians left hundreds of worn sandals, apparently as part of a religious act at the end of a pilgrimage. *Courtesy: The Peabody Museum of Archeology and Ethnology*

In caves of the Grand Canyon area, Indians left figurines like this, which they constructed out of split twigs. Archeologists still do not know exactly when or why the figurines were left. The one shown here was found in a cave below Yaki Point on the South Rim of Grand Canyon. *Courtesy: The Museum of Northern Arizona and the Western Speleological Institute*

Indian artifacts and the desiccated body of an Indian found in Mammoth Cave. *Courtesy: National Park Service*

The first written record of a white man's visit to a cave in the United States was made by the Spaniard Friar Berreda who in 1693 stayed in what is now part of Florida Caverns. If he ventured a little way into the cave, he saw scenes such as these young tourists are being shown. *Courtesy: Florida State News Bureau*

During the War of 1812, miners dug petre-dirt from cave floors and leached it in wooden vats like this. Here Roy Davis stands beside a vat nearly one hundred and fifty years old in Henshaw Cave, which is one of the entrances to Cumberland Caverns. *Courtesy: Cumberland Caverns*

A series of logs hollowed by a large auger made a pipeline which brought water into Mammoth Cave during the saltpetre mining operations there at the time of the War of 1812. After the water had passed through vats holding petre-dirt, it was pumped up to the cave entrance through a second wooden pipe. There it was boiled with wood ashes, then cooled in order to obtain nitrate crystals that were essential to the manufacture of gun powder. *Courtesy: National Park Service*

This close-up shows how the wooden pipes in Mammoth Cave were fitted together. *Courtesy: National Park Service*

Courtesy: National Park Service

Vats and equipment used in leaching petre-dirt in Mammoth Cave. *Courtesy: National Park Service*

CHAPTER EIGHT

The First Speleologists

As the exploration and commercial exploitation of caves picked up momentum in the nineteenth century, it was almost inevitable that a real speleologist would appear on the scene. It was almost as inevitable that Horace Carter Hovey would be that pioneer cave scientist. The talk in his home, from the day in 1833 when he was born, was about rocks—their amazing variety and astounding habits. Horace's father was a geologist on the faculty of Wabash College in the small town of Crawfordsville, Indiana. And Crawfordsville lay within the northern limits of the great limestone and cavern area of Indiana.

When he was nine, Horace made a small sensation in the geological world by finding and collecting superb specimens of fossil crinoids—prehistoric plantlike animals that had limy skeletons. It wasn't long before the best museums in the world sought examples of these Crawfordsville crinoids. From fossils Horace Hovey moved on to caverns, and poked into more and more of them as he grew up and went through Wabash College. At nineteen, Hovey again showed his initiative and scientific promise by making a geological survey of southern Indiana in which he included data on his cave explorations. The ardent young enthusiast must have been very much encouraged when the leading newspaper in the country, Horace Greeley's New York *Daily Tribune*, published his report.

Even when Hovey entered professional life as a minister, he kept expanding his field of exploration. Though burdened with pastoral duties (at some times in the Congregational Church and at others in the Presbyterian), and with a wife and four children to support, he joined the list of those who had got "cavin'" in their blood, and he somehow found time to visit cavern after cavern. He looked at sea caves around the Bay of Fundy in Nova Scotia; he tramped through the Cave of the Winds near the foot of Pike's Peak in Colorado, and through others in between. He covered a lot of country and poured out articles on his favorite subject for most of the leading magazines, including those for children. By the time he was forty-nine—a bearded and respected author of many published sermons and historical papers on church and family history—he had assembled much of his knowledge about caves in a book, *Celebrated American Caverns.* This classic in speleological literature was the first important volume produced in this country on our subterranean wonders. In fact, it was the only *general* book on American caves published between 1882 and 1955.

Hovey's interest in caves was all-inclusive. He described with zest—and accuracy—every feature along every route he traveled in Mammoth and Wyandotte and Luray, and he followed these routes to their then-known limits. Wearing a close-fitting cap, which was his nearest approach to a hard hat, swinging a lard-oil lamp at his side for light, always carrying a walking stick which he considered indispensible spelunking equipment, he probed into passage after passage of caves that were famous and of caves that he felt deserved to be. He wrote lengthy and detailed accounts of many of them, even producing a large guide book to Mammoth, where he spent weeks wandering around. Every bit of cave literature that could be collected was in his library. And near his work desk, to remind this unconventional cleric of an underworld that held no terrors for him, he kept a little pet cave rat in a revolving cage.

As his writings became well known, he was called upon to lecture, and lecture he did on caves and related topics all over the United States and Canada. Many scientific organizations, which elected him to membership, published his contributions in their journals.

Caves and the name of Hovey were inseparable, and he carried his investigations far beyond his native land. He entered some of the deep perpendicular shafts in the Pyrenees in France and visited caverns in Russia and even Siberia. Hovey was a tourist par excellence, but he was much more than that. He was endlessly eager for *facts* in all the sciences connected with speleology.

What was to be known about cave temperatures, which usually seemed to remain constant the year round? Checking with his own thermometer as well as with data from other scientific sources, Hovey confirmed the fact that the temperature of cave air tends to be the same as the mean surface temperature in the vicinity of the cave.

What kinds of plants and animals could live in the lightless cave environment? Hovey discovered and collected and described in minute scientific terms a new species of fungus in Luray Caverns. He examined crayfish in Wyandotte and was familiar with various species of blind fish. His *Celebrated American Caverns* lists, with their scientific names, forty-six species of cave fauna, and at various places in his writings he shows familiarity with the then-existing literature of the subdivision of science that is now called biospeleology.

What was the genesis of caves? In a time when Darwinism and evolution were highly controversial topics in church circles, Rev. Hovey turned not to the Bible but to science for an explanation of the immensely long geological processes that created and then decorated caverns. There were learned men who stoutly maintained that caves were formed by gas bubbles arising from the decomposition of animals that perished in the great flood of Noah's day. Hovey, following the more advanced science of his time, was convinced that acid-bearing water seeped down into limestone and dissolved it, leaving cavities. He knew also that underground streams could play a role in enlarging cavities once they had formed.

What could caves reveal about the past of human life on this continent? A great deal, Hovey was sure, and he recorded much of interest with a minimum of romantic speculation. What had long passed for bear wallows in Wyandotte Cave he correctly identified as pits created by prehistoric Indian flint-miners, and he richly documented his case to prove that this great cave was a source of considerable archeological interest. News, scarcely widespread in 1882, that cave shelters in the Southwest were filled with ancient Indian dwellings and artifacts fascinated him. He recognized unmistakable evidence of the antiquity of man on this continent in the form of human bones he saw embedded in flowstone in Luray. He described in detail Indian remains found in Kentucky caves. And he debunked mummies—desiccated bodies—carried into Mammoth to titillate tourists. (Those bodies were genuine Indian remains preserved by the dry air in the upper chambers of nearby caves, but Hovey felt compelled to note that they were not authentic finds in Mammoth itself. Long after Hovey's day an authentic Indian body *was* found in Mammoth.)

Although Hovey recognized the unreliability of much of the data about caves and was scornful of obvious fakery, he was never captious when sets of data about a common subject differed. Speaking of the then-extant maps of Mammoth Cave, he said, "A critic would hardly recognize them as representations of the same locality. Few can appreciate the difficulties of an underground survey, amid rugged and tortuous paths, deep pits and lofty domes, all wrapped in darkness but imperfectly scattered by lamplight. Imagine a map of Pike's Peak plotted from observations taken by torchlight, on a series of moonless midnights!"

Whatever he reported was clothed in more than adequate prose. He wrote in the idiom of his era, but made it as ample and rich as his interests, yet as firm and clear as words should be when they deal with facts. And Hovey, bless him, had a sense of humor, which is not a universal occupational requirement of either the ministry or speleology. The owner of Luray, for example, invited him to think up descriptive labels for speleothems and passageways. A puckish footnote comments on this: "Perhaps it was because christening is in the author's line that he was requested to name most of the objects and localities of special interest...." One can only regret that it was the nineteenth-century minister who did the "christening" instead of the man who could poke fun at himself for doing so. In Luray, as in most caverns, the names for fascinating objects are singularly dull.

The curiosa of caving, no less than the technical aspects, interested him as much because of his broad humanity as because of his deep concern with his specialty. He did not hold back from trivia. For example, he became well acquainted with Andrew Campbell's trip to a place known as Water Cave.

"Contriving to pass the wet and slippery entrance that had hindered previous explorers," Hovey reports, "he delighted himself a while with what he called 'a water piano,' where charming echoes were awakened by tossing pebbles into a crystal pool that nearly filled the room he had found within. While thus engaged he noticed a low, small aperture at the farther end of it, and his curiosity led him to stoop down and hold his candle so as to light up whatever might lie beyond. To his surprise an object was thus brought to view that was large and hairy. Our explorer was not easily frightened, and accordingly observing that the object did not stir, he crept up to it, and found—an old hair-covered trunk!

" 'Now my fortune's made,' said [Campbell] to himself, 'for this can be nothing but some kind of treasure concealed during the [Civil] war. Probably a lot of gold and silver, or valuable jewelry!'

"The trunk was carefully dragged out from its hiding place. It was found to be securely locked. Using the end of a stalactite for a hammer, Mr. Campbell forced open the lid, and there, before him, lay exposed to view, in the gloom of that dim ante-chamber—*a skeleton!*"

Hovey relished the fact that a cave could offer tantalizing surprises, some of them of an elusive Grand-Guignol variety. Though a minister of the gospel, his writing is singularly free of the moralizing so popular even among laymen of his day. It was as if Hovey said, "Nothing human is alien to a cave."

Curiously—or perhaps not so curiously—Hovey's sweeping gaze had not caught sight of caves in Missouri where it is now known that large numbers of them exist. The Ozark Mountain region was a remote section of the country, and its people for the most part kept their affairs to themselves. One eminent zoologist, Samuel Garman, a contemporary of Hovey, after making a search of all the scientific literature, found only one sentence about one cave animal in southwestern Missouri. The fact seems to be that very few people knew anything about caves in an area where frontier conditions lingered on very late, although as early as 1819 Henry R. Schoolcraft had written about caves of the Ozarks in connection with a report he made on the lead-miners of Missouri. However, a woman, Ruth Hoppin, in Jasper County, somehow became interested in exploring caverns. Whether or not Miss Hoppin was stimulated by Hovey's *Celebrated American Caverns* is not known. But five years after the appearance of the book, she became an ardent collector and student of cave fauna in her part of the Ozarks. Her interest was obviously encouraged by Samuel Garman, to whom she sent a specimen of the blind white cave fish *Typhlichthys sub-*

terraneus. Garman was excited by the curious fish and asked Miss Hoppin to employ an assistant and look for more specimens. Delighted to be of use to the scientific world, she set about cave-crawling, with a young boy as her companion.

Soon Garman was receiving specimens not only of fish but of frogs, crustaceans, mollusks and insects, some of which, he was pleased to report, were new to science. Down on hands and knees in the sticky gumbo of cave floors, Miss Hoppin patiently observed the habits of crayfish in an effort to determine whether they ate the little white fish. She found the blind creatures most difficult to catch with her net (though lacking eyes they had unfailing ability to avoid anything that moved toward them in the water). After she had spent one frustrating day along an underground stream with muddy banks that constantly broke off and roiled the water, her spirits remained high, although she had obtained only five specimens. "I am much encouraged," she wrote to Garman "...I realize there is ever so much I can learn." In a true scientific spirit, she extended her learning beyond mere collecting. She rigged up an experiment and came to a conclusion about the sensory organs of blind cave animals with which biologists still agree. After catching one of the little white fish, she kept it in a tank at home, observed how it reacted to light, studied what it ate. In addition, the no doubt decorous lady stood beside the tank and screamed with calm scientific passion in order to find out whether *Typhlichthys* would respond to sound waves. *Typhlichthys* ignored her, and she decided that, since he reacted only to motion in the water, he must have a highly developed tactile sense. Ruth Hoppin in the late eighties must have derived real satisfaction from being a pioneer three times over—she was an early scientific explorer of caves close behind the Middle Border; she was a woman engaged in activity of a kind that fell far outside the limited world in which nineteenth-century women were supposed to live; and she made real advances in the field of cave biology, where her name has achieved a modest immortality. A crustacean she was the first to collect has been named after her—*Asellus hoppinae faxon.*

By a coincidence which no one has explained, another woman, Luella Agnes Owen, made speleological history in southwestern Missouri ten years later. Miss Owen was associated with the Missouri State Geological Survey—in itself a rather amazing accomplishment for a woman in the nineties. There is no doubt about where she acquired some of her interest in caves. She knew Horace Hovey and his writings. (In the American Museum of Natural History is a copy of her own book, *Cave Regions of the Ozarks and Black Hills,* inscribed in her hand, "Dr. H. C. Hovey, with the cordial regards of the author.")

Luella Owen was a woman of real spirit and real scientific attainment. But though she was unusual in being a geologist and spelunker, she did not venture beyond the conventions of her day insofar as her spelunking clothes were concerned. Overalls, which were recommended to her when she visited Marble Cave, she considered "an objectionable costume." Even if she had to pay dearly for her conservatism—she found it impossible to visit some parts of the cave—she insisted on "the superior claims of a divided skirt. If it is properly made, only the wearer need be conscious of the divide." Rubber boots and a "waterproof protection for head and shoulders" completed her spelunking outfit. "Not exactly an artistic creation," she remarked, "but it is suited to the requirements of the occasion and makes the explorations far more easy and profitable than they otherwise could be."

The utter novelty of having a woman visit Marble Cave (now called Marvel Cave) apparently put its owner, Truman S. Powell, into a fit of chivalry. Miss Owen stayed at his home the night before she was to enter, and at breakfast Powell gave the usual blessing, then became lost in a fervent prayer for the "safe and successful accomplishment of our undertaking." Thereafter Miss Owen entered the cave without mishap. Once inside, she surveyed its beauties with the trained eye of a geologist, but also with the common interest of any human being. There in a room called the Auditorium was a dance floor, and she noted a piano that had been lowered into it through a sinkhole thirty-five feet deep. At various points along the route, Powell indicated that more cave lay ahead in one direction or another, but out of consideration for the gentler sex, he avoided some of the more difficult areas. Miss Owen reports that "further down Total Depravity Passage we were not urged to go." Nevertheless, at one point the lady in the divided skirt had to crawl seventy feet; later she had to squirm through another tight-fitting passage which, fortunately, was dry. There was climbing to be done, too, and the combination of activities began to weary her. But recalling her host's ardent prayer at breakfast, she decided it would seem "inconsiderate not to present the reassuring appearance of inexhaustible endurance"—and she went on.

Later, still as Powell's guest, she asked to visit Fairy Cave, which apparently he and one of his sons had been the first to enter only a short time before. It required some doing to get into this cavern, for there was a hundred-foot straight drop-off from the surface to the floor of a great, domed room. The Powells had rigged a hand-turned windlass, and anyone who wanted to be lowered into the cave had to sit astride a stick at right angles to the end of a rope. (Here the divided skirt would certainly come in handy.) On the day when she was due to make her descent, Powell set out early on horseback to go from farm to farm, in hope of enlisting man-power to run the windlass. Miss Owen, who like Ruth Hoppin had a small-boy spelunking companion, traveled along a different route by carriage. When they arrived, after getting lost on the way, they found that Powell, alas, had not succeeded in mustering a large enough crew to man the windlass. The descent had to be called off, and Miss Owen was forced to rely for her description of the cave on a report prepared for her by Powell. Fortunately the resourceful gentleman had been able to see the great domed room in its entirety—no thanks to electricity, either. He discovered that every day at about 11 A.M. in a certain season the sun shone directly into the cave through the hundred-foot-deep entrance. After descending by windlass, he had a large mirror sent down to him. At the moment the sun's rays struck the bottom of the cave, he maneuvered the mirror so that reflected light showed him what neither candle nor kerosene lantern was capable of revealing.

Her curiosity whetted by what she had learned of Missouri caves, Luella Owen journeyed to South Dakota, where caves had been discovered although little was yet known about them. In the Black Hills she studied the extensive and rugged passages of Wind Cave in as great detail as she could—given the handicap of her voluminous divided skirt, which she stubbornly clung to in preference to the overalls which cave-crawlers here, as in Missouri, recommended. The good lady who had not been led down Total Depravity Passage in Marble Cave, here ventured into W.C.T.U. Hall and was impressed, not by the name, it must be reported, but by the unusual speleothems she found. Boxwork, a kind of honeycomb calcite formation, exists in profusion in Wind Cave, and in very few other places. How did this boxwork come into existence? Miss Owen wondered. But beyond that, how did Wind Cave itself form?

She knew very well that acid-bearing water dissolved out caves from limestone, but this one was different from any she had seen. To explain the difference she postulated geyser waters that she believed must have been responsible for the solution of rock in the Black Hills and for the unusual type of speleothem.

Scientists now disagree with her explanation. Wind Cave and others in the area, they say, were formed by solution along fractures in the limestone. The boxwork also was formed along fractures or joints which were minute. Calcite filled in the tiny crevices and later the more soluble limestone dissolved away, leaving calcite in angular crisscross patterns.

Perhaps Miss Owen's geology was faulty, but the findings of many early students of caves have been corrected by later ones. And no one, so far as I know, has disproved the account she gives of the discovery of Wind Cave.

It seems that Tom Bingham, a pioneer, went hunting one day in 1881 on a South Dakota hillside that had belonged until recently to the Sioux Indians. Suddenly he heard a mysterious sound coming from a clump of brush—a low kind of whistling noise. Bingham approached cautiously and found a ten-inch hole in the ground which seemed to be the source of the whistle. A wind was blowing out of the hole—strong enough to lift his hat into the air. This was a wonder sufficiently strange to keep Tom sitting by the hole for an hour watching the wind raise his hat time and time again.

He reported his discovery to his brother that night, and his brother, knowing the frontier, promptly asserted that Tom had been drunk. But Tom stoutly defended his sobriety and his tale, and in the end the two agreed to go back and investigate further. On arrival, Tom, full of confidence, placed his hat over the opening, but instead of flying upward the hat disappeared into the ground. The hole which had blown out air on one day was sucking in air on another!

Later a little digging enlarged the hole so that explorers could go in, and they found a rough, magnificent cavern. Air continued to blow in or out of the enlarged opening. Apparently the cave was like a very large bottle. When atmospheric pressure increased, air flowed in. When atmospheric pressure decreased, air flowed out.

Tom Bingham, who discovered this blowing cave on the frontier only five years after the Sioux wiped out General Custer and his forces on the Little Big Horn not far away, was part of a general pattern. Pioneers, or those with pioneering spirit, have been the ones more often than not who located caves. Louella Agnes Owen certainly had this spirit when she journeyed to Wind Cave, studied it and issued her very intelligent report on it in 1898.

Louella Owen and Horace Hovey, alone among early speleologists, wrote popular books summarizing their knowledge, but many a scientist took an interest in one phase or another of the cavern frontier which throughout the nineteenth century opened up more and more. These men confined their publications to scientific journals, and so their substantial achievements are not widely known. Mention of discoveries that they made in just a few caves will serve to suggest that a rich story remains to be told about these pioneers, how they made their finds and what these meant to the advancement of knowledge.

As early as 1832 a botanist, Constantine Schmaltz-Raffinesque, had visited and made notes on his findings in Kentucky caves, and in 1834 he looked into Durham Cave on the banks of the Delaware River in Pennsylvania. Years later in 1856 (a year before the publication of Darwin's *Origin of Species*), Dr. H. D. Rogers, the State Geologist of Pennsylvania, examined the same cave, and as often happens, discovered things of interest that had been overlooked earlier—the bones of twenty different species of mammal. Even Rogers' search was not complete. Dr. H. C. Mercer—racing against quarry-workers who were destroying the cave in 1893, and no doubt spurred on to new and painstaking endeavors by the vast interest in evolution that had developed since Rogers' day—found the bones of more than a score of animals, including several that were extinct in the area.

Scientists ran another race against quarry-workers in Port Kennedy Bone Cave, Montgomery County, Pennsylvania. In the 1870's

Charles Wheatley removed about three hundred tons of clay and fossil bones from this, the most important bone cave in the entire country. (At that time the minds of most scientists, at least, had been liberated from the theory that fossils were unsuccessful experiments tossed aside on the fifth and sixth days of Creation, or that they were a kind of divine hoax deliberately placed in the earth to test the faith of questioning geologists.) Wheatley dug down in Port Kennedy Cave as far as the water table, and there he had to stop. A few years later D. N. McCadden and S. N. Rhoads were able to dig a bit deeper. By 1895 steam pumps were at work drawing water out of the quarry, and this made it possible for new excavation to be undertaken. Several paleontologists, including Dr. H. C. Mercer, labored until they had removed another three hundred tons of clay and bones. It was apparent that for every bone that had been dug out perhaps two still remained in the cave, but the pumps were unequal to the task of giving the excavators dry areas in which to work. Water took over, and after that a nearby factory began dumping great quantities of sludge into the quarry-cum-cave, thus effectively sealing off the rich treasury of clues to the story of prehistoric animal life. Altogether, the bones of eighteen species new to science came from this one cave.

Nineteenth-century scientists by no means confined their investigations to caves so well known as to be the scene of quarry operations. Dr. Joseph Leidy, who has been called the first speleologist in Pennsylvania, visited many a cavern, together with his student Edward D. Cope. Latter-day spelunkers, who have felt a sense of elation at discovering what they thought was a new cave, have more than once found the initials of these two pioneers deep within some supposedly virgin passageway.

By the turn of the century, scientists had done a good deal of such underground adventuring in various parts of the country that had long been settled. Meanwhile laymen with a pioneering turn of mind were still moving into areas that had only recently been wrested from the Indians. Among these were cowboys, one of whom was soon to make a major discovery.

CHAPTER NINE

Cowboy Cavers

Jim White had been riding range on the Triple X Ranch in southeastern New Mexico for ten years, and he was now twenty, but never in all those years had he seen a sight like that which startled him at dusk one summer evening in 1901. Just ahead of him, in the foothills of the Guadalupe Mountains, a funnel-shaped whirlwind appeared to be outlined against the sky. But whirlwinds always moved along above the surface of the dusty desert, and this one stood still. Besides, the odd shape in the air was dark—darker than desert dust would be, even at twilight.

Jim decided to investigate, and before long he found himself lying on his belly among cactus plants at the edge of a deep, shadowy pit. The funnel-shaped mass rose out of the pit all right, but it wasn't as motionless as Jim had first thought. It consisted of thousands—no, millions—of bats flying rapidly upward in a counterclockwise spiral and then heading off over the rim of the hill toward the Black River. Jim was utterly fascinated with the windy whir made by hundreds of thousands of wings and with the singular rotary flight-path which produced the funnel effect, and perhaps he felt a certain kinship for a few mavericks who broke out of the conventional vortex of their fellows to fly in any direction that pleased them. He may not have been so attracted to the strong musky odor their bodies left in the air about him, but at any rate the bats set Jim White to wondering.

How deep was the hole that could disgorge so many of them? He built a fire of dead cactus, then threw one of the burning stalks down into the chasm. The flame went out before he could be sure the stalk had reached the bottom. So he pushed the whole fire in and watched the embers fall. The drop-off, he calculated, must be

101

straight down, at least thirty or forty feet—quite a drop, but there must be a lot more hole than that to house so many bats. Jim determined to come back for another look.

Two days later he was on the scene again with equipment that he as a cowboy understood—rope, lots of it, wire (of which the fence-mending crew at the cow camp had an abundance), an axe (which any cowboy hated but knew how to use), and a kerosene lantern. The afternoon sunlight fell directly into the hole, and he could see that the pit, as he had suspected, was the opening to great depths that obviously lay beyond. His equipment would come in handy. First he set to work with his axe chopping down tough desert shrubs to get rungs for a ladder. He fastened the rungs to ropes with wire, and then eased himself into the big hole. From the bottom of the ladder he had to scramble down a ticklish, steep pile of broken rock till he reached a solid floor. There he paused and lit his lantern.

Ahead of him a high-vaulted tunnel led off to the left and to the right. The passage to the left looked smoother, so he went that way, but not for long. The floor was covered with a deep layer of bat droppings. In that direction, then, lay the vast home of the little creatures that had brought him here. The floor of the other tunnel was free of guano. Jim began moving cautiously along it by the dim light of his kerosene lamp.

The immensity of the silent space through which he advanced was almost overwhelming. He had never been in any cave before, let alone a cave so huge that it made the Guadalupe Mountains above seem hollow. He had never read about caves—for the reason that he had never gone to school and couldn't read. But even if he had been a learned speleologist, Jim White could not have felt more sure that he was venturing into a place that was unique. When he came on the first stalactites and stalagmites, his sense of wonder grew. Here was a sight as beautiful as any man from cowboy to world-explorer had ever seen.

On and on Jim went, and he grew forgetful of his lamp. Suddenly it sputtered out. A paralyzing panic came over him in the absolute darkness. His hands shook as he tried to pour kerosene from his emergency can. Even for an unworried man, this would have been no easy task in the total darkness, but he finally got the light going.

Still terror-stricken, he dashed back the way he had come. Only when he rammed his head into a sharp stalactite which cut through his Stetson and his scalp did he come to his senses. Then, more cautiously, he followed the line of broken stalactites he had left at intervals on the ground to mark his trail—with the small end pointing toward the entrance—a practice frowned on by modern speleologists, who wish to conserve cave beauties that have been centuries in the making.

Back on the ranch at last, he told the other cowpokes of his marvelous discovery—and got well hooted at for his trouble. Not a one would deign to go and see proof of the incredible tales he told. Not one, that is, except a fifteen-year-old Spanish-American boy known only as the Kid. Across the barrier of language—neither Joe nor the Kid could utter more than a few words of the other's tongue—arrangements were made. Jim rigged up kerosene torches to take this time instead of the clumsy lamp, and five days after his first visit he returned with the Kid as partner.

The Kid proved as fearless—and as fascinated—as Jim himself. The two of them spent three days in the cave, looking, looking, and marveling, and finding ever bigger underground rooms and formations.

Near a huge boulder that had dropped from the ceiling at some distant time, Jim discovered a human skeleton. Someone, no doubt an Indian, had been here before him and had perished, possibly for lack of light and food on the dangerous narrow ledge where his bones lay. Some of the bones fell to pieces at Jim's touch, but the skull was solid, and he took it with him in his grub sack as a souvenir. Not long after this Jim himself almost became another skeleton in the cave. The can in which he carried his reserve supply of kerosene received one too many bangs on the rocks over which he was constantly struggling. The can sprang a leak, and the kerosene saturated his clothes. He was on a ledge at the time, with no safe space in which to try to remedy the situation, and the Kid was close behind him—too close. The Kid's torch set fire to Jim's back. Frantically he scrambled along the ledge with a brilliant flame from his own leather jacket lighting the way—and revealing the deep drop-off below the ledge. The Kid sped at his heels, and when they touched solid ground, the quick-witted boy saved Jim's life by using his own coat to smother the flame. Jim for his part smothered the blazing oil can with his Stetson.

The three-day exploration ended then and there. Jim had to get out of the cave to take care of his burns.

Even now, with the Kid to vouch—in Spanish—for the truth of his story, Jim was not able to convince the hands on the Triple X that he hadn't imagined all the wonders about which he couldn't help speaking. Cowboys and ranchers had long known there was a "bat cave" in the area, but bats didn't excite them, and who would believe that anything of interest lay in a hole in the ground? Most people in the nearest town, which was then called Eddy, shared with the cowpokes the general feeling that Jim was telling a tall tale— or else was more than a little *locoed*. One man, only, believed the story, and then only up to a point. He had visited Mammoth Cave in Kentucky. He knew what a cave could be like, and he could also read. He showed Jim pictures in encyclopedias, and Jim described the similarities—and dissimilarities—between the formations he had seen and those which appeared in the illustrations. But when Jim claimed that his cave was bigger than Mammoth, his friend balked. Nothing, he was dead certain, could be bigger than the underground world in Kentucky.

Jim's list of converts to a belief in the existence of his immense cavern remained at two, and soon one of them—the Kid—drifted on to some other ranch, possibly in Texas, and was lost forever. Jim remained at the Triple X Ranch. After a few years he found a way not only to be near the cave but to spend all his time there. Men interested in mining the bat guano for fertilizer had located this seemingly endless supply, and they hired Jim as foreman of the digging crew. Now in his free time he could explore to his heart's content, and he took other miners with him on some of his expeditions.

Jim worked at mining whenever his employers had orders to fill, and when they didn't, he kept on expanding his knowledge of the cave. After the end of World War I there was very little activity in the guano works, but Jim and his wife stayed on in a shack near the entrance. The years of guano excavation had proved to a growing number of people that Jim's cave really did exist, but so far he had not succeeded in luring anyone—except the Kid, his loyal wife and a few miners—underground to see its beauties. In fact, it was nearly twenty years after he first discovered the place before any sight-seer asked to look at it.

The request came from two young men touring the country in a rattletrap car who had somehow heard of the cave and found their way to it across the desert. Jim was more than happy to take the pair on a trip, and they succeeded in getting a photographer from the town twenty-seven miles away to come along. Two dozen pictures resulted from this first conducted tour. When the photographer's neighbors saw them, they quit kidding Jim and besieged the single-minded cowboy to guide *them* on a tour. He led a party of thirteen into the cave, and all of them were delighted and amazed at the vastness and the beauty of the place. Jim found himself in business as a guide.

In the days of guano-mining, a shaft had been bored into the section of the cave inhabited by the tiny bats that had left at least 100,000 tons of droppings on the floor. To hoist out the guano, a little gasoline engine dropped a round bucket straight down the shaft 180 feet, and two passengers could ride standing up in it. Clumsy though this elevator was, it provided a much easier means of reaching the cave than did the natural entrance. Jim continued to use it until the crowds grew too large. Meantime, he hacked out paths and drove discarded automobile axles into crevices to hold safety lines across dangerous spots.

Business men began to take an interest in Jim's tourist attraction, and they gave him some financial help. Outside the cavern entrance he built cabins for his visitors, who found it took most of a day to reach the place on the uncertain road from the town that had changed its name from Eddy to Carlsbad. Mrs. White provided meals for the travelers. Altogether it looked as if Jim's long devotion to what became known as Carlsbad Caverns would pay off in dollars—in addition to the immense satisfaction he got from showing off his great discovery.

But Jim was no business man. Time and again he enjoyed whole days giving free trips to his erstwhile doubting neighbors from nearby ranches. He spent too much money on building cabins for tourists and on improving trails. It was the story of Lester Howe all over again, except that Jim White never owned his cave, so he could not lose it.

The General Land Office in Washington heard of Carlsbad and sent a skeptical mineral-examiner, Robert Holley, out to have a look at it in 1923. Holley's doubts quickly changed to excitement and awe. He spent a month making the first survey of the cave, and he couched the hard facts of his report in some purple prose that is not too memorable. But memorable indeed was his recommendation that the Caverns merited establishment as a national monument. Within the year President Coolidge acted on Holley's suggestion.

Jim White stayed on at Carlsbad as Chief Ranger for a few years, watching increasing thousands of people take delight in his discovery. The Caverns had become a gigantic and complex enterprise. Jim had long dreamed that his cave would be famous and that millions of visitors would enjoy it, but now that his dream had come true, he had to step aside.

Today Jim White's memory is kept very much alive by his widow. Daily she descends in the elevator to the huge underground dining room, 750 feet below the surface, and there at a small stand where one of Jim's handmade kerosene lamps is on display, she will autograph a quaint booklet relating his adventures. Mrs. White will tell you if you stop to chat with her that her husband felt quite sure he had never reached the end of every passageway in the cave. The guides agree that there may well be more than the twenty-three known miles of corridors and enormous vaulted rooms.

Jim White discovered a cavern that can be talked about only in superlatives, but he was by no means the only cowboy who found caves or knew about them. The great Edwards Plateau in central Texas is limestone country, full of sinks and underground passages, and the early cattlemen no doubt located some of the caves in the same way Jim White found Carlsbad Caverns. Vast columns of bats have issued from Frio Cave and Ney Cave since time immemorial. The colony in the latter still numbers between twenty and thirty million. Frio Cave houses many millions, and so does an awesome hole in the ground known as Devil's Sinkhole.

No one now remembers what cattleman first reined in his horse just in time to avoid plunging to death at the bottom of Devil's

Sinkhole, 407 feet below the Texas prairie. Except when the bats are flying, there is no surface warning of any kind to indicate a hole 75 feet across. But apparently, at about the time when Jim White first entered Carlsbad, some rancher not only looked into the great pit but climbed down into it. He could only have done so with the aid of ropes, for the sink is jug-shaped—its diameter gets progressively greater as it goes down. At the bottom he found massive stalactites, tiny helictites, bacon rind, flowstone, and something that meant a good deal more to him than any of these things—clear, cool pools of water.

With a kind of Gargantuan ingenuity, the rancher somehow rigged pipes from the pool to the surface, where a windmill ran a pump. But it took more than drinking water to turn this bleak prairie with its scrubby growth of mesquite into good cow country. The rancher and his cattle moved on, leaving the place to sheep and goats. The Devil's Sinkhole is still there to be explored. Only a few hardy souls have ventured into it in recent years, and they are the first to admit that they don't know where the great hole might lead or how far their underground journey might take them.

At least one Arizona cowboy—a Negro named Crane—knew of a large cave in the side of Rincon Peak, twenty-seven miles southeast of Tucson, and so did four other men who may or may not have been cowboys. One day in 1884 these four gentlemen had urgent business at the cave. They had just robbed a Union Pacific train of $62,000 in gold coin, and they wanted a quiet place in which to lie low. On their way to the underground hide-out, they stopped and forced Crane to trade them fresh mounts for their exhausted horses. Before long Sheriff Bob Leatherwood had trailed the bandits to Crane's place and from there to what Crane called "the hole in the ground." When Leatherwood and his posse reached the mouth of the cave, they were welcomed with gunfire. The sheriff's object was to capture the bandits and recover the loot—not to engage in suicidal heroics in some dark underground passageway. So he and the posse camped near the cavern mouth and kept close watch, feeling sure that they could starve out the train robbers. But at the end of two weeks a cowboy rode up to Leatherwood with interesting news. Four men were in a nearby town boasting that they had fooled the sheriff from Tucson.

Leaving some of his party to keep an eye on the cave, Leather-wood went to check up. The braggarts turned out to be the bandits, and a western-style gun battle ensued, in which three of the bad men bit the dust. The fourth was captured.

Then began a unique chapter in the history of cave exploration. The Wells Fargo Express Company, whose agents had been in charge of guarding the $62,000 on the train, sent detectives to the scene because it was assumed that the robbers had hidden their loot in the cavern. For three long months the detectives poked around in the dry labyrinthine passages of what is now known as Colossal Cave. They turned up absolutely nothing of interest in the way of gold coins, and certainly nothing of interest to speleology. They didn't even find the obvious explanation of how the bandits had slipped through Leatherwood's guard in the first place. Indeed, it was years before anyone noticed there was a second entrance to the cave, only a quarter of a mile from the posse's camp.

In the meantime, the surviving bandit had paid for his sins with a twenty-eight-year stretch in prison. Wells Fargo agents, still hopeful of recovering the $62,000, were waiting inconspicuously nearby when he stepped out of the prison gates. They tailed him to Tucson. There, after several days, he shook them and disappeared. On the hunch that he would return to Colossal Cave to pick up his savings, the agents rushed off and once again searched the place. Once again they found nothing. That ends the story, except for the small fact that years later some of the Wells Fargo sacks which had contained the gold coins *were* found in the cave—empty.

Whether the bandits knew it or not, they had chosen as a hide-out a cave that really deserved the name it was later given. Colossal has an estimated thirty-nine miles of explored passages, and its end has never been reached. In terms of linear measurements, this makes it bigger than Carlsbad.

But no known cave is as spacious or has such vast rooms and enormous passageways as Carlsbad. Its Big Room alone is nearly three-quarters of a mile long and in one place, 285 feet high. Few caves anywhere have such massive stalagmites—although New Cave nearby has one formation bigger than anything in Carlsbad itself. Few caves have such a profusion of well-preserved speleothems—

although only about 5 per cent of Carlsbad is still alive, with water dripping and giving lustre and translucence to growing deposits of calcite. On the 1,100-foot level, which can be seen from above but not visited by tourists, cave pearls are growing in rimstone pools.

Far below the desert surface of the land, water from the infrequent rains still seeps down, carrying with it calcium bicarbonate in solution and depositing calcite in the hollowed vastnesses created by water when the land was moist and the water table was high. For sixty million years this great cave has been forming in Capitan and Tansill limestone that was laid down in a shallow sea about two hundred million years ago. Fossilized evidence of the marine life of the Permian sea, in which the limestone was built, exists in the walls. And every year a half-million people learn something about the grandeur and complexity of the world's evolution as they view the spectacle opened to them by Jim White, who could neither read nor write but who had the precious ability to respond with persistent action when his imagination was stirred.

CHAPTER TEN

Cave-Crawling Scientists

The stupendous cave that Jim White discovered and explored was bound to attract scientific investigators. In 1923, both Robert Holley of the General Land Office and Dr. Willis T. Lee of the United States Geological Survey studied Carlsbad. The following March, Lee returned at the head of a full-fledged expedition sent out by the National Geographic Society. His party set up housekeeping in rough shacks left over from the days of guano-mining, and when hot weather came to their wilderness camp, they were glad to have the ready-made refrigerator which the cave provided. The steady 56° F. temperature underground was a considerable improvement over that outside, which ranged daily from 100° to 115°.

As Jim White guided the explorers through the cavern, they began to find almost immediately something most unusual in caving history: Time and again the actual measurements they made proved that passageways and rooms were *bigger* than had been reported. Even back in Hovey's day, a "cave mile" was famous for being an infinitely elastic unit of length. Depending on who did the walking, it could mean anything from two hundred yards up to a little less than a mile. But in Carlsbad Jim White and the other early guessers had been remarkably modest.

Lee did not attempt a full mapping of the cave—no complete map has yet been made—but he did go down to the lowest known level. Modern spelunkers will be amused by the method he used to keep from getting lost. He relied on the old ball-of-twine technique, unrolling the string behind him when he entered unfamiliar passageways, but he also did one thing that cave explorers still do— he used arrow-shaped markers pointing toward the exit. Even with these precautions, Lee admitted that he had been confused at times in passageways with which he thought he was quite familiar.

Spelunking gear had not been perfected in his day. He often had to improvise on the spot. To descend one ninety-foot drop he and his helpers fashioned a ladder of sorts out of wire. In another place a more or less permanent ladder was made of wood, and it can still be seen leading down to the lowest level in a great abyss known as the Jumping Off Place.

Lee was not only fascinated by the cave which he was the first scientist to study intensively. He also kept a close watch on his companions and their reactions to extended periods underground, and he noted that some of those who were new to caving felt apprehensive as they faced the prospect of unknown hazards. Others were buoyed up by a high sense of adventure. But, he reported, one and all in his party showed the effects of tension after long-continued labors far from the light of day. Many more recent exploring parties working in other caves for shorter periods have experienced this same tension. It is a strain, sometimes a very great strain, even for old hands to face danger and the unknown day after day.

When Lee returned from Carlsbad, he wrote two articles about the cavern for *The National Geographic Magazine*—and tourist trade at Carlsbad promptly began to be the extraordinary phenomenon it still is.

Obviously many more expeditions into the deep recesses of Carlsbad would be required before anyone could say the cave had given up even a major part of its secrets. The same can be said of most big caves, including Colossal in Arizona. Even before Lee took his party into Carlsbad, another expedition, with a scientist along, had entered Colossal and there, in 1922, had establishing a spelunking record that stood for many years: they remained underground six days and seven nights. Frank Schmidt, who devoted his life to Colossal much as Jim White devoted his to Carlsbad, led this expedition which included three other men—a geologist remembered only as Dr. Hibberd; Alex Kerr, who apparently had some caving experience (he had explored a cave in Australia for the British government); and a Mexican or Spanish-American identified only as Angel.

The four men, all equipped with miners' carbide lamps, dressed in levis and wearing soft rubber-soled shoes, entered the cave with very little idea of what hazards they would have to face. They suspected that they would find no water, and they were right. They expected to stay underground a long time—and they did. In their packs they carried dehydrated food, quantities of water, sleeping bags, four 50-foot lengths of ⅜″ Manila rope, a surveyor's chain, an altimeter, a safety light, a compass, a thermometer, and two pedometers. On the first day, Angel's pack weighed 110 pounds, and the other men carried 65 pounds each. After one night in the pleasant 72° temperature of the cave, all of them abandoned their sleeping bags.

The party proceeded systematically to explore each passageway in turn and to make a rough survey. Along the main passage they chalked arrow-marks pointing in the direction of the exit. On parts of the wall that were dark, they used light chalk; on walls where the color of the rock was light, they used dark chalk. Side passages, too, were marked with arrows, and when the men withdrew from one after examining it, they methodically chalked a line across the tail of the arrow at the mouth of the passage as a memo to themselves.

Following the dry bed of an ancient underground river and its tributaries, the small group plodded along what they estimated to be a total of thirty-nine miles of cave. But before they had reached the end of the main channel, they had to turn back. They faced and were unable to cross an intangible but very real barrier that has defeated many an expedition: They ran out of supplies. With no adequate support party to keep them furnished with food and particularly with water, the four weary men retraced their steps. No man has gone beyond the point they reached, and Colossal Cave still remains a major underground frontier.

As technological advances in the twentieth century sped up, more and more scientists became aware of the fact that caves in general presented a new frontier for their investigations. Industry and science had been stimulating each other at an ever-increasing rate, and as a result of man's increased knowledge, his ability to be curious about caves also increased. The very large number of known caves offered scientists ready-made laboratories in which to make their observations. Before long the thinking and writing of American geologists began to reflect a tremendous interest in the hollow places within the rocks which it was their business to study. One who had been maturing his thoughts for most of his eighty years, W. M. Davis, brought out in 1930 a theory of the origin of limestone caverns which stimulated controversy and further study of the subject. Unlike many geologists of the time, who thought that cavities in limestone developed *above* the water table, Davis emphasized his belief that most caves originated *below* the water table. A. C. Swinnerton also pointed to the very plausible evidence of cave formation in the saturated zone, but he insisted that solution took place for the most part *at or just below* the water table. He also allowed for the fact that caves were enlarged after they were drained and above the water table. Several years later Clyde A. Malott placed great emphasis on the carving action of underground rivers *above* the water table as the major shaping factor in large caves, after they had been primitively developed below the water table and then drained.

By 1942, J Harlen Bretz of the University of Chicago had visited about a hundred caves of widely varying types and had studied each to see whether it could be explained by previous theories. He concluded that most of these caves could only have originated *below* the water table, but he recognized the important changes that had taken place after caves were above the water table. However, he attacked one argument of those who placed great emphasis on the importance of underground streams. This argument ran as follows: There is a great deal of clay to be found on the floors of many caves; clay is washed from the *surface* by streams; therefore, if clay exists in a cave, a stream must have washed it there. Bretz said not so. Much of the fine-grained clay in caves, he believed, consisted of insoluble material once contained in the limestone itself, and it settled to the floor when the cave was completely filled with water— that is, while it was still in the saturated zone.

Bretz's curiosity about the subject did not end with the publication of his theory, which stirred great interest among scientists. Since then he has visited perhaps two hundred more caves and has prepared a book on those of Missouri. For the lovers of curiosa, it may be reported that a constant companion on these trips has been a dog who seems to be quite as avid a cave-crawler as his master.

Biologists as well as geologists began in the 1920's to take an increased interest in what caves had to offer. A year after Willis T.

Lee headed his expedition to Carlsbad, Vernon Bailey spent a great deal of time there studying cave life, particularly bats, and he embodied his findings in a book.

At about the same time, an experiment with bats in Texas reflected the rising curiosity about the little creatures. Dr. Charles A. R. Campbell was fascinated with the problem of how bats could leave the utter darkness of a cave, fly away at dusk and on into the night, then somehow make their way back into deep underground recesses. To test the extent of their ability to find their way home, Campbell went to a bat cave (probably Ney Cave) and captured two thousand in a big net. He then took them in his car thirty miles from the cave, doused them in a mixture of powdered chalk, water and gum arabic, and let them loose. The bats streaked off toward their home cave, and so did Campbell. According to his report, he got there first and very soon began to observe his white-marked specimens plummeting down into the cavern entrance. Their flying speed seemed to be about thirty miles an hour, and he believed he had proof of highly developed homing ability.

Biologists felt that Campbell had not performed a thoroughly scientific experiment (he did not try to capture any of the marked bats as they returned), but his critics were aware that they themselves had much to learn about the habits and hows and whys of bats. For example, no one yet knew how bats could fly in complete darkness. One theory, widely held but never tested by experiment, maintained that they had extremely sensitive nerve ends in their wing membranes which reflected differences in air pressure. Nor had anyone figured out why some bats hibernated and why some seemed to disappear altogether during the winter. In his careful study of the bats of Carlsbad, Vernon Bailey never discovered that most of them left the cave during the cold months and moved far south into Mexico. The unknown far exceeded the known. But any area of ignorance is a challenge, and with bats—which seem singularly remote from human life—as with a great many other things, the disinterested search for facts led in the most unexpected way to things of practical, even sensational, importance to man.

Charles E. Mohr, an eminent naturalist and speleologist, was among the first to make persistent studies of the little creatures. He wanted a way of following the movements of individuals—something more permanent and specific than the whitewash that had already been tried. So he borrowed a technique from the field of ornithology, using very small bird bands which identified the animals to which they were attached. Mohr wasn't the first to do bat-banding, but he was the first to carry out long-term, systematic investigation. His work began in May, 1932, and has continued up to the present.

In the fall of the same year, a young Harvard student, Donald R. Griffin, also started putting bands on bats to identify them, and he too has persisted. Others—there grew to be about thirty banders working at any one time—joined in and began haunting caves and abandoned mines. Sometimes they swept the air with oversized butterfly nets and captured the bats as they flew in or out of the entrance. More often the batmen and batwomen gently plucked the sleeping or hibernating animals from their roosts far back in the darkness. Gradually they worked out techniques that are now standard practice.

A bander first examines a bat to determine its species and sex, then deftly slips on an identification tag. This is a delicate operation. The band, a tiny strip of metal, must be pressed around the bat's forearm tightly enough so that it won't fall off, but not so firmly that the wing membrane is pierced by the ends of the band. (At various times the bands have been put around the legs or through the ears. But it was difficult to see the former when bats hung in a cluster, and clips in the ears were apparently harmful.) The featherweight bit of metal, placed loosely on the forearm, seems not to do any harm and can be more readily seen than a leg band. If the bander can, he finishes his work before the bat is thoroughly roused. Not that he is afraid of being bitten when it becomes lively. Very few cave bats have teeth that can pierce the human skin. But the bander does want to keep his specimen from waking up. A dormant bat's body is normally at just above cave temperature, but when handled, it begins to wake and to warm rapidly. This means it soon uses up its energy reserve, which is stored for hibernation in the form of fat, and since it lives on insects which are not available during winter, it may quite possibly die of starvation.

Each tiny bat band is marked with two sets of numbers. One set is that which has been assigned to the bander by the United States

Fish and Wildlife Service. This same number appears on all the tags he uses. The second set of figures identifies the bat. The bander notes in his records, next to each number, the species, sex, place of discovery, and he sends a copy of this record to the Fish and Wildlife Service in Washington. When any bander anywhere examines a bat that already wears a tag, he in turn notes the number, exact time and place, and sends this information to the Fish and Wildlife Service, where it is entered in the records. A note then goes from Washington to the bander who originally tagged the bat, and to the finder, who is told when and where the bat was first banded.

By 1955, more than 90,000 bats in the United States had been individually identified, and over the years a more and more complete picture has begun to show what bats do while human beings sleep or merely look the other way.

For one thing, it is now clear that migratory bats usually return to the same places year after year. There is increasing evidence that they do have homing tendencies. When transported in cages for distances as great as 156 miles, they have found their way back to their customary roosts. Regular seasonal migrations from one place to another have been traced. Donald Griffin found, for example, that some bats traveled from Cape Cod, where they summered, to caves in Vermont, where they hibernated. He also discovered that one species from the United States wintered on the island of Bermuda. The longest migration on record so far was made by a bat from Carlsbad, which was recovered 810 miles to the south in Mexico.

From banding we now know something of how a bat lives and how long it lives. Apparently ten years is a good ripe old age attained by many individuals, but there are some who have lived to be twelve, and thirteen years old. One veteran carried a band for sixteen years, and no one knows how old he was when he was first tagged. Other curious facts have come to light: There always seem to be more adult males than females, although the sex proportion among baby bats is about 50-50. What happens to the females? Do they die in the process of reproducing and rearing the young? A mother has the burden not only of suckling her newborn infant but of carrying it along, clinging to her belly, when she flies in search of food. (Most species have only one offspring a year.) No one has found proof, however, that female bats with infants have a high mortality rate. Could it be, then, that many females take advantage of a peculiar biological fact and hibernate in places as yet undiscovered, which are far distant from the roosts of the males? Mating of bats takes place before the hibernation period. The female retains the sperm in her body, but the ovum is not fertilized until she awakes from the period of dormancy. So far, no one has found a place where large collections of hibernating females would give proof to the theory that after mating the sexes go their separate ways. However, it is known that females very often establish "nurseries" in secluded spots where few if any male bats hang around. In the nurseries, the half-grown young are left together while the mothers forage for food.

The list of discoveries about bats is constantly growing—but so is the list of unsolved mysteries—and both our knowledge and our ignorance have stimulated many kinds of research. By the 1930's, scientists faced up to the fact that they didn't really know how bats could fly in the dark. They had no proof—only a hypothesis—that nerves in the wings accounted for so uncanny a sense of direction. Experiments were set up to determine which of the bat's sense organs actually was responsible for its extraordinary ability. In a soundproof room wires were hung crisscross about a foot apart. Blindfolded bats released in the room missed the wires every time. This confirmed the Italian experiment made a century and a half earlier. Another investigation, almost as old but less well-known, had shown that bats had great difficulty in flying if their ears were plugged. Now bats with their ears taped down were released in the experiment room. They collided with the wires. Obviously the sense of hearing had something to do with flight. Bats whose mouths were taped shut likewise had difficulty in flying, even if their ears were open. A connection between these two facts seemed most likely. The scientists reasoned that a bat must guide itself by the echoes of its own voice. Its ears must be able to catch sounds pitched higher than a human being can hear.

Bat "sonar" remained another unproved hypothesis until Donald Griffin devised a method of testing it. He found, by the use of a delicate microphone and a piece of electronic equipment called an oscillograph, which together could convert sound waves into light waves, that he could indeed detect ultrasonic vibrations caused by bats' vocal cords. Careful study of photographs of the light patterns on the oscillograph screen revealed that bats utter sounds of extremely short duration, each one lasting one two-hundredth of a second. The sounds are not given out singly, but in little groups or bursts, and there may be as many as sixty bursts per second. Plainly the bat's ears are able to pick up the echoes of these high-frequency sounds in the infinitesimally short silent period between bursts. The nearer an object, the shorter the interval between a cry and the return of the echo. The object may be a wire only a few inches away, but the bat can avoid it.

Not only do bats use their "sonar" to detect obstacles in flight, but apparently they also remember echo patterns and can return again and again to the same spots deep in caves. Quite possibly the spiral flight pattern they make as they issue from Carlsbad and some other caves is nothing but a mnemonic device. The bats may be rehearsing the echo patterns of the cave entrance before they take off on long cross-country flights to their feeding grounds, where night insects flourish. However, bats are not infallible pathfinders. They can get lost in caves just as people can. Explorers have found occasional skeletons or desiccated bodies far inside caverns, away from normal roosting places.

It was no easy task to arrive at an understanding of bat "sonar," and it involved, as do most speleological studies, a lot of hard work in caves. It also involved risk—in one case, risk of drowning in a sudden underground flood, a hazard dreaded by all cavers. One Thanksgiving weekend, Griffin with five others went to record bat sounds in Aitkin Cave, Mifflin County, Pennsylvania. He had banded bats there before and was thoroughly familiar with the place. The scientific party set up their tents near the mouth of the cave and their oscillograph equipment inside. Before they went to work, rain began to fall. Fearing a rise in the small creek that entered the cave, Griffin and his assistants moved their equipment to high ground in an underground passage, then prudently went outside—and a lucky thing they did! The rain increased; the water rose with great rapidity and in a very short time literally filled the cave as if it had been a bottle. The scientists escaped, but the bats did not. All were drowned except a few that Griffin had captured and taken out in a cage, and a handful of others that were hibernating in one air pocket. If the men had been incautious or inattentive to the weather and the level of water in the creek, they could have been trapped and drowned, as six of eight speleologists had been in France only two weeks before Griffin's trip. The French researchers entered a cave to study insects, and were caught by a sudden rush of water following an unsuspected rainstorm outside.

What Donald Griffin found out by lugging his equipment into caves and "listening" to bats seemed singularly remote from human affairs, although scientists were interested. However, his discoveries led to an unexpected reward for himself and—more important—for humanity. During World War II he applied his knowledge in devising new ways for blinded soldiers to guide themselves by the use of echo-location, and his efforts won him high government recognition.

For all their research, scientists still can't answer many of their own questions about bats. Why do some hibernate when the food supply runs low with the coming of winter? Why don't *all* of them migrate? What is the physiological mechanism that triggers either migration or hibernation?

Why is the bat population steadily decreasing? Is it because bats are disturbed too much by cavers? Or has the use of DDT cut down their food supply or possibly even poisoned the bats themselves? Or is there another reason?

What causes the homing of bats? Is it some sort of electrical response to magnetic fields?

What is the source of rabies in bats that are insectivorous? Are they bitten by vampire bats while on migration far south in Mexico or Latin America? The vampire bat is the only one in this hemisphere that feeds on animal blood, the source of rabies infection. But it does not range as far north as our southern border.

Members of at least two species found in Mexico—the Hognose and the Longnose bats—spend about three months of every year at Colossal Cave in southeastern Arizona, and there was a time when scientists found them completely puzzling. These creatures are fruit-eaters. But, between early May when they arrive and late July when they leave, this part of Arizona has little or no fruit to offer. What, then, could the bats find to eat? External evidence led to an "educated guess." Both species have elongated noses and unusually long tongues. Could it be that they fed on nectar? Examination of the stomach contents of specimens revealed a liquid and bits of solid material. The latter proved to be pollen from two kinds of desert plant that bloom in profusion near the cave—the saguaro cactus and the shin dagger or amole. Moreover, the blossoming season of these plants almost exactly corresponds to the arrival and departure of the bats. Apparently the animals not only live on the nectar but also help to pollinate the flowers.

Here again the solution of one puzzle led to another. Scientists discovered that the migrant bats who appear in the spring are all pregnant females. They spend just enough time in the Colossal Cave area to bear and rear their offspring; then, when flowers wither and the food supply gives out, the youngsters with their mothers set off presumably for Mexico. But where do the males spend the months of May, June and July? What is the chemistry of bodily processes that sends females on the journey to Colossal and males who knows where?

Dr. E. Lendell Cockrum of the zoology department at the University of Arizona has determined to find at least some of the answers. In two years he and a group of his students have banded several thousand of these fruit-eating bats—mothers and their young who, of course, include both male and female. Dr. Cockrum hopes that in the near future enough specimens of both sexes will be recovered somewhere in Central America to show where the females spend nine months of their time and where the males spend all of theirs.

Complexity increases as bio-speleologists learn more and more. Not only bats but also less numerous cave creatures have presented scientists with an endless variety of problems to solve. One example is enough to illustrate what they face—in addition to the difficulties of the cave itself—when they embark upon a project. Says Anita Cruise Ley in the National Speleological Society *News*:

A speleologist finds himself a herpetologist, an evolutionist, an ecologist, a collector, a taxonomist and a photographer when he goes spelunking for salamanders. The herpetologist seeks an amphibian with an elongated body and tail which persists throughout life; a scaleless animal with or without gills which lives in water, on land or a combination of the two. The evolutionist deliberates on the explanation of the reduction of eyes and the depigmentation of many of the cave salamanders. The ecologist notes the presence of a twilight zone and a dark zone with species typical of each habitat, and is inspired to become a collector with a wire strainer and a bottle of FAA (formalin, acetic acid, alcohol). He himself may be a taxonomist or may solicit the assistance of one who will be concerned with identification of the catch. . . .

Among the constellation of sciences that make up speleology none is of greater practical, immediate importance to man than hydrology, and no science is more dependent upon caves. Hydrologists look for water supplies beneath the surface of the earth. In limestone country this means looking for cavernous passages that are wholly or partly filled with water. When a deep-well driller strikes water in limestone country, he in fact finds a cave passage—possibly very small, but nevertheless a water-filled cavity. It follows that the more a hydrologist knows about the caves of an area and its pattern of underground drainage, the better will be his chances of success when he says, "Drill here."

The amount of information a hydrologist needs from a cave is enormous if his detective work is to be good. He requires an accurate and detailed cave map, not only in two dimensions but in three. The map must relate the cave in its entirety to the surface features of the land, including, of course, water drainage. The nature of the rock in which the cave was formed is also important. In which directions do the bedding planes tilt? What is the pattern of seepage as revealed by stalactites and flowstone? Are there more stalagmites than stalactites? Has some movement of the earth's crust slipped one mass of stone upward or downward past another? The evidence a hydrologist collects includes the temperature of cave water, its chemical content, the direction and rate of flow—and not just at one moment. He may find information of great importance to him in the seasonal variations in the rate of flow.

In a large sense, of course, he wants to know where underground water comes from and where it goes, so he traces the course of streams by using a dye called fluorescein. Rivers and brooks in limestone country have a way of appearing and disappearing, aboveground and underground as well, and the dye is a most convenient way of finding out whether streams A and B are the same or totally different bodies of water. Out of such details, together with a knowledge of geology in general, hydrologists draw conclusions that are increasingly important to ordinary mortals, for life itself depends on an adequate supply of water; and as population and industry increase, the need for water becomes ever more pressing.

On the other hand hydrology, which finds caves so useful, has at least once returned the favor. A few years ago the operators of Luray Caverns noted that moisture was ceasing to drip down some of the speleothems. In a short time this would mean that the stalactites and stalagmites would become lusterless, and in the long run they would turn to papery flakes and dust. But what had caused the cave to dry up? There had been no important decrease in rainfall, the source of the seepage water that kept the speleothems alive. Investigation proved that the hardwood trees on the land above were responsible. They had been growing steadily and giving off increasing amounts of moisture into the atmosphere through their leaves.

With the cooperation of federal conservation experts, many of the big trees were logged off. The twigs and branches were left on the ground to protect the soil, and a certain number of new varieties were planted—softwood trees that give off less moisture through their leaves than do hardwoods. Far below in the cave, drops of water reappeared on the speleothems, retaining for them the luster that is such an essential part of their beauty. Men had successfully intervened in the operations of nature, and increased the volume of water below the surface of the earth. A small miracle was performed because someone had a little knowledge of hydrology and botany.

In addition to the well-known achievements of archeologists and paleontologists in caves, promising investigative work has been done by other scientists. Bacteriologists have examined cave earth in the hope of finding new antibiotics, and have inquired into the possibility that nitrogen-fixing bacteria, using inorganic materials, are the creators of the nitrate crystals found in some places where there is every indication that the crystals are not a product of bat guano. Physiologists, too, have discovered in caves a useful environment for the pursuit of knowledge. A few years ago Dr. Nathaniel Kleitman and Bruce Richardson chose Mammoth Cave as an ideal spot in which to find out whether or not the bodies of human beings can adjust to a time-schedule other than that of the twenty-four hour solar day. Where there was no sunlight to distract them, the two men started living as if the day were twenty-eight hours long, with time allotted for work, recreation and sleep. Richardson, the younger man, adjusted perfectly to the new schedule; Kleitman had some difficulties. Although they drew no sweeping conclusion from the five-week experiment, it seemed clear that the human body is not mechanically or magically limited to a twenty-four hour cycle.

Nor is the human mind held within a prison of the facts that are already known. The advances in speleology have been startling. Practically the whole gamut of sciences has had something to give caves or to get from them, and most scientists have found that solitary cave-crawling is inadequate to their purposes. In the nineteenth century, European speleologists began to pool their knowledge and resources. Today there are at least 125 speleological societies in 20 different countries of the world. In the United States a great number of those individuals specially concerned with caves have banded together in the National Speleological Society, about which there will be more in the next chapter.

One team of scientists in California became the active workers in a learned society known as the Western Speleological Institute. Although the Institute is not a membership organization, it has financed and conducted archeological excavation and intensive surveys of many individual caves, each survey lasting at least a week. In addition it has made general surveys of all the known caves in Nevada and is in the process of completing a similar survey of all the known caves in Arizona. One—and only one—of the Institute's achievements has been the discovery of many new caves in the Grand Canyon.

Such discoveries by scientists and by laymen have been made at an outstanding rate in recent years. A century ago only fifty caves were known to geologists in this country. Five thousand or more are now listed in the files of the speleological societies, and those who are most active on the cave frontier are the first to say that exploration has only begun.

CHAPTER ELEVEN

Spelunking Grows Up

"An institution is the lengthened shadow of a man," the saying goes, and William J. Stephenson is a husky man who casts a very vigorous shadow in the form of the National Speleological Society, which he founded.

No single dramatic event turned Steve's attention underground. The fact seems to be that his interest in caving developed gradually. He had more energy than Washington, D. C., could absorb in the 1920's when he was a young government worker preparing himself for a career as an examiner in the Patent Office. He added hiking to swimming, which had been his college sport, and on weekends he headed for the out-of-doors.

On one occasion, while he was leading a hikers' group of the All Souls Unitarian Church, he happened to look into a cave, the first one he had seen. After that he visited more of them. He wanted exercise and wasn't averse to a little excitement. He found both in wild caves, and more, too. For instance, the behavior of one particular cluster of hibernating bats intrigued him. He noticed on successive visits that they had moved from one location in the cave to another during the period when they were supposed to be totally inactive. Why? Scientists could offer no explanation—if, indeed, they had ever observed such a phenomenon.

By 1941, Steve had collected other unanswered questions. He had also collected numerous friends who enjoyed caving. Together they organized a group that became the National Speleological Society. Few, if any, of the charter members then considered themselves speleologists. They were spelunkers rather than serious investigators in any of the sciences connected with caves. The NSS—an abbreviation soon dictated for reasons of convenience as well as by Washington's love of using initials—was primarily a group of sportsmen at the outset. But cave-crawling is an odd sport: it leads its devotees easily into a pursuit of scientific explanations for the wonders they behold. For one thing, the infant NSS found its collective curiosity piqued when it sought information from any quarter, governmental or private, regarding the location of caves in which it could spelunk. Nobody since the days of Hovey, who himself had scarcely been discovered by twentieth-century cavers, had bothered to assemble all the available data on caves—and there was all too little to assemble.

The amateurs in the NSS pulled themselves—had to pull themselves—up by their bootstraps. There were almost no reliable maps of caves, so they set about making them. They set about observing mineralogical phenomena that mineralogists had often ignored because these things were inconveniently underground—where, after all, most minerals occur. Some of the early NSS members realized, as had Hovey three generations before, that caves held much of archeological interest. Other members sought far and wide for data on the plant and animal life they observed in caves, and they found precious little at first.

The obvious earnestness of the group—in spite of their amateur status and their unfeigned interest in the delights of exercise and adventure underground—soon attracted scientists who themselves did not have nearly all the answers to the amateurs' questions. A partnership, which could well be emulated by many branches of learning, quickly developed between people professionally trained in science and pioneering laymen—spirited John or Jane Does—who from the early days in our country up to the present have discovered a good many more caves and explored a good many more than scientists have.

As this partnership expanded, with the experts really dependent in many ways on the skills and interests of the sportsmen, the society grew and spread outward from Washington into cave areas. Local groups called themselves "Grottoes" after the name often given to small caves within larger caves. (Recently the national organization has urged local groups to call themselves "chapters." Because the name "Grotto" has been in use up to the time this book went to press, it will appear throughout.)

The serious scientific interests of the organization were reflected in the men who succeeded Stephenson as president. One was Ralph W. Stone, former State Geologist of the Commonwealth of Pennsylvania and editor of *The Caves of Pennsylvania;* another, Charles E. Mohr, a leading authority on cave life and director of the Audubon Nature Center in Greenwich, Connecticut. The latest to assume presidential duties is William E. Davies, Assistant Chief, Military Geology Branch of the United States Geological Survey, author of *The Caves of Maryland* and *Caverns of West Virginia.*

Typical scenes of NSS activity suggest the nature of the collaboration that goes on between laymen and those who have special technical training. A scientific study of all the caves in New York State is in progress. It is a volunteer project, entirely financed and conducted by the members and the Grottoes of the northeastern states. When published, the study will be a valuable source book in half a dozen sciences, as well as a guide for spelunkers who want to know where caves are and what to look for. In addition, the book will supplement a folklore and human interest survey already made by Clay Perry in his *Underground Empire.* Since the project has serious goals but will be conducted in part by amateurs and by scientists unused to caving, it is necessary to set standards for all hands. So the leaders devise a model demonstration survey. They invite cavers from all over the northeastern states to spend a weekend of learning by doing, in Becker's and Spider Caves near Schoharie, New York.

The plan is this: a coordinator will set up work groups—one to make a survey of the surface terrain above and around the cave; one to map the cave itself; another to study the geology and mineralogy of the cave; others to inquire into paleontology, biology and hydrology. In addition, a photographer will take pictures of significant cave features and of the scientific teams at work. An artist, working in black and white, will make drawings of things which can be more clearly recorded in his medium than on film. A first-aid expert is on hand in case of mishap. A cave-master will stand at the entrance directing traffic—and making sure nobody is left inside when activities end.

Preliminary findings of each group will be reported to the coordinator, then discussed on the spot at a meeting of all members of the expedition. The final results of their studies will appear in published form.

Such is the blueprint. Now an amazing variety of very human human beings set to work carrying it out. A few—mostly those who have brought their children along—settle down in the hotel in Schoharie. (One prominent caver smuggles his dog into the hotel, too.) A tall man in a business suit clumps around the lobby in his caving boots—he has forgotten to bring any other shoes. The majority of the expedition camp out in sleeping bags and tents in the city park on top of the bluff above Becker's Cave. In the middle of the camp, one member sets up a shop on the tailgate of her station wagon, with carbide, spare lamp parts, literature for sale—profits to go to the NSS. Little gasoline stoves come out of cars and heat up suppers on picnic tables. The coordinator of the work parties hauls from his car a reference library of scientific books that may come in handy. Without a word to anyone, a young man passes a rope around a tree, crawls into his caving coveralls, which have special leather patches in the crotch and over one shoulder, and suddenly disappears over the bluff—a straight drop-off of sixty or eighty feet, and a wonderful place to practice the mountaineering techniques that are useful underground.

Saturday morning: the coordinator, who is a young science teacher, makes up his lists for the work parties. Who wants to go with the biology group? Anyone interested can sign up to accompany the leader. This party is the first to be organized. It has priority in a cave because later groups will disturb the underground creatures and muddy the water where living things must be visible to be observed or collected.

The crew which will make the surface survey also gets an early start.

Next come those who will accompany the hydrologist. He, too, wants to study the water before it is muddy or disturbed. With him he carries a can that has roused interest among the neophytes in the party. It contains the brilliant red powder fluorescein. Everyone has heard by this time that the powder turns a livid fluorescent green when dropped into water, but in spite of its poisonous color it is harmless to human beings or to water life. The hydrologist expects to dump the chemical into a small lake reputed to be at the end of one channel in Becker's Cave, the object being to see whether the dye will turn up later in a spring some distance away. If green water does appear, some knowledge will have been gained about underground drainage in the area. Volunteers go off to sit—they don't know for how long—watching at the spring for the dye. (As it turns out, they don't have to wait very long, swatting mosquitoes. The underground lake is found to be a tiny puddle with no evidence of flow in any direction.)

The geologist, with his volunteers, collects specimens of the limestone formation in which the cave lies, and makes notes on what he calls "dip"—that is, the angle of a bedding plane in relation to the horizontal—and "strike"—the compass direction of a line at right angles to the dip. (This kind of information may help explain the shape of a cavity in limestone, the underground drainage pattern, and its relation to surface topography.)

A young paleontologist, a graduate student at Columbia University, finds fossil crinoids in the limestone outside the cave and more of them inside. With a geologist's hammer and chisel he collects specimens. Peering through a huge magnifying glass, he hunts for fossilized specimens of smaller forms of life.

A student from Rutgers University heads the cave-mapping party. He has a tough assignment. He can't use a transit—there are too many low crawlways and squeezeways and curves for such a bulky instrument. So he must get accurate measurements and sights with a steel tape and a delicate Brunton compass. The problem is to sight over the compass, from the entrance of the cave to a point as far back in a straight line as possible, note the exact direction and distance, then take another straight line from that point, and so on, wherever the passageways lead. It is necessary to measure at the same time changes in elevation, and the varying widths and heights of passageways. The surveyor also has to record, in their exact locations, streams, mud banks, any breakdown and important speleothems.

The discomforts and frustrations of mapping a cave like Becker's have to be witnessed to be appreciated. It is mostly work on hands and knees (the rocks on Becker's floor seem particularly sharp) or flattened out on belly or back. Even then the man trying to sight the flashlight ahead of him in the cramped quarters is likely to call to an assistant who is wedged in between, "Suck up your guts! I can't see."

The leader of the party, though a large man, wriggles nimbly through all the tight places, rather like an oversized and very animated amoeba. To the astonished novices present, it seems that he is working wonders. The fact is that bulky cavers can become very efficient contortionists. There always seems to be some arrangement of angles for hips and shoulders that will render negotiable the kind of hole which spelunkers have nicknamed "meatgrinder," "keyhole," "lemon squeezer," or "fat man's misery."

The accomplishments of the head surveyor do not end with surveying under conditions that would defeat most civil engineers. He is head of an NSS group that has mastered the technique of underwater cave exploration. Now, after finishing up in Becker's, he puts on a diving demonstration in a chilly creek (46° F.) which emerges from underground not far away. The creek possibly connects with the cave, but nobody has ever investigated. Later a fully equipped party may probe farther.

The NSS is always probing farther into caves—and each one presents special problems. The skills needed to get into Elkhorn Cave near Masonville, West Virginia, are as exciting as the underwater techniques but very different. The Philadelphia Grotto arranges ahead of time with the farmer under whose land the cave lies for a visit and permission to camp in his pasture. Experienced riggers in the Grotto arrive before the main party. Elkhorn can be entered only through a perpendicular fissure with a drop of 160 feet—which is roughly comparable to descending the elevator shaft of a sixteen-story building. The riggers have to figure out a way to get fifteen or twenty people safely down—and back up.

A ladder made of rope or steel cable would do the trick. But a climb of 160 feet on a free-hanging ladder is exhausting. So speleologists who have turned sportsmen for the occasion join assorted other spelunkers and begin maneuvering ropes with skill and assurance that would win a word of approval from any professional rigger.

The entrance to the cave is a hole, two or three feet across, at the bottom of a small sink. Around the sink grow several large, well-rooted trees which will soon come in handy. The problem is to lower the explorers, one by one, down the shaft with block and tackle. This means that the block must hang directly above the opening. The riggers bridge the gap between trees with heavy rope, to which they attach the block by means of a karabiner—a sort of king-sized safety pin made of steel and capable of holding weights up to two tons. Next they uncoil about two hundred feet of the best-grade Manila rope and pass it through the block. In the end which will go down into the hole, a member of the crew ties a large but simple knot that has long been the friend of sailors and firemen—a French bowline. This is a variation on the simple bowline that every Boy Scout learns to make: It has two loops instead of one. A caver crawls into the loops, testing whether one is the right size to sit in and the other the right size to go around his chest, under his arms. The loops fit, and he has a seat which holds him snugly for the descent.

Now the rest of the rope is straightened out, free of kinks, ready to run smoothly over the wheel in the block when the first passenger descends into the hole. More cavers arrive, and their man- and woman-power is welcomed. They line up at intervals along the outstretched rope and take a firm grip on it. They will act as brakes, holding back and lowering the passenger slowly into the shaft.

The most experienced underground mountaineer will go first. Before stepping off into the void, he attaches a safety line around his chest—just in case. This line is not much thicker than a telephone cord, but it is made of nylon, and it can take the shock of his total weight if for any reason he should fall. At one side of the opening, an experienced woman caver sits with feet firmly braced, ready to pay out the safety line, which passes around her so that her whole body and both hands can act as brakes on it if necessary.

The first-man-down gives a last check on his personal gear. A whistle he will use for signaling hangs around his neck. He carries a flashlight fastened by a lanyard to a coil of light rope which he wears belt-fashion and which he may need for a dozen different purposes later on. Attached to his hard hat is his carbide lamp, but he doesn't light it. He wants no open flame that might set fire to the ropes on which his life depends.

"Here goes nothing!" he calls out cheerfully.

A man stationed at the cave mouth gives three blasts on his whistle—the signal for those holding the long rope to lower away. The woman acting as anchor on the safety line begins to let it out.

The top of the hard hat disappears into blackness, and for a time there is no sound but the turning of the wheel in the block. The members of the lowering crew grip the rope and walk slowly toward the pit as the rope slides over the wheel. When the man at the head of the line reaches the pit, he releases his grip, then runs back to grab hold again behind the last man in line. Finally the rope goes slack. A single whistle signal from the depths calls a stop to the lowering. It is followed by a shout that can barely be heard up at the cave mouth. The first man is down. Two whistle blasts relayed from below by the watcher over the entrance are an order to "up" the ropes.

The young woman hauls up the safety line. The rope crew walks away from the pit raising the double-loop seat for the second passenger.

Meanwhile one end of an additional rope—a guide line—has been lowered to the man in the pit. He will use it to help others make an easy landing when they come down.

"Next?"

Several old hands at this kind of thing—both women and men— disappear into the hole. Then comes the turn of a novice. Others check and double-check the knots in the French bowline and the safety line to give him reassurance. They point out which way to face, as he starts his descent, so that he can use his feet to push away from the wall if he swings in too close. Whistle signals sound in his ears, but he forgets their meaning as mixed eagerness and apprehension rise up in him.

"Take it easy—but take it!" somebody calls.

He slithers a little awkwardly into the opening. His left hand holds onto the Manila rope in front of him, and with his right he plays the flashlight onto the rock wall very close to him. He kicks away from it, as he has been told. Then suddenly the light goes out. It is temperamental anyway, and he has neglected to repair it. Frantically he shakes it and pounds it against his leg. The usual remedy doesn't work. He tips his head and looks longingly at the last rays of light from the opening. A slight bend in the shaft cuts off the entrance from view. He is in complete darkness—and going down, it seems, at express-train speed. Actually the rope crew outside is walking as slowly as usual to lower him. But it doesn't feel that way to the man in the loop.

From somewhere comes a single whistle blast. His descent stops, and he is dangling now in space. Below and to one side he can make out carbide lamps. What has gone wrong? Maybe the rope is jammed in the block—or worse, stuck somewhere in a niche between projecting rocks. Then what? There is no explanation from below—no word from above. The novice is just there, and without a light, but too proud to show his concern by yelling out any questions. Doggedly he hangs on, while the rope on which he sits cuts into his buttocks. His hands tighten their grip, as if that somehow will help.

Two more whistle blasts. He feels himself rising, but only a few feet before a single shrill toot calls a stop. Two more and he drops again. Whatever is wrong, they're working on it.

"Hold your legs out straight," comes an order from below.

All too willing to do anything that will help, he straightens his legs. At the same time, he looks down. "A little airy"—the phrase he has heard spelunkers use in speaking of certain chasms comes grimly to mind as he stares down into dark space. Then a sudden brilliant flash fills the shaft with light. Whistles blow; the rope runs again; he drops—and seems unaccountably to be swinging sideways toward the cluster of carbide lamps. His feet touch solid rock, and he stands dazed and a little shaken while hands work him free of the ropes.

The photographer, after packing away his used flashbulb, gives a sheepish grin when he realizes that his model was not one of the old hands, but a neophyte. "How did you like the trip?"

"Fine!" the novice answers—and wonders at himself for really meaning it.

The cave that opens out at the foot of the shaft explains why all this trouble has been taken. There are magnificent flowstone formations, one of them sweeping down into a series of rimstone pools. A delicate miniature grotto holds myriad tiny stalactites, reflected in a tiny lake. The utter calm and beauty of this seldom-visited cave make a sharp contrast to the strenuous excitement of the descent. Both are a part of the fascination of caving which attracts so many to the NSS.

Training of new members of the Philadelphia Grotto does not usually start with trips to caves like Elkhorn. In fact, it starts above ground. The Grotto, once or twice a year, runs a school to teach the use of ropes and rock-climbing techniques on Breakneck Ridge, a high sheer cliff along the east side of the Hudson River. There the best mountaineers in the group and the beginners camp out together. (Camping is one of the informal social activities that act as a magnet to members.) Instruction starts with simple rock-climbing problems at the base of the cliff. Learners, ranging in age from high-school kids to grandfathers, find that a rope, plus the right use of arms and legs, can give them amazing security—and the ability to master what seemed an insoluble problem. Before the weekend is over, a grandfather may be dropping rapidly down the face of the cliff like a yo-yo, with nothing but the friction of the rope around his body and the pressure of his uncalloused hands controlling the speed of his descent. Of course his safety line will catch him if his grip fails, and he has seen proof that the line will do its work.

One self-sacrificing instructor has the job of demonstrating what happens if a climber misses his footing and takes a fall. He approaches the task with mixed emotions. He knows perfectly well that the safety line will hold him. He feels it is his duty to give the beginners confidence by proving this fact. But he also knows that photographers on the expedition have him at their mercy. There's no telling how long they will keep him dangling at the end of the line high on the face of the cliff, preferably upside down, until they get just the shots they want.

When it's all over, "graduates" of the school are qualified to enter caves where only mountaineering will make exploration possible. Some of these trips will be initiated by individual cavers, and the groups will be small. Others are organized officially by a Grotto and even by several Grottoes working together.

In a number of areas Grottoes hold annual conventions—one is called a Cave Carnival. And the yearly National Convention brings people together from all over the country. These gatherings are held in areas where members can do a lot of caving, but that is not their entire purpose. They serve as social get-togethers, as opportunities to transact NSS business, and—particularly in the case of the National Convention—as a meeting where learned papers are read and reports made on scientific developments.

In this unique organization, it is a routine thing for scientists and laymen to meet as equals—not only when field work goes on in caves, but also when specialists report the results of their studies. Publications of the Society also reflect the dual nature of its membership. The annual *Bulletin* contains a great deal of serious scientific information, plus some articles of particular interest to the sportsman-caver. The monthly *News* reports various spelunking activities but also has items of scientific interest. From time to time, special technical documents appear as *Occasional Papers*. As if this were not a large enough publishing program for an organization consisting of about 1,600 active members, a number of Grottoes publish mimeographed periodicals which serve as a record of their own activities. A master file of information about all known caves in the country is constantly being expanded in the national office in Washington, where the Society also has a library of cave literature and a file of color slides available for loan.

The organization is busy, extremely busy, and its work—except for the services of a part-time secretary—is conducted entirely by volunteers. No rich angel or foundation or government subsidy aids in the continuous exploration and scientific study that goes on. It is estimated that the data in the possession of the national office has cost $350,000 to assemble—and all this has been contributed in time or money by the members.

Among NSS members only the very small minority who operate commercial caves make a living in the field to which all are dedicated. The others, aside from the scientists, pursue almost every conceivable type of occupation. In one Grotto there are a machinist, a telephone operator, an assistant manager of a business-machine factory, a lawyer, a librarian, an artist, several secretaries, doctors and dentists, a chiropodist, a dietitian, several commercial photographers. The list goes on to include both high-school and college students, a real estate broker, an egg farmer, and a number of housewives. The Protestant, Catholic and Jewish religions are all represented, and there are those who profess none. The only considerable population group not represented is the Negro portion, but leaders of the Grotto say they will welcome anyone who wants to belong. Of course, this is a Northern Grotto. NSS members from the South have been known to fly the Confederate flag over their tent on a spelunking expedition—not a very good device for adding the resources of Stephen Bishop's descendants to the organization. On the other hand, artificial barriers of another kind do not stand between scientific advance and the human resources that can aid it. Perhaps alone among American scientific organizations, the NSS accepts laymen and experts as equals and aids many laymen to make real contributions.

One contribution is the discovery and preliminary reconnaissance of caves. In a sense, the spelunkers are pathfinders—and they have a wonderful time being just that, as two stories out of scores published will indicate. In March, 1955, NSS members Robert Hudson and Gordon Danz demonstrated with a certain amount of Texas flourish what spelunkers could accomplish. In twenty-seven days they discovered forty hitherto unlisted caves; they entered and explored each one up to a point, and fretted and fumed because they had leads to more than fifty others, also unlisted, which they had not time to visit.

One of their missions was to find out whether there is a basis for a legend concerning a cave that is supposed to run *under* the Rio Grande River in the Big Bend National Park area. It took a lot of climbing along a cliff, a thousand feet *above* the river in 110° temperature, to confirm their own belief that no such cave existed. But they did find a small den which they were pleased to note was unoccupied at the moment—it was obviously in current use by smugglers. In the mouths of other caves they met rattlesnakes, and just as they reached the last one they had hoped to explore, they encountered four wild hogs called javelinas. "A javelina has been known to tear a man to ribbons with the sharp tusks on his lower jaws," says Hudson. "As the cave had a crawl-in entrance, and might afford good opportunity to get the hogs cornered, where they would be very dangerous, we decided there was nothing to that cave after all."

The special thrill of being the first to enter and see a cave is a rousing experience. In October, 1953, five NSS members were looking for a deep pit called the Banshee Hole near Crossville, Tennessee, when two of the group, Tank Gorin and Roy Davis, suddenly found themselves peering down into a great chasm which was not the one they were searching for. They dropped a rock and waited. Seconds passed before it hit bottom. A hole that deep had to be investigated. It was obviously an abyss of the kind that French spelunkers call a *gouffre*—and the Gouffre this Tennessee cave became. Later the party found that it was known locally as the Blowing Hole. In the meantime they set about rigging ropes for the descent, and one member, Bill Cuddington, was selected to go down. Here is Roy Davis' account of what followed, complete with the mountaineering terms that spelunkers use as a matter of course (those unfamiliar with the terms will find them explained in Chapter 19):

It was an agonizing few minutes that the surface crew spent before Bill Cuddington's greatly muffled voice shouted, "On bottom!"——"How deep is it?" we shouted back——"Over 250 feet!" came the reply—— Silence prevailed—— A fifteen-minute investigation period was given Bill to look about and decide if others should come down. It was less than five minutes, however, before he shouted up, "Send Roy down!"

I nervously attached my rappel pads, prusik knots and other equipment to my person, and, donning my leather gloves, climbed over the ledge, got in rappel, and began to descend into the black abyss.

Fifteen feet below the entrance the shaft enlarged and remained a constant 40 feet in diameter over 100 feet. The well was smooth and round, fluted in places by the never-ending action of the dripping water. There were no ledges and no overhangs, the rope hugging the wall from top to bottom.

Approximately 100 feet down, the well belled out into an enormous chamber, the blackness of which exceeded the blackest night. As I entered through the ceiling of this cavity, I looked in vain for the walls or floor—and I wondered, indeed, if it would not be long before I should come to the "end of my rope."

"Hello," I shouted—amazed at the volume of echoes my voice created—"Where are you?" Bill climbed over a rock far below and shouted a reply—his carbide light producing barely a spark in the immense gallery. I was amazed to learn that I was still 150 feet from the as yet invisible floor of the "Gouffre"—and that the total depth of the shaft was 254 feet!

I continued my descent in silence, except the shouts of amazement that escaped me when I chanced to pass a small opening in the wall that apparently connected with a parallel well nearby.

At length the bottom was reached, and, refueling our lamps, Bill and I set forth to explore the giant room—after first informing the surface crew that they would hear no more from us for one hour.

At the bottom of the drop, a steep talus slope ran downward for at least 50 additional feet to the actual bottom of the cave. To the right of the entrance drop a sparkling waterfall tumbled from a dome in the high ceiling to the floor below, where it immediately sank in the gravel. Beyond this waterfall, a clay bank rose from floor to ceiling—what might be above and beyond the slope could not be determined as the incline was too slippery to scale without the aid of ropes and mineral hammers, which were not at the time available.

Crossing the room lengthwise, past the waterfall and entrance drop we encountered a passage to the left, which, upon investigation, opened into a series of three domes, each of which were decorated with stalactites, stalagmites and helictites. One such dome, because of its unusual symmetry and beautiful decoration, was named the "Chapel."

Returning to the main chamber, a turn to the left brought us to another clay bank—this one inclined less steeply, which we climbed. At the top, the floor continued level for a short distance before it terminated in a low "belly-crawl." The estimated size of this huge chamber is, roughly, 150 feet wide, 150 feet high, and 350 feet long!

Several "high" leads were noted which were not explored, due to lack of equipment, leaving two wells, two high leads, and the clay bank to be conquered on some future trip.

As a whole, the "Gouffre" was quite impressive, with its lofty ceilings, distant walls and massive size. Dangling from the slender rope, gazing downward to the invisible floor over 150 feet below, where the feeble flame of Bill's lamp glows dimly, brings about an acute sensation of awe and wonder at the matchless skill of the Divine Hand that carved these towering walls and amazing depths.

After an easy ascent on prusik knots (40 minutes apiece), we emerged from the "Gouffre" into the darkness of an autumn evening. Tired, muddy and cold we descended the mountain-side—but with high spirits and a deep joy from having experienced a wondrous, rare adventure in a "virgin" cave, in the "basements" of Tennessee.

CHAPTER TWELVE

Bigger and Tougher

Spelunkers with more exuberance than surveying equipment have found a good many "biggest" caves at one time or another. Almost every commercial cave has the "most" or the "longest" or the "rarest" of something or other. Superlatives go with enthusiasm, and enthusiasm goes with caving. So it is little wonder that there are many rivals for the title of "best." However, cavers generally unite in their feeling about Higgenbotham Cave near McMinnville, Tennessee: It *is* one of the very best—extensive and magnificent. But these were things not widely known until a very short time ago.

Local inhabitants named the cave in 1810, or thereabouts, when a surveyor who lived nearby noticed a hole, three feet by three feet, in a limestone outcropping close to an old Indian trail—the Chickamauga Trail—that led in the direction of what is now Nashville. This surveyor, Aaron Higgenbotham, looked into the hole and, having looked, grew interested.

According to legend, he lit a pine torch and proceeded to explore. Deep in the cave, while he was crawling along a ledge, his torch went out and he was plunged into total, terrifying darkness. Fearing to move, Higgenbotham perched on his ledge for three days. At the end of that time, friends who must have followed his tracks to the cave mouth finally located him and led him out to sunlight, where it was all too apparent that the shock of his experience had turned his hair white.

About two years later, when the search for saltpetre became a matter of desperate importance to the young republic, someone found another cave entrance three-quarters of a mile from the entrance to Higgenbotham. This cave, which later became known as Henshaw's, proved to be a source of petre-dirt. Mining went on there during the War of 1812, and it was resumed under the Confederacy during the Civil War. Still, explorers apparently did not penetrate far into either Higgenbotham or Henshaw. Then one Shelah Waters grew fascinated by Higgenbotham and left his initials and the date 1869 at many points deep within the cavern. He seems to have used only torches for light, and as far as anyone knows, his ventures into the unknown were solitary affairs. But if Waters liked to explore alone, he did not keep the news of his finds to himself. Others began to learn about the excitements the cave offered.

After a while the citizens of McMinnville eight miles away took to hiring "bandwagons," with long seats on either side, for outings to Higgenbotham. Guides for these parties in the early 1900's were three young men, including Tom Barnes, a mail-carrier who later became a local historian and the source of all information about the early history of the cave. Using kerosene lanterns for light, they led what they considered long trips in the cave. Neither Barnes nor anyone else was aware that most of Higgenbotham lay ahead—undiscovered.

Knowledge of the caves rested there until the day in the late 1940's when ardent cave-explorer, Dr. Edward McCrady, now Vice-Chancellor of the University of the South, went farther than any man had gone before. Dr. McCrady discovered new and magnificent regions and some bobcat bones, perhaps thousands of years old, which interested him greatly since he was a biologist. Higgenbotham was on the verge of a period of intense and exciting revelations that unfolded one after another.

Prominent among the cavers irresistibly drawn there was a large, round-faced youth whose quiet bearing belied an ardor that was highly dramatic. With a rare singleness of purpose and clarity of mind, Thomas Calhoun Barr, Jr., had become a real speleologist by the time he was seventeen years old. He had visited many caves, where he studied in particular the curious life forms he found there. He was fascinated by the relationship of cave creatures to their environment, and while still in high school he wrote a paper on the specialized subject of cave ecology. This paper, together with his home laboratory (and possibly also his clarinet-playing in the school

band), won him a scholarship in a national competition. Tom Barr
went to Harvard.

New England caves are very much smaller than those of Tennessee, but Barr visited them and even made the first careful report
on a remote cave in Maine, one of the three known in the state.
When he returned to Tennessee as a graduate student in biology at
Vanderbilt University, he continued his exploration and his studies
of cave life. By 1949 he had accumulated a list of more than two
hundred caverns in his home state. Six years later his list had grown
to more than eight hundred and it is still growing.

It was in the nature of things that Barr would enter Higgenbotham sooner or later, and in 1948 he made the first of nearly one
hundred trips to the cave. On one expedition his party emerged into
a large room with a waterfall. Nearby they saw in another passage
a huge snow-white calcite column which Barr believed then and
still believes to be the most beautiful speleothem he has ever seen.
They were not the first to discover this Monument Pillar—no one is
sure just which explorer first beheld it—but, like all other parties
who had reached this area, they were stopped by very deep vertical
pits beyond.

In September, 1950, Barr, with cavers Charles B. Fort and Bert
Denton, pushed into new territory. Insufficient time and another
deep drop-off called an end to this trip. Charles Fort would have
liked to go on with his exploration, but Army duty kept him from it
until December, 1950, when with three other soldiers he entered the
cave one evening. Cavers, unlike mountaineers, are not limited to
daylight hours: a cave is no darker at midnight than at noon. Fort
and his party spent most of the next twenty-four hours walking,
climbing and crawling along virgin passages.

"We were finally stopped," Fort reported in *The NSS News*, "by
an onyx curtain extending from floor to ceiling in the passage. There
was one hole in the curtain, too small to permit passage of our
bodies but through which we could look into another large grotto.
. . . Here we suspected our proximity to a second entrance. There
was dung on the floor, and from a small underground lake, raccoon
tracks led through the hole into the grotto beyond. Two other indications were the exceptionally heavy draft, and small tree roots
protruding through the ceiling." Although a possible exit apparently

was very near, the explorers had to back-track a considerable distance with some very rough going on the way.

Fort, tied down by military duty, could do little about continuing exploration for a while, but others were interested in the cave, too, and determined to reach its limits. One of these was a seventeen-year-old high-school boy. He was fairly familiar with the cave—he had been in it five or six times—and during a Christmas holiday trip, he tried two things no spelunker should ever do. He attempted to climb a rope hand-over-hand—and without a safety line. As a result he fell forty feet and was fatally injured. The boy's needless death saddened but did not deter other explorers.

Fort wrote to Bert Denton and told him about the hole in the onyx curtain. Perhaps Denton, who was slender, could get through it. Denton could and did. He found more evidence of the proximity of the room to the surface—hickory and walnut shells, and a thick tree root growing through the cave wall. "Thus there is an entrance," he said, "yet where?"

Once more Fort tackled Higgenbotham with a party which included Denton, Jack Reccius, Bill Lawson and Jim Neil. But this time they decided to investigate the vertical drops that had stopped Tom Barr when he first entered the area then known as the New Discovery. In order to give themselves as much time as possible for exploring, they planned to camp overnight far underground. After a very late start, they reached their campsite, deep in the cave, at 6:00 A.M. and turned in. Fort's own words in *The NSS News* describe the rest of the two-day assault on the unknown.

> After six hours of fitful slumber we were finally routed out of our sleeping bags by Bill Lawson's harmonica playing. Bill . . . claims that harmonicas sound twice as good in caves due to the added resonance. Of course, if you don't like Lawson's harmonica music, following this line of reasoning, they sound twice as bad.
>
> We ate a hearty dinner of pork and beans heated on cans of Sterno and were ready for the day's project. This was a descent into the black void beneath the jumping off place behind Monument Pillar in the New Discovery. After half an hour's hard scramble from the Big Room, through the Devil's Quarry, and into the New Discovery, we arrived at our location. We let

down Bert Denton's 100 feet of half-inch Manila and Bert was first down. He made a body rappel to a small ledge 90 feet down the 60-degree slope and reported that he was resting and safe but did not have enough rope to go farther.

In reply to our questions, Bert answered that he could not see too much where he was with his light, but that the bottom really dropped out of things beneath him. Bill Lawson and I then rappelled down to join him on the ledge, bringing my 120 ft. of 7/16″ mountain nylon. We found ourselves midway on the sheer walls of a giant well. We looked up at least 60 ft. to the top of the dome while the pit beneath our feet dropped into a seemingly bottomless abyss.

Directly across from us was a small hole in the wall of the well which seemed to be a passage leading on. Bert found hand- and footholds while Lawson, on belay, safetied him over to it. He reported that after about eight feet the bottom dropped out into another well. It seemed to me that we had entered a system of vast inter-connecting wells. This not only proved to be the case, but we also found that we were somewhere on the other end of an already known but unexplored system that drops from a passage beneath the waterfall in the Waterfall Room. Acting on a hunch, Jim Neil, at the top of the slope, had made his way to the jumping off place there. Ten minutes later we heard his voice loud and clear coming to us through the wells. We could not see his light, but we judged him to be about 150 ft. away and on the same level. An interesting route to have followed would have been the completion of a traverse through the wells to Jim and the Waterfall Room, but we lacked pitons and expansion bolts and probably the rock climbing experience to accomplish it.

In the hope of finding a lower level passage, I let down the nylon rope and jumped off our ledge in free snap-link rappel of 70 ft. to the bottom of the well. At the bottom I was able to scramble into the bottoms of two other wells, but was unable to find any other outlet. There was no place to go except back up and I began the long ascent of the standing rope on prusik knots.

On the way up I ran into some difficulty. The rope must have been twisted, as I spun like a top on a good part of the ascent, and it was also fouled with mud so that the prusik knots could not be pushed up too easily when their tension was released. It was with a great deal of relief that an hour later I rejoined Lawson and Denton on the ledge. The three of us then, using the Manila rope for direct aid, easily made the 90-ft. ascent up the slope to rejoin Jim and Jack at the top. This reconnaissance of the New Discovery's inner wells had taken all day and it was 10 o'clock at night. We returned to the Big Room and turned in.

The next morning Jim and Bert guided us on a trip in an older partially explored section of the cave which I had not as yet visited. As we proceeded in an easterly direction through a gallery that opened from the north end of the Big Room, I began to suspect that until now I had missed some of the most beautiful and spectacular parts of Higgenbotham Cave. After walking about a quarter of a mile, we entered an immense gallery expansion and stood at the foot of an underground mountain, which had been formed by the partial collapse of the passage roof eons ago. On the rock breakdown slopes of this mountain, onyx pillars growing to heights of 15 and 20 ft. reminded us of the petrified stumps of a giant primeval forest. While the rest of the party remained at the foot, I ascended to the top, lighting magnesium flares on the way to illuminate this vast expanse. They estimated the height of this mountain to be 150 ft. After everyone had ascended to the peak, we passed over the top and continued down the gallery beyond.

Wonders did not cease as we left the Mountain Room behind. The next gallery expansion we appropriately named the Roundhouse. This [was a] huge chamber . . . with a flat, unsupported ceiling 40 ft. high. Along one whole side we viewed a massive ornamentation of draperies and columns growing from ceiling to floor.

After following this known gallery system for perhaps half a mile from the Big Room, the party was temporarily stopped by a breakdown extending from floor to ceiling in the passage. Bert found a way through and we jumped off into virgin cave. As we proceeded the gallery gradually dried out and we soon were passing glittering encrustations and flowers of gypsum on the 50-ft. high passage walls. The party was finally brought to an abrupt halt, after following this virgin passage . . . by a dirt fill from ceiling to floor. As to what lay beyond . . . only speculation could conjure. . . .

Not every exploring party could lug in sleeping bags and spend two days underground, and much time and energy were wasted in crossing the known areas of Higgenbotham before spelunkers could reach the unknown. If the suspected second entrance could be found, it might solve the problem. So Milford Gardner, who had spelunked with Fort, took up the search, and cannily he enlisted as a member of his party Duane Fertig, who was very slender.

Fertig managed to wriggle through the now-famous hole in the onyx curtain which only Denton had been able to negotiate so far, and he, too, was convinced by the evidence that if animals could burrow into the chamber, a man could burrow out. After an hour's careful examination, he found something that Denton had over-looked—the end of a rotten log embedded in the wall. Fertig managed to dislodge the log, looked through the hole it had left, and saw daylight. Some brisk digging enlarged the opening, and Fertig anglewormed up through it and stood outside—the first man to pass through Higgenbotham's second entrance.

Triumphantly he returned to his bulkier companions, who were serving the cause of discovery as best they could by sitting and waiting inside the curtain. With them he made the long trek back to the old historic entrance. It was still a mystery on what wooded hillside the new entrance lay because Fertig had been unable to recognize landmarks during his brief look-around.

At the first opportunity, Fort and Gardner, with other compan-ions, returned to enlarge the hole in the curtain and thus make a complete journey through the cave—in one entrance and out the other. When they finally emerged from the opening that Fertig had dug, they were amazed to find that their rugged mile-and-a-half trip had brought them out just 250 yards from the familiar entrance they had passed through hours earlier.

The new entrance did save time in reaching some portions of the cave, but not enough to suit Tom Barr, Standiford (Tank) Gorin and Dale Smith. At Eastertime in 1953, they decided to take a good look through Henshaw's Cave in the hope of finding, as Barr suspected, that it connected with Higgenbotham. The party spent fruitless hours trying to dig a trench through a clay-filled crawlway. Then Smith squirmed into a very tight passage that might lead nowhere. He wriggled along with difficulty until suddenly he found himself in a large room—one that quite obviously had been visited by a lot of other spelunkers. This "Meatgrinder" did, indeed, connect Henshaw's Cave with Higgenbotham, and it was a real short cut.

Among the cavers interested in Higgenbotham was the indefatigable young explorer Roy Davis, who first saw its splendors in 1952 and thereafter spent hundreds of hours in the place. On one occasion, believing a tall tale which his friend Tank Gorin had related, Davis and a party of other students from David Lipscomb College began a search for the mythical region of wonders in the cave which Gorin had described. As it turned out, the joke was on Gorin. After only three hours of nosing around, the group found the area now known as the Great Extension, which is in the neighborhood of three miles long. But size was not the most interesting feature of this virgin territory.. It contained a breathtaking wealth of rare speleothems—cave pearls and large gypsum flowers; long, thin needle-like gypsum crystals, some of them extending upward from the cave floor as much as three and a half feet; gypsum snow and gypsum that looked like nothing so much as cotton.

Still other discoveries were to come. In 1954, Davis and a companion entered considerable virgin cave in an upper level. In 1955, Tom Barr, who by this time had spent at least five hundred hours in the cave, came upon virgin territory just off an area that was very well known. He and a companion found a new series of rooms and passages filled with beautiful stalactites, draperies and flowstone. One of Higgenbotham's deep pits held up advance at one place in the new area. The pit and several nearby leads still challenge explorers.

No one yet knows the total length of Higgenbotham, but there is general agreement that it is possible to walk through thirteen miles of corridors and rooms. In addition, many crawlways have been probed, and all this explored area lies under only one-third of the mountain in which the cave has been hollowed out. Few caves have so great a range of fascinating features, and its fame among spelunkers has kept pace with the ever-expanding exploration. No wonder, then, that two from among its many devotees, Tank Gorin and Roy Davis, took on, in 1955, the hard physical work—and the financial risk—necessary to open it commercially. By the time this book appears, Higgenbotham—renamed Cumberland Caverns—should be nearly ready for visitors.

It is amusing to wonder if Tank Gorin may be carrying on an old family tradition. An early owner of Mammoth Cave was named Gorin. As for Roy Davis, he is definitely repeating a distinguished pattern in American caving history. This young enthusiast, who could convert anybody to a love of caves, plans, as Horace Hovey did a hundred years ago, to go into the ministry, and, like Hovey, he spends every spare moment caving.

Gorin and Davis have advantages in opening Higgenbotham (Cumberland) that no commercial operators ever had before. In a sense, they are the beneficiaries of all the work that has been done by the spelunkers and speleologists in the NSS. An almost loving care of speleothems marks the attitude of most NSS members when they go underground. The organization is made up of zealous conservationists. Although by now hundreds of people have passed through one brilliant chamber of Higgenbotham known as the Sewing Room, its dazzling display of long gypsum spines remains intact. A touch can destroy one of these crystals—but there they are, and there is the lavish collection of gypsum flowers, almost equally fragile. The children, even, who have gone with NSS parties through parts of the cave feel a sense of responsibility, though touching and feeling and handling are part of their normal process of learning and enjoying. They have left its perishable wonders undisturbed.

Exploration of Higgenbotham has not been a highly organized, scientific probing into the unknown, although scientists have done methodical work there. It has rather reflected a spilling over of the considerable energies and talents of a lot of people, laymen and scientists alike, who have found a place they just plain love.

A similar but much thornier emotion has drawn small, devoted groups of cavers to Schoolhouse Cave, which runs under a ridge in Pendleton County, West Virginia, not far from commercialized Seneca Caverns. The devotees of Schoolhouse are relatively few in number because of the cave's extraordinary hazards and difficulties. It is often called, by the handful of those qualified to make such statements, the toughest American cave. Beauty is not the magnet that attracts men and women to its terrifying abysses and to its seemingly unscalable walls (Schoolhouse has only a limited display of speleothems), and there are a great many other caves where scientists can get better results per man hour of laborious research. But no cavern in the United States presents so many different kinds of challenge to the rock climber in so short a space as does Schoolhouse. Experienced mountaineers need from eight to ten hours or more for the grueling round trip, which is only sixteen hundred feet each way, as the bat flies, from entrance to end.

A cross-section of Schoolhouse resembles a tortured series of mountain peaks separated by deep chasms, and over it all is a flat stone ceiling which consigns every cliff and ledge to perpetual and utter darkness. In order to get anywhere in the cave, it is necessary for the explorer to descend the chasms and scale the cliffs, each of which puts its own special demands on the mountaineering skills of those who are audacious enough to accept the challenge. Even the names that spelunkers have given to features in Schoolhouse are quite different from those in most other caves. Here are no Fairy Pools, Elfin Rambles, or Queen's Chambers. Instead, the Groan Box, Nightmare's Nest, the Rib Fiddle, Nick of Time, the Big Bite, Grind Canyon and Sam's Struggle show the wry realism of those who have triumphantly suffered through them.

A minimum requirement for Schoolhouse is that a spelunker be able to rope down steep pitches, then drop off into space on a single or double strand of rope, swinging free over a deep pit, until his descent stops on another slope. In one pit, he must swing through space like a pendulum, then come to rest on a ledge. At a place called the Upper Window, he rests for a while astride the window sill with his left leg hanging into one deep well and his right dangling into another. Then, like a human fly, he moves on and up to Angel's Roost, which is nothing but a dangerously sloping ledge covered with clay. In another spot he can make his way laterally along a high wall, near the ceiling, "by means of fingerholds which are much like a picture molding," according to the cave's first surveyor, who adds, "There are no footholds for about thirty feet of the traverse, and the slope is so steep that friction doesn't help much."

A misstep or false motion in any one of these situations could mean death to the underground mountaineer who fails to use a

safety rope. But cavers are not suicidal maniacs. They enter Schoolhouse only if they have adequate equipment. A portable telephone
has even proved to be desirable because, for one thing, explorers
could be drowned on the lower level if an unexpected rainstorm
came up outside. Skill based on long practice, plus good physical
condition, is a common-sense prerequisite for a trip through the
cave. But these must be reinforced with good equipment. One
young man fell eighty-five feet to his death at the Jumping Off
Place because he used a faulty rope which broke and because he
had no safety line attached to his body. (The NSS points out with
unhappy pride that the youth was not a member of the organization, and that no NSS member has ever been killed in this cave—
or in any other.)

The history of exploration in Schoolhouse is short but intense.
It was known during the Civil War, when saltpetre-miners worked
the entrance room, which is not difficult to reach. At least one
unknown adventurer went beyond this room. A cedar pole he
obviously carried in extends from the Jumping Off Place to a ledge
below. But beneath the ledge is a great chasm, and no explorer
ever got down into it—or left his bones as evidence that he had
tried—until 1939, when a group from Washington, D. C., the forerunners of the NSS, brought rope ladders and made a serious though
unsuccessful effort at full exploration. Experienced mountaineers in
the Potomac Appalachian Trail Club then took up the challenge.
They launched a series of assaults on the cave, with full equipment.
Each of several expeditions went farther than the previous one,
and finally, in 1941, a party reached the mud bank that marks the
end. Later that year a team headed by H. F. Stimson achieved the
seemingly impossible task of surveying and mapping Schoolhouse.

Aided by the map, and falling heir to the mountaineers' experience, teams of spelunkers have been entering the cave ever since
then. Notwithstanding the advantage of knowledge, technique and
equipment—plus some permanent aids, such as expansion bolts that
have been driven into the wall at a few points—none but the most
experienced cavers can explore Schoolhouse—or should even attempt it.

Another cave so tough and dangerous that its entrance has been
padlocked is Neff's Canyon Cave on the north side of Mt. Olympus

near Salt Lake City. Because the entrance is small—some husky spelunkers have been unable to squeeze through it—the only gate necessary was a single chain fastened to eyebolts fixed in the limestone. But beneath this lemon-squeezer opening lies a cavern that may be even deeper than Carlsbad.

Neff's Canyon broke into the news in March, 1949, when three boys got stuck inside the cave and had to be hauled out by a rescue party. One of the youngsters persisted in his folly and made more trips underground, luckily without further mishap. Teen-age talk about his exploits reached the ears of NSS members in Salt Lake City, and ten of them decided to investigate the cave. Equipped with eighteen hundred feet of half-inch rope and other supplies, they started out by truck, then took to horses, and finally dragged their equipment through snow for the last half-mile up the mountain. Those in the party small enough to get through the narrow entrance roped down a drop of eight or ten feet and found themselves in a long, narrow passage, the bottom of which sloped at a 45° angle, with occasional drop-offs ranging up to forty feet. How far the passage went they could not even guess, for they penetrated no farther than had the three boys who were trapped. Beyond that point yawned a sheer drop of at least a hundred feet.

A later NSS expedition, better equipped, probed farther and conquered more steep drop-offs. Still the main passage kept going down and down. Like Schoolhouse, Neff's Canyon Cave offered little to attract the eye. Far inside, explorers did find one tiny alcove holding a clear pool and a wealth of dog-tooth spar crystals, and nearby a single small room decorated with a row of paper-white stalactites, stalagmites and three-foot columns. Utah's Timpanogos Cave had much more beauty to offer. But, for rugged spelunking, Neff's Canyon Cave was perfect. Not only did it require difficult rope work, but much of the rock was soft and crumbly; handholds and footholds gave way under pressure.

The Wasatch Mountain Club decided to test its mettle in Neff's Canyon and made a further advance. Then the Salt Lake Grotto of the NSS spent two days inside the cave in early October, 1953. Later that same month, members of the Mountain Club returned, led by Harold Goodro. These experienced mountaineers came out with their clothing in rags after fourteen hours in the narrow, abra-

The author in Haynes Cave, Monroe County, West Virginia, inspecting a wooden winch at the top of a deep shaft. During the Civil War this winch was used to raise loads of petre-dirt from a lower level of the cave. It has been perfectly preserved and is still in working order. *Courtesy: National Speleological Society. Photo by Charles E. Mohr*

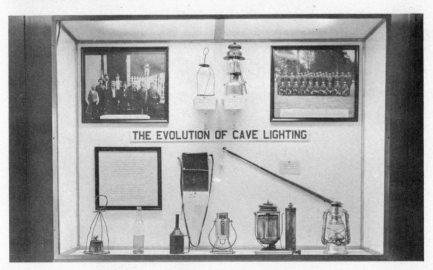

The lights used by explorers and guides in Mammoth Cave have ranged from pine torches (not shown here) to gasoline pressure lamps. From the very early days, guides have practiced the art of flare throwing in order to illuminate inaccessible spots. With a rod like the one in the lower right corner, all present-day guides toss burning kerosene-soaked rags with amazing accuracy onto high ledges or across deep pits. In the upper left corner appears a photograph of early guides, Negro and white. Uniformed Park Service tour leaders appear in the upper right corner. *Courtesy: National Park Service*

A stone hospital hut, still standing in Mammoth Cave, built by Dr. John Croghan, owner of the cave, in 1843, to house tuberculosis patients. The doctor mistakenly thought that cures could be effected by the pure cave air. *Courtesy: National Park Service*

Mammoth Cave attracted many celebrities in the nineteenth century. Among them was the singer, Jenny Lind, who sang as she sat in this natural chair which still bears her name. *Courtesy: National Park Service*

Lester Howe, the first explorer in Howe Caverns, made his way through passages like this, unreeling a tape behind him so that he could find his way out. A well-constructed walkway now follows one of the routes he took. *Courtesy: Howe Caverns*

After squeezing his way through two tight crevices, Andrew Campbell entered this room in Luray Caverns in 1878. An entrance for tourists was later dug and stairs were installed. *Courtesy: Luray Caverns*

Some of the many legends about Penn's Cave, Centre Hall, Pennsylvania, concern an upper dry level which can be entered on foot. Nowadays tourists visit the lower portion of the cave by boat. *Courtesy: Penn's Cave   Photo by Kepler Studio*

In several caves operated for the public, visitors can eat lunch underground. Here is the vast lunchroom, 750 feet beneath the surface in Carlsbad Caverns. From this point new high-speed elevators whisk tourists up out of the depths. *Courtesy: National Park Service*

Close-up of a fragment of boxwork from Wind Cave, South Dakota. *Courtesy: National Park Service*

Preparing a cave for visitors can be a large undertaking. Here Emergency Relief Administration workers, in 1939, carried the master light cable up a winding mountain trail which tourists still have to climb in order to reach Timpanogos Cave in Utah. *Courtesy: National Park Service*

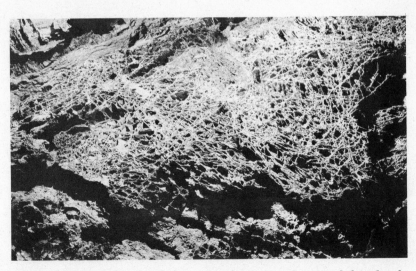

The pioneering speleologist, Luella Agnes Owen, was fascinated by this boxwork phenomenon in Wind Cave, South Dakota. More recent scientists found the explanation for it. Calcium carbonate filled cracks or joints in the limestone of the cave ceiling. Then acid-bearing water later dissolved the limestone which was more soluble than the secondary deposit of calcium carbonate. The photograph shows the ceiling of the Elks' Lodge Room in the cave. *Courtesy: National Park Service*

Jim White, the first explorer of Carlsbad Caverns, reported his discovery of these wonders—and was laughed at by his fellow cowboys and by the citizens of the nearest
community twenty-seven miles away. *Courtesy: Santa Fe Railway*

Courtesy: Santa Fe Railway

Large parties travel on carefully worked out schedules in Carlsbad Caverns which are visited every year by about half a million people. Here a party near the great stalagmite known as the Rock of Ages listens as a guide explains the cavern. *Courtesy: Santa Fe Railway*

Train robbers in 1884 hid themselves and their $62,000 loot in Colossal Cave, Arizona. This modern administration building now stands near the spot where a posse camped for two weeks in the hope of starving out the bandits. Present-day scientists are interested in the cave because it is the summer home of fruit-eating bats which feed on the nectar of the saguaro (left foreground). *Courtesy: Pima County Parks and Recreation Department*

Courtesy: Pima County Parks and Recreation Department

The first explorers of Colossal Cave were Wells-Fargo detectives hunting for money bags containing loot which train robbers had supposedly hidden in the cave. The detectives searched unsuccessfully in spots like these (*above and lower left, opposite*). Years later some of the money bags were discovered in the cave—empty. *Courtesy: Pima County Parks and Recreation Department*

Many speleologists believe that the total length of passages in the cave system in Flint Ridge, Kentucky, is the greatest in this country. The three pictures (left, below and upper right) show explorers at work in this rugged and varied underground labyrinth. *Courtesy:* Sports Illustrated *Photo by Robert Halmi*

The Flint Ridge cave system, entered by way of Floyd Collins' Crystal Cave, has been the scene of the most ambitious and intensive cave exploration project yet undertaken in the United States. *Courtesy:* Sports Illustrated *Photo by Robert Halmi*

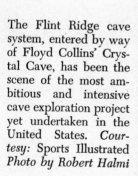

Courtesy: Sports Illustrated *Photo by Robert Halmi*

Bio-speleologists have found out a great deal about bats, but there is still much more to be learned. By banding some of these, which issue nightly in the summer months from Carlsbad Caverns, they have discovered that the creatures winter far to the south in Mexico. *Courtesy: National Park Service Photo by Kennicott*

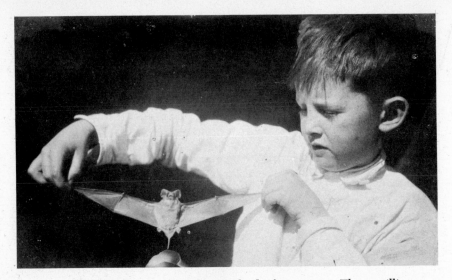

A Mexican Free-tailed bat weighs only one-third of an ounce. Three million or more of them make their summer home in Carlsbad Caverns. Some caves in Texas house even larger numbers. *Courtesy: National Park Service*

A few years ago the guides in Luray Caverns, where this picture was taken, noticed that water was ceasing to drip in part of the cave. This meant that pools would dry up and the stalactites and stalagmites would lose their luster. A piece of scientific detective work, reported in Chapter 10, disclosed the cause and cure of the trouble. *Courtesy: Virginia Chamber of Commerce Photo by Flournoy*

Mrs. Russell H. Gurnee and Mrs. Roger W. Brucker enjoy caving as much as their husbands do, and they take their babies along. Borrowing a trick from the Indians, Mrs. Gurnee made these cradle boards which are here being used in Wyandotte Cave, Indiana. *Courtesy: National Speleological Society   Photo by Albert C. Mueller, Jr.*

Exploration still goes on in many commercial caves, far from the smooth paths traveled by tourist parties. This spot, about a mile from the entrance to Floyd Collins' Crystal Cave, is near Scotchman's Trap, a small hole in the floor through which the .explorers had to pass in order to reach the vast wild portions of the cave they were surveying and mapping. *Courtesy: Floyd Collins' Crystal Cave Photo by W. T. Austin*

Where caves are still being enlarged by underground rivers, small portable boats are standard exploring equipment. In water that ranges from ten to twenty feet deep, Donald Egbert and Tank Gorin paddle their way through a part of Snail Shell Cave, one of the biggest in Tennessee where 800 caves have been found and where more are constantly being discovered. *Courtesy: National Speleological Society*

Photo by Roy Davis

With the aid of his carbide lamp, Larry Smith, a Louisville caver, looks down to see what his foot has discovered. *Courtesy: Floyd Collins' Crystal Cave*

Photo by W. T. Austin

Is the passage too small or is the caver too large? Spelunkers often find themselves asking this kind of question. *Courtesy: National Speleological Society Photo by John L. Spence*

Cavers ascend a steep pitch on a steel cable ladder. *Courtesy: National Speleological Society Photo by Ann Meuer*

What lies around the next corner? This caver, wearing a football helmet to which he has attached a special holder for his carbide lamp, struggles up around a tough spot in order to answer the question that always drives explorers onward. *Courtesy: National Speleological Society*

Photo by Ann Meuer

These four Mammoth Cave guides went cavin' on a day off from their official duties in 1938 and discovered a vast new section of the cave. Here they stand in front of a natural dam built up of calcium carbonate deposits from the water it held back. *Courtesy: National Park Service*

sive channel—with the triumphant announcement that they had reached the end, and to prove it to the next party in, they had left their names in a tin can tied to a spike they drove in the terminal wall. The mountaineers estimated that the cave channel was four thousand feet long and that its bottom was two thousand feet lower in altitude than the entrance. If their estimate is right, Neff's Canyon Cave is the deepest known in the United States. But fear that incompetent cavers would try to equal the achievement of Goodro and his companions led to the closing of the entrance. Forest Service Rangers now have to be satisfied that spelunkers know their business before the key to the padlock will be released to them.

Experiences in Neff's Canyon, in Schoolhouse, in Higgenbotham and in dozens of other caves proved that NSS members were able to tackle ever larger and tougher caves. Their know-how had increased even during the war, when to many of them caving became a patriotic search for underground areas of potential military usefulness. By 1953 the organized speleologists and spelunkers felt ready for something really big. Reports persisted—and they were confirmed by reconnaissance parties—that Floyd Collins' Crystal Cave in Kentucky was almost incredibly vast and interesting. Moreover, its layout was such that explorers invariably went down to defeat through fatigue and lack of supplies. They were stopped by what came to be known as "the endurance barrier."

Cavers could crack this barrier in only one way: they had to establish one or more camps, deep within the cavern, where, during an entire week, they could explore, then eat and rest, while supply teams took on the burden of lugging in food, fuel, and additional equipment if it turned out to be needed. This might sound like a remarkably simple plan—and perfectly obvious. But NSS members who had visited the uncommercialized part of the cave knew in their vitals that a great gap existed between the simple blueprint and its realization in action.

For one thing, every man and woman, every ounce of supplies, would have to pass through a crawlway thirteen hundred feet long, which meant literally *crawling*. At one point a keyhole exactly ten inches high, but wide enough for a human being to squeeze through, determined the size of any freight to be delivered to the underground frontier beyond.

Joe Lawrence, Jr., a young electronic engineer, accepted leadership of the project and put his considerable executive ability, as well as his spelunking experience, to work. He and a planning group devised a blueprint for the adventure. Then they enlisted men and women to carry it out. The roster included individuals professionally trained in geology, biology, hydrology, meteorology and map making. The active exploring teams, all experienced cave-crawlers and rock climbers, came from vocational backgrounds as diverse as the American scene can provide—stenographer, scenario writer, sheet-metal contractor, draftsman, a man who taught dancing, a woman who trained dogs, engineer, real estate broker, college student, farmer, bacteriologist. Loyal and capable people agreed to do the grueling and less glamorous work of dragging in supplies for the explorers. They included an engineer, school teacher, marine, student, administrative planner, mathematician, bricklayer, bookkeeper, government sales representative, mover. A team took on the by no means simple problems of laying and servicing a long cave telephone system. (It was essential to have communication between those inside the cave and the general staff at headquarters outside.) On this chore a cabinet-maker, a museum guard, an electronic technician and a museum curator went to work.

There were others, a total of sixty-four in all, whose active help at the cave was needed if a handful of explorers was to keep pushing out into areas where no man had ever been before.

All had to be ready at the same time, in February, 1954, and most of them had to wangle vacations at that unlikely season. All had to be physically fit. A spelunking doctor prescribed a set of exercises designed to ready people for the kind of activity that lay ahead. For example, he instructed nurses, telephone linesmen, photographers and scientists to crawl daily under the chairs in their living rooms—crawl until they were good and tired. Every minute of ludicrous discomfort at home would pay off in efficiency when they began inching on hands and knees along that 1,300-foot passage through which every soul on the expedition had to suffer before reaching the *terra incognita* on the as yet undrawn maps.

The leaders assembled not only people but also the necessary gear, including scientific equipment, mountaineering gadgets, food of the kind that was both portable and palatable. Each individual member looked to his own personal equipment, one indispensable item of which was a pair of rubber knee-pads such as miners wear. But it was impossible to carry all of this stuff into the cave in any usual way. When packs and duffel-bags did get through, they had to be hauled along at times tied to explorers' ankles. Everything had to be dragged for thousands of feet over rough rocks and around corners, pulled through holes and thumped over ledges. What could stand up under such a beating? What kind of container would not snag or get stuck? Nothing that existed. Something new must be designed, and the NSS had among its members two men who came up with the answer. One was John L. Spence, the 57-year-old chief photographer of the expedition, an industrial designer by profession. The other was Russell H. Gurnee, sheet-metal contractor. Spence and Gurnee set their minds to work and invented an odd, bullet-shaped metal container that could be attached to a rope and dragged by the small end so that it slid with a minimum of resistance over or around any obstacles that lay in its way. Now famous among spelunkers as the Gurnee can, it was exactly ten inches in diameter because the cavers had no more leeway than that through which to haul it or push it at one point.

The doctor gathered equipment for a first-aid station in the cave and for a dispensary topside. Beyond that, he gave physical and psychological examinations to all expedition members. He wanted to know what happened to bodies and minds when people spent many active, tense days underground.

The February deadline arrived. Members of the expedition rolled in from states all over the East and South and Middle West. In their wake came photographers and reporters, including William Burke Miller, who had won the Pulitzer Prize for his reporting of the death of Floyd Collins in nearby Sand Cave almost thirty years before.

Joe Lawrence, like a general, marshaled his forces and sent them into action. An advance group established a camp deep underground, two miles from the entrance, complete with space for sleeping and cooking, a safe water supply, a place for a latrine. The telephone crew stubbornly fought the cave in their effort to lay wire where the support parties wouldn't break it or get tangled in it. A spool of wire could be intractable at times, or could break loose and roll down into a deep pit.

Finally the whole complex job of getting the expedition under way seemed done. But almost immediately a crisis developed above-ground. A forest fire broke out in the neighborhood, and all available manpower had to help put down the flames. This meant many long hours' delay in delivering supplies to the advance party. It also meant that many members of the support teams were so exhausted from fire-fighting that they could not immediately resume the struggle of hauling Gurnee cans. For a while, explorers went on short rations. But operations continued. Exploration went on around the clock, with people working and resting in shifts. (The difficulty of supply had dictated that there could be only one sleeping bag for each three members.)

Joe Lawrence, expedition leader, and Roger W. Brucker, explorer and surveyor, give a graphic story of the trials, the grim periods of frustration and the high moments of discovery in their book *The Caves Beyond*. Since this record, rich in human and technical detail, is readily available, it is enough to say here that the expedition gave ample proof that cave exploration in this country had reached a high level of maturity. In the few years since caving had become a serious sport, it had grown up. The NSS was very well prepared to pioneer the "caves beyond"—that is, the possibly vast sections of Floyd Collins' Crystal Cave unreached by the expedition.

Just such exploration continued for almost two years, and it produced sensational results. In the last week of 1955 NSS leaders, in a special session on speleology at the annual meeting of the American Association for the Advancement of Science (in Atlanta, Georgia) made an announcement that became front-page news. Exploration and surveys revealed, they said, that Floyd Collins' Crystal Cave was "a nucleus of a cave system larger than any other known in the world." Thirty-two miles of passages had been explored, of which twenty-three had been surveyed and scores of leads remained to be entered and examined.

There were indications that the cave might connect with Sand Cave, as Floyd Collins suspected thirty years ago. It might even connect with Mammoth Cave, which lies under the next ridge. But questions immediately arose in many people's minds about one point: how could scientists so confidently imply that Crystal Cave is larger than Mammoth, which has long enjoyed the reputation of having 150 miles of passageways? One answer seems to lie in the likelihood that the Mammoth Cave figure is based on legend and tradition rather than on careful surveys. Lee Heiman, writing in the Louisville *Courier-Journal*, January 29, 1956, states, "National Park Geologist Bennett T. Gale and National Park Service Naturalist Paul Schulz now acknowledge that the [long-accepted survey] figure probably is an estimate rather than an actual measurement."

Only an impartial comparison of the surveys of the two neighboring and rival caves—one under public ownership and the other under private ownership—can settle this point. Even then the title of longest cavern in the world may rest uncertainly with any cavern that claims it. What about Colossal Cave in Arizona, for instance? Records reportedly made there in 1922 indicated that 39 miles of passageways were traversed before the surveyors had to withdraw from the cave without reaching the end. The records and map of Colossal were apparently destroyed after the death of the geologist who made them, but a new survey should be made before this admittedly vast cave can be eliminated from the list of contenders.

Furthermore, are American cavers right in assuming that the biggest cave system in the United States is the biggest in the world? Many vast caverns, largely unexplored, exist in eastern Mexico. The Soviet Union, which covers approximately one-sixth of the earth's land surface, has the kinds of rock underlying a very large part of its area in which caves can and do form. Large caves have been discovered in little-explored Africa; and in other parts of the world there are huge caverns already known, with many more undoubtedly to be found.

As a matter of fact, Hölloch Cave in Switzerland, which NSS leaders believed, on the basis of published reports, to be thirty miles long, has already turned out to be longer than its American rival. Word has reached this country that Hölloch has thirty-*three* miles of explored passageways.

Since authoritative figures about caves all over the world, including the United States, are still to be carefully compared, it seems premature to call any one of them the largest. Meanwhile, the persistent and heroic work of the explorers in Floyd Collins' Crystal Cave has itself become an achievement that has won the admiration of speleologists everywhere.

CHAPTER THIRTEEN

What Use Is a Cave?

The week-long pioneering effort of sixty-four people in Floyd Collins' Crystal Cave, and the thousands of other underground expeditions in recent years, can give rise to legitimate questions: Are caves worth all this trouble? What *use* is a cave?

"No damn use at all," one eminent and peppery speleologist has been known to answer. At the other extreme, certain laymen addicted to science fiction seem to believe that in this atomic age the very survival of the human race depends on making caverns into underground bombproof cities. Both the quipping scientist and the queasy romanticist are wrong. The scientist knows this, of course. He *uses* caves all the time—for research and recreation. And an astounding variety of other Americans have found ways to get practical value out of caves. Saintly Quakers once turned them into hiding places for fugitive slaves; counterfeiters, assassins and assorted villains have sometimes made the word cave and crime almost synonymous; hermits and publicity-seekers alike have seen that caves could provide a suitably exotic background to their antics.

The most *practical* use for a cave is in the industrial area—and there have been industrial uses on a grand scale. Saltpetre-mining was the earliest. It began during the American Revolution and became crucial to the continued existence of our nation during the War of 1812. During the Civil War many caves were worked by the Confederate side, which felt the pinch of the Union embargo. Some Confederate soldiers did nothing throughout the war but mine saltpetre, and one of them told his story to researchers in 1954 when he was a spry 106-year-old. Apparently it was considered necessary for the South to use military personnel and prisoners of war instead of—or in addition to—the slave labor that had been adequate in

the earlier war. Scholars looking into the facts might find evidence
that slaves were a good deal less than eager to help their masters
win this particular war, which held the promise of their freedom
if the men in gray lacked gunpowder.

Today perfectly preserved evidence of nitre-mining can be seen
in Mammoth Cave. The air is dry in the section that was mined,
and the wooden leaching vats and water pipes have not rotted.
Protected now by the National Park Service, they should remain
indefinitely. Many other caves also contain well-preserved relics of
saltpetre works. Organ Cave, one of the three commercial caves in
West Virginia, has a large number of hoppers used in leaching the
earth, and some of the original straw that lined the hoppers to act
as a sieve is still in good condition.

From the time men began to mine petre-dirt until well after the
Civil War, caves that lay near the shifting frontier—and were therefore far from transportation—did some business in furnishing pioneers with powder for their guns. Recently in Arizona spelunkers
found a saltpetre cave that must have been worked in the not too
distant day when the West was still wild.

In Texas, the saltpetre-mining took a different form. There it was
not cave earth but enormous deposits of bat guano that yielded
nitrate for gunpowder. One of the biggest of the Texas bat caves,
Frio Cave in Uvalde County, has a more or less continuous history
of mining from the Civil War up to the present. Its entrance chamber is so vast that oxcarts could be driven in and loaded from small
cars that ran on wooden rails, bringing the guano from deep within
the cavern. After industry had found cheaper ways to make gunpowder, mining in Frio Cave still went on, since guano proved to be
valuable fertilizer. So valuable was this source of nitrogen for agri-
cultural purposes that even caves like Carlsbad, which lay miles
from any railroad, became the scenes of mining operations. In spite
of transportation difficulties, guano from Carlsbad reached the citrus
orchards of California. At least one cave much nearer the orchards—
Bat Cave in Nevada—is still a source of fertilizer today.

Mining of other kinds has been attempted, sometimes successfully, in widely scattered caverns. A small cave in Real County,
Texas, is probably unique as a source of celestite in commercial
quantities. When the light-blue crystals of this mineral burn, they

give off a bright red flame, and so they find a use in fireworks, tracer bullets and signal flares. Wyandotte Cave produced Epsom salts in the early nineteenth century. Lead-miners in Missouri found easy access to the ore they sought through cave channels. Onondaga Cave, also in Missouri and now commercially operated, has chambers that were mined for the beautiful onyx that could be polished and used as rococo decoration for buildings in a bygone day. Mining of onyx still continues in many caves—to the great detriment of their beauty and possible future scientific usefulness.

In pioneering days, when farmers took their corn to local gristmills, one imaginative miller got water power for his machinery by damming up the entrance to Onondaga Cave, thus creating a large underground reservoir. At the present time, the Pittsburgh Limestone Company utilizes Cove Run Cave, near East Brady, Pennsylvania, as a reservoir. Several caves have been used from time to time as veritable mushroom growing factories.

Not only does industry take things out of caves; it also puts some of its products back in. The early brewers of St. Louis stored their beer in natural underground refrigerators, and caverns still make the best place for aging certain kinds of cheese.

But far and away the most impressive conversion of a cave to the purposes of industrial man is the Natural Tunnel in southwest Virginia, which makes it possible for the Southern Railway to take a short cut through a mountain. This enormous cavern, extending for fifteen hundred feet between two openings, is just what its name implies—a natural tunnel. The railroad trains, and the telegraph lines paralleling the tracks, are dwarfed by the great height and width of the passage.

Construction engineers have looked longingly at other natural tunnels through mountains but have found few that met their specifications. Those interested in a different kind of transportation had better luck. Conductors on the Underground Railroad, which spirited passengers northward to freedom before and during the Civil War, made extensive use of caves. According to the latest researches, about half a million slaves escaped from their owners and found their way sucessfully to the North and to Canada. Not all of these followed the highly organized Underground Railroad, but every one of them traveled along secret routes of one kind or another, and much of the journey had to be made at night. Since professional slave-hunters were always on the prowl, there had to be good hide-outs for fugitives during the daylight hours. What better spot could exist than a subterranean passageway with its round-the-clock darkness? Well-known though it was, Mammoth Cave occasionally served as a station on the Underground Railroad. So did caves in West Virginia, of which Tory's Cave in Pendleton County may well have been one. Whether it was or not, will perhaps be determined one day by excavators. A legend has it that the mouth of this cave collapsed, entombing a group of fugitives. There is no doubt that a collapse did occur at some time, and it has so far defied all efforts to force an entrance. Behind the dangerously poised rocks which have frustrated explorers may lie tragic evidence of one of the most exciting episodes in American history.

Meramec, a very large cavern in Missouri, was a station through which hundreds passed. Other stations saw less traffic but were equally necessary. Clay Perry reports that Horatio Hough secreted passengers in a cave in Lewis County, New York, which was admirably designed for safety against those who attempted to enforce the Fugitive Slave Act. Hough's cave had two openings several hundred feet apart. If pursuers entered the first, the passengers could depart through the second.

Another cave station with two entrances lay in the banks of the Delaware River near Montague, New Jersey. Not many years ago spelunkers discovered to the last detail how it was used. They entered innocently from the river bank, and before long they found themselves in the cellar of a nearby farmhouse. Here was an entirely concealed passage between the river—where the "railroad" ran— and the house in which an abolitionist family, to its own great risk, gave food and shelter to the hunted passengers who had a one-way ticket to freedom. The present-day owner of the farm has grown weary of having historical-minded spelunkers turn up unannounced directly beneath his parlor. He has bricked off the end of the passage.

Two entrances are also reported to have existed in a cave that was not simply a station on the Underground Railroad but a literal roadbed—and one of a most unusual kind from a geologic point of view. Near the city of Pittsburgh, on the north bank of the Ohio

River, are two cavities known as the Bellrock Caves. One of these reputedly was the northern exit to a cave that had an entrance on the southern bank of the Ohio. Thus a tunnel crossed *under* the river and was apparently water-free. If, as is most unlikely, this unique passageway existed, it still remains to be rediscovered by modern explorers.

In the pre-Civil War days, the North itself had a large number of aggrieved citizens who used caves in a dramatic kind of guerrilla warfare against the vestiges of feudalism. Farmers in the Helderberg Mountains west of the Hudson River were for a good many years in revolt against the owners of huge estates that dated back to old Dutch times. Although nominally free citizens, these farmers had an almost serf-like status. One and all, they determined to cease paying exorbitant rents and to become owners of the land they tilled. This brought them into conflict with armed law-enforcing agencies, and the farmers formed an underground organization that made use of Indian costumes for camouflage, and of meeting places that were literally under ground. They sometimes plotted and hid in caves in the Helderberg area, and in the end their use of caves and costumes—and their persistence—paid off. The Anti-Renters, as they were called, ended feudalism in the Hudson Valley and won the passage of the Homestead Act, to boot.

Possibly some of them, and certainly a great many other farmers, have found peaceful uses for caves. Numerous farmhouses have been built over or near cavern entrances which were used as refrigerators, storerooms and root cellars—and still are today. A cave now called Ski-Hi, near Fort Knox, Kentucky, has a natural chimney near the entrance, a flowing stream, and a strong draft of fresh air. And so in the old days it made an ideal, prefabricated slaughterhouse for hogs. There the farmers could butcher and scald, while the smoke and the odor went off up the chimney.

A poultry-raiser in Indiana recently thought of a way to get his six thousand chickens out of the oppressive summer heat which was killing many of them. He rigged lights in a cave where the temperature is a constant 56°, screened off rooms, and covered the floor with corn shucks and cobs. With the addition of water, which had to be piped from above ground since the cave is dry, he moved his entire poultry establishment underground.

Excessive heat and drought in southern Tennessee nearly drove another farmer off his land not long ago. His crops withered, and even his drinking water disappeared. However, Keith's Cave, on his property, was still moist although it had no running water in it. Where there is one cave, the farmer reasoned, there might be another. He looked over the ridge above his fields—and he found one. The new cave held the water he sought, ample for irrigation, and pure enough for household use, too. Thereafter he prospered to such a degree that instead of leaving his land, he has been able to build a new home on it.

By no means all cave water is pure. Farmers have long been in the habit of using sinkholes for a purpose that is more honored by time than by the test tube. Where nature offered a ready-made hole, they dumped dead animals and saved themselves the trouble of burial. (A dog-catcher also used Dead Dog Cave in West Virginia as a disposal place for carcasses.) When a cattle train was wrecked in Pennsylvania many years ago, the remains of the mangled beasts were heaved into a sinkhole; and sinks have often been used as garbage pits. Future paleontologists and archeologists may one day be fascinated by the heaps of bones and debris in these sinkholes, but for today the result is that many an underground stream is polluted, and more than one community has sought in vain for the mysterious source of the pollution.

Spelunkers, with the help of fluorescein dye, have rendered valuable civic service by tracing the origin of microbes in one city water supply in West Virginia. They found that the water picked up disease germs when it flowed under a large sinkhole used by all the farmers in the area as a dumping ground for dead animals.

But pollution can be a two-way proposition. A community may be the source of unsafe water as well as its destination. For example, another town in West Virginia, which is entirely built in a huge sink, has no municipal sewage system. The good citizens merely drill straight down beneath their houses to an underlying cavern. As yet no one knows for sure where the stream flowing through the cavern finally emerges to the surface. The best guess is that the water remains underground for many miles, carrying sewage with it. Geologists base their guess on these facts: no stream comes to the surface near the town. The limestone formation containing the underground stream does not itself appear at the surface for a long distance in any direction. Where it does crop out, a stream gushes from the rocks at an elevation which would allow for continuous downhill flow from the town's hidden cesspool. If this guess is accurate, a vast underground cavern system awaits study by speleologists—and public health authorities.

At least five communities in Pennsylvania have used caverns as cesspools—in some cases inadvertently. One of these cities discovered not long ago that its main sewer pipe discharged very little sewage. Spelunkers found the reason. The pipe had burst and was draining into a cavern that lay beneath the city.

The possibility of pollution on a gigantic scale is obvious in a region where extensive underground drainage exists. Recently cavers have expressed some alarm at reports that the waste products of the atomic age might be dumped into caves. Since a great many caves are connected with labyrinthine streams—the course and outlets of which are frequently unknown—the hazards of such dumping seemed very great. Apparently, however, the Atomic Energy Commission and other interested agencies are aware that caves offer no simple solution to the problem of radioactive waste disposal. So far as is known, no experimental atomic cesspool has been created in a cave.

However, some of the perfervid writers of alarmist prose, and some civilian defense enthusiasts with more than usually high blood pressure, have dreamed that caves might save large sections of the population in the event of atomic attack. Put this down as merely bizarre Americana of the mid-twentieth century. The fact is that the old song is right—"The rock cries out, 'no hidin' place.'" There are too few caves near large cities to shelter even a small part of the population. Furthermore, if an atomic bombardment should occur, there is no security in caves. In the first place, cavern ceilings are very likely to collapse under the shock of an atom bomb; in the second, it would be virtually impossible to prevent contaminated air from seeping into cave shelters. One expert, Bahngrell W. Brown, a member of the American Institute of Mining and Metallurgical Engineers, has this to say:

... Even if the natural caverns, many of which nature has precariously carved from cherty and brittle limestones, could withstand a seismic force of a proximate blast without major roof failures, there is a more serious argument against the blanket use of natural caverns as a first line of defense. In addition to the force of the blast, there is always the danger of poisonous or radioactive gases. In a natural cavern break-throughs cannot be predicted, and positive protection against inroads of gas is impossible. A fracture in the limestone may lead into a hidden chain of caverns connecting directly with the terrorized gas-filled outside world. These gases will probably not be persistent and their effects could be neutralized by ionization in a collective protector while the danger persists. But pure breathable air can be maintained only where there is positive control of ventilation. . . .

Short of the utterly simple and sensible idea of doing away with atom bombs, the only halfway sure protection for even a small minority seems to lie in man-made shelters dug deep into strong rock strata where ventilation can be adequately controlled. Indeed, natural caves have very little military usefulness of any kind these days. Some can be made into storage vaults for supplies or valuables, but as a rule mines are far better for this purpose. The time has passed when caves can camouflage the whereabouts of important troop concentrations, as they did during the Civil War. Stonewall Jackson found Melrose Caverns useful for this purpose, and another cave was big enough to hold a completely equipped stable for two hundred horses ridden by the Confederate raider Mosby and his men.

At least one novel military use was made of a cave during the first World War. The Bethlehem Steel Company turned one of the Reddington Caves, east of Bethlehem, into a firing-range for testing artillery shells. Already archeologically-minded spelunkers have dug there for weapons of a bygone age. To be sure, they don't turn up Sandia points or Folsom points, but they have found shells— many of them unexploded. Since the blow of a pick or shovel might easily detonate one of the projectiles, Reddington should be avoided —and let future generations of archeologists beware!

A cave by-product—bats—did seem for a while to have military usefulness during World War II. Bats were the origin and center of a grisly development that came very near sending shudders through all mankind, just as did the destruction of Hiroshima and Nagasaki. In fact, it was apparently only the impending "success" of the atomic bomb experiment that relegated the bat-weapon to limbo. A mechanically-minded doctor, doubtless hoping to serve decent ends, invented, with bats as a starting point, a most devastating type of bomb, but one which could not be aimed with precision. It was quite as likely to destroy innocent civilians as military objectives.

The doctor-inventor, who had seen the nightly flight of bats from Carlsbad Caverns, conceived the idea of using the little animals to deliver tiny incendiary bombs behind the enemy's lines. Experiments showed that a Mexican Free-tailed bat weighing only one-third of an ounce could take off and stay in the air with a load three times as heavy as itself, and it could fly for ten, even twenty, miles with its burden.

The military was definitely interested and gave active assistance in developing one-ounce time bombs, capable of burning for eight minutes, which bats could carry clipped to their bodies. If the bats were released, it was reasoned, they would take off for the kind of roosting place they liked. Lacking caves, many of them would find secluded spots under the eaves of buildings. Japan offered millions of such spots, many of them under the overhanging roofs of flimsy wood and paper homes. It followed that if large numbers of bomb-carrying bats could be released over Japan, large sections of the islands would burst out in flames. Naturally, there was no way of training bats to commit suicide only under the eaves of military targets.

The bats would have to be captured first, of course. In front of bat caves in Texas, large wire enclosures were built with doors that could be left open to give the bats freedom of motion, or closed when they were to be harvested. Keeping the captured bats alive was the next problem. Experiments had shown that this could be done most easily by refrigeration in a humid atmosphere which kept the creatures dormant as if they were hibernating in a cool, damp cave. Accordingly, bats by the tens of thousands were stored away hanging upside down in special containers.

The problem of releasing them over Japan had to be solved. Bomb-shaped cans were designed, each capable of holding from one thousand to five thousand dormant bats, equipped with capsules of destruction. Attached to a parachute, a can would drop slowly enough for the bats to be warmed into activity, and at an altitude of one thousand feet a mechanism would release them into the air. The timing device on each incendiary bomb was set to give its bearer ample opportunity for locating a roost. Then, when it was hanging under the eaves of a building, the bomb would go off.

There was no doubt the plan would work. The Air Force had found this out to its sorrow when some loaded bats escaped by accident near an airfield in New Mexico and set buildings on fire. Quite probably the useful little denizens of caves would have been sent out to do their work of destruction but for the fact that the military became obsessed with the potentialities of the atomic bomb.

The bat-bomb story does not quite end the record of caves in World War II. Some zealous patriots who lived deep in the Ozarks had learned that the government was concealing much of the information it had about the weather, for fear the Nazis might find the data valuable. It happened that a certain blowing cave in the Ozarks predicted the weather unfailingly by breathing out when the barometer fell and breathing in when it rose. Obviously, duty called for thwarting the traitorous hole which persisted in giving military secrets to the enemy. A dead-serious group of men plugged it up so that it could not act as a weather prophet.

It is nowhere stated that these saviors of the nation were encouraged by the product of a well-known local industry, but it *is* known that Ozark caves, as well as caves in Kentucky, West Virginia, Pennsylvania and other states, served as quiet hiding places for moonshine stills. Smokehole Cavern in West Virginia has on display an apparatus for making corn liquor which was part of its proud record.

Counterfeiters, too, have found caves convenient studios in which to practice their art, or sometimes simply hideaways from unfriendly critics. Wyandotte in Indiana was such a hideaway a hundred years ago, at the very time when it was beginning to receive visitors commercially. Two men appeared there one day in 1856 and sought employment. They were put to work digging, through heavy clay, an eighty-foot trench that was designed to provide—and still provides—a walkway for tourists who would otherwise have to crawl. The job was arduous, and the pay by no means equal to the income the two men expected from their usual profession, but it served its purpose. Not until the ditch was finished and the men had emerged permanently into daylight did the Rothrock family, owners of the cave, discover that they had unwittingly harbored counterfeiters who were on the lam.

There is apparently no basis for thinking this particular pair found ways of carrying on their trade while they were supposed to be swinging pick and shovel. But counterfeiters had better luck in some New England caves and at Cave-in-Rock on the north bank of the Ohio River in Illinois. In the latter they even left some of their molds, to the great delight of upright antiquarians who found them years afterward.

Jesse James seems to have been more interested in authentic coins of the realm than in imitations thereof, but he too had a special liking for caves. His name is associated with several in Kentucky, and in Missouri he apparently made extensive use of Meramec Caverns. Publicity stories recently gave lavish hints of proof that James used another Missouri cavern which was about to be opened to the public. The "proof" took the form of $100,000 in gold which James was supposed to have secreted there. To be sure, no witness has testified that he actually saw all the loot, but newspaper reporters have turned up fascinating clues. Clue number one: gold currency must, by law, be exchanged for other currency, and a United States Treasury Department armored truck was seen in front of the cave-owner's premises. Clue number two: a local banker said he had seen $10,000 in old gold coins that had come from the cave.

There the matter rests, as far as I am aware, but matters seldom really rest when large sums of money are involved. The chances are that a good deal more is known—or may be someday—of the truth about Jesse James's hidden hoard.

News of another cave treasure-hoard went out across the country a few years ago on the AP and INS wires from Hot Springs, New Mexico. In this case, too, more is doubtless to be learned, either proving or disproving a story of skulduggery which bridged over several centuries and included at least two murders—to the satisfaction of city editors.

In Spanish days, according to legend, a priest discovered a cave in the San Andres mountains and concealed there a large treasure made up of coins, bars of gold bullion, a big ruby, a diamond-encrusted crown and weapons. How a lowly priest in the American Southwest came into possession of such riches—especially a European-sounding headdress like a crown—is not very clear. Nor is it clear why a Spanish soldier felt called upon to murder the priest when that good man, who wouldn't talk, had the only clue to the whereabouts of the treasure. However, that's the story, and nothing much was done about it until the turn of the century, when a certain Col. A. J. Fountain of Las Cruces reportedly discovered the cave and its riches. Before he and his son could remove so much as a bar of gold, the two men vanished permanently, leaving no trace behind them. Then, in 1937 (or 1941, depending on which paper you read), a man by the name of Noss, who presumably knew nothing of the Fountains or the Spanish priest, rediscovered the cave and, in due course, the treasure. According to his wife, he found gold bars, each weighing from thirty-five to fifty pounds and piled up like cord wood. The other precious paraphernalia of the old Spanish legend were all there, too.

Noss supposedly removed everything, then changed his mind and returned it all to the cave for safekeeping while he considered what he'd better do about such a fortune. Before he came to a conclusion the draft caught up with him and whisked him off into uniform. After World War II, he apparently returned to recover his treasure, but not to reclaim his wife. By now the mouth of the cave had collapsed, and Noss needed equipment and financial backing in order to dig his way in. This he seems to have obtained from a man by the name of Ryan. It wasn't long, however, before Noss was fatally shot and Ryan was charged with the murder. Thereupon the estranged Mrs. Noss, who had never known the cave's exact location, took out a prospector's permit in order to look for it—and the treasure. Whether her search was fruitful is not yet a matter of record.

Not only have murders and other crimes been committed in caves —and in connection with them—but caves themselves have been used as prisons to hold a wide variety of characters who have fallen afoul of the law or at least fallen into the clutches of those who had the power to enforce what they wanted to be the law. One such is Marvel Cave in Missouri. Just who the "goodies" and the "baddies" were in the local disturbances that led to its use as a prison is a bit obscure. (The answer probably depends to a considerable extent on which local gang your own ancestors belonged to.) But it *was* a prison—and a spacious one at that. It is reported to have about fourteen miles of passages.

A much smaller place that started out as a cave is Newgate Prison in Connecticut, known in the eighteenth century as Simsbury Mines. Prisoners were kept in the place before, during and after the American Revolution, and it had all the atrocious features of English prisons of the time, plus the additional horrors of dampness and constantly dripping water. Newgate, still open as a show place for tourists, with manacles and chains to demonstrate how prisoners were fastened to the cold wet walls, is only a cave by courtesy, if that word fits in such a gruesome context. Beginning as a small natural cavern in the seventeenth century, it became a mine by stages when the surrounding limestone proved a profitable source of copper.

While we can feel some relief that the employment of caves as prisons has fallen into disfavor, we can only note with curiosity another custom that dates back a long time and is apparently increasing in popularity—and not because more and more people have taken up caving as an avocation. Since the mid-nineteenth century young couples have fled from the light of day into dark chilly caverns in order to go through religious wedding ceremonies.

Perhaps the earliest such ceremony was held in Howe Caverns when Lester Howe's daughter and a young man who was willing to please his prospective father-in-law took the marriage vows on a high ledge which the begowned bride could reach only by climbing a tall ladder. Most other commercial caves have at one time or another had elaborately staged weddings, and one commercial-cave owner, Miss Lydia Neubuck of Natural Stone Bridge Caves in New York State, inveigled her aviator fiancé underground into Carlsbad Caverns for their wedding ceremony.

Credit must go to another young lady who, in the nineteenth

century, lived to regret a solemn spinsterish oath she had taken, no doubt in a moment of justifiable irritation with the male half of humanity. This young lady had vowed never "to marry a man on the face of the earth." When she had a change of heart, her out, of course, was to marry the gentleman *under* the face of the earth— in a cave.

Latterly, the motives for underground weddings are less devious. Cave after cave offers the free use of a stalagmitic altar for the ceremony. It is no small inducement also when cave-owners, for their own reasons, pay the minister and provide free music. One even boasts a guide who can thump out a semblance of "Here Comes the Bride" on vibrating calcite columns in the bridal chamber. A cave in Missouri, sufficiently interesting for the massive flowstone that extends all along one wall, has made a special feature of weddings, complete with recorded music and a selection of ministers from an interdenominational' panel. Bridal Cave this one is called, of course, and during a good week four or five marriages may be performed there.

Burials are another thing, however. Floyd Collins' remains rest, perhaps appropriately, in a sarcophagus in the beautiful cave he discovered and near which he died. Collins did not ask to be buried in a cave, nor, apparently, have any other latter-day explorers. Much as they love caves, they do not go there to die. An occasional spelunker of frontier vintage did choose a cave as his final resting place. Daniel Boone's brother, Squire, by name, was one. But certainly the most colorful character of this kind was a man known only as "Cave" Wilson. In 1822 he moved into a Missouri cavern with his wife and a large brood of children, and there he stayed until 1855 when he died.

"Cave" Wilson had his own ideas of what should be done with his carcass, and his wife followed his instructions to the last detail. She had his viscera removed and the body cavity filled with salt, after which he was placed in a coffin and packed round with more salt. The coffin was then left in the cave—together with a keg of corn licker which was to remain intact for seven years.

In 1862, as many of his friends as could assemble under war conditions met, just as he had planned it, to open and enjoy the cave-aged refreshment. At this crucial point, history breaks down and there are two schools of thought. Congenital optimists claim that everything was in order and a good drunk was enjoyed by all. Skeptics, of whom I am one, claim that the reunion at "Cave" Wilson's coffin was a failure. The only one pickled was Wilson, in his briny resting place. The whisky keg had long since been emptied.

Although this sabbatical wake was, in my view, far from the gay thing it should have been, revels have been held in more than one "Stygian cave forlorn." Lost River Cave in Pennsylvania, now called Lost Cave, once had a specially constructed floor on which "many a youth and many a maid, dancing in the chequer'd shade," spent hilarious nights. Dances went on there, in fact, as long as the cave provided the best illusion of being far from home. When mass-produced automobiles and good roads could really put a distance between teen-agers and their parents, the underground dance hall fell into disuse.

Henry W. Shoemaker has dug up the story of another Pennsylvania cavern in which youths held country dances secretly, in defiance of the puritanic customs of their elders. Every Saturday night the younger people gathered in a hemlock grove east of Coburn, made their way through a heavy growth of ferns, and climbed down a ladder into Stover Cave. There they had built a floor, and the rock walls adequately deadened any sound of laughter, shouting or music that might betray their hideaway.

Hard-working Nevada miners a generation ago had a different idea of how to spend Saturday night in a cave. They discovered that a pool of water in Devil's Hole was very warm—a perfect place for weekly baths. This cave, for reasons not yet known, is far above normal temperature, although the pool water has cooled a great deal since it was first discovered.

When everything has been said about the odd or incidental or accidental uses to which caves have been put (and I have by no means completed such a listing), the total does not add up miraculously to one of those believe-it-or-not statements which we would usually be better off not believing. Neither the destiny of man nor the workings of nature revolve around underground recesses as their central point. But caves *are* fascinating, and their two major uses are very real and of widespread importance. First and foremost, caves are a vast and ever expanding section of the nation's playground and recreational resources. It bears repeating that over a million visitors pay to enter commercial caves every year. The operation of all these show places taken together is a considerable business. In addition, a growing number of sportsmen and sportswomen—about two thousand of them—do consistent spelunking; and there are unknown thousands of others who have fun, on occasion, looking into wild caves.

Of tremendous importance, though little mentioned in this book, is the work done by the National Park Service of the Department of the Interior in preserving splendid caves and in making many of them available to the general public. Some states have done an excellent job of protecting and exhibiting caves. At least one county—Pima County in Arizona—has performed a valuable service by maintaining Colossal Cave as a show place.

Cave operators, whether public administrators or private owners, have usually been careful custodians of the wonders which they are in a position to display. Under both individual and civic control, caves serve a public purpose—they invite the ordinary citizen to learn and relax and enjoy—and let the Philistines wail that their use for recreation is not a legitimate and very important one.

The second great utilitarian function of caves lies in the area of research. Scientists find them a boon to their never-ending efforts to notch up our understanding of the world we live in. And it is always wise to avoid predicting in what direction scientific curiosity and ingenuity will lead. Enough has been said elsewhere in this book to suggest that the hollows under the earth are of value to science, and it is surely not necessary to demonstrate the obvious— that science is of use to man. It may be worth-while, however, to realize that highly trained investigators, including historians, have yet to learn a great many things about caves. The frontiers these investigators have still to cross are in their way as considerable as the number of caves which no modern man has entered.

CHAPTER FOURTEEN

Cave Mysteries

When early cartographers faced up to the fact that there were areas about which they had absolutely no knowledge, they were inclined to embellish the blank spots in their drawings with sea monsters or other mythical and terrifying creatures that seemed a good deal more authentic then than now. Present-day mappers of caves are more modest than were their forerunners a few centuries ago. When they reach the point beyond which no transit has been lugged nor Brunton compass sighted nor steel tape stretched, they leave a vague opening at the end of their confident lines that show cavern walls, or else they suggest where an unexplored frontier lies by extending dotted lines a little way in that direction. The number of maps of large and famous caves that have channel after channel trailing off in this fashion toward *terra incognita* is astounding.

What lies beyond the point where the solid lines on the maps end? Here is a cave mystery, preliminary to all others, which keeps the explorers busy. There is no early prospect that they will run out of new territory to enter, and upon their success in following caves, big and little, to their farthest points, depends the solution of certain speleological problems that plague scientists.

Until the exact—and full—nature of more caves is known, the debate on how caves were really formed will continue. Until the shape and the nature of a very great variety of cavern passageways is known down to minute detail, and known in relation to every feature of the rock in which they occur and to the landscape above, there can be no sure, verifiable explanation of the origin of every kind of cave. Though existing theories are substantial, there seem to be caves for which no present hypothesis is adequate.

How, for instance, was Cave-in-Rock carved out of the limestone on the north bank of the Ohio River? There are speculations, but some fact about this cave always punctures each of them. Many caves in the area show extensive enlargement by underground rivers. But Cave-in-Rock, which looks as if a river had been at work there, ends in a solid limestone wall in the rear. Only a small sink-hole, draining a small area, could possibly have introduced a stream into the cave, and the stream could never have been large enough to do the erosion manifest here.

Did the Ohio River wear away at the limestone from the outside and thus gouge out the cavern? This seems impossible, as George F. Jackson has pointed out. The cave is much longer than any other known to have been formed in this way, and invasion by river waters could apparently never have been achieved except at flood times—and floods come during only a small part of each year. No known uplift of the mass of limestone that contains Cave-in-Rock is known to have occurred. There is no evidence that it is all that remains of a larger cave which the river has destroyed.

How then did Cave-in-Rock come into existence? What is the theory which will explain it? No one yet is absolutely sure.

Is it possible that one vast, interconnecting water-filled cavern system extends from Kentucky westward, under both the Ohio and Mississippi Rivers? This theory has been suggested by those who have no other explanation yet for the wide dispersion of one variety of blind white fish.

These sweeping questions are easily followed by more specific ones. What is the deepest cave in the United States? Is it Carlsbad or Neff's Canyon or some other? Carlsbad is generally believed to be the deepest, and at least one geologist thinks it likely that one or more levels exist below the eleven-hundred-foot depth that has been reached. But the only explorers who claim to have reached the end of Neff's Canyon estimate that this Utah cave is two thousand feet deep. Which cave is longest—Mammoth, Floyd Collins' Crystal Cave, Colossal Cave or some other?

The questions move on to more detailed matters. For instance, how are helictites formed? Mineralogists have widely differing theories to explain the contorted and even upward-growing shapes of these speleothems. What causes the special disk-shaped deposits of calcite known as shields or palettes? What is the explanation for moon milk? How exactly do gypsum flowers and long needle-like gypsum crystals grow outward from their base? What is the real secret that lies behind the formation in caves of both calcite and aragonite, which have the same chemical formula but different crystalline structure? Mineralogists hold sharply opposing views.

One of the early explanations for helictites was that their curious wandering structure resulted from air currents that blew lime-bearing drops of water off their true perpendicular course and started the growth of deposits at various odd angles. This theory, no longer taken very seriously, originated in the fact that air currents—sometimes very puzzling ones—do exist in caves.

Meteorologists are fascinated by the problems they meet in trying to account for the movement of air in some underground passages. For example, no one has yet been able to explain a phenomenon first observed by the veteran spelunker Burton Faust in a cave near Burnsville, Virginia. One day while waiting at the mouth of a crawlway for other cavers who had gone on through it, Faust noticed that the air about him was moving strangely. He lit a candle and watched its flame lean in one direction for a while, then stand upright, then lean in the opposite direction. He lit a cigar. The smoke drifted into the crawlway, came to a stop, then drifted back out and stopped once more. It looked for all the world as if the largely unexplored passageways beyond were breathing—in and out. The cave became known as Breathing Cave.

On numerous trips, observers have checked Faust's report. The cycle lasted sometimes eight minutes, sometimes more—but "breathe" the cave did and still does. Nobody can explain why. One theory proffered, which does not meet all the conditions in the cave, is that in some unexplored portion a room may fill with water, thus forcing air into other passages, and then drain, thus allowing air to come back. The draining could be done, the theorist says, by means of a siphon arrangement in passageways which carry water out of the room. Siphons are known to exist in caves, but no evidence has yet turned up that Breathing Cave has a water supply that could produce the periodic rapid filling of a chamber. Siphon action has explained another phenomenon which was once a per-plexity to cavers. The levels in some springs rose and fell in a pulsing manner. There was no correlation between the pulsing and rainfall.

It was just "magic," or just "one of those things," according to the kind of evasion most congenial to the commentator. But, as with everything, there was a rational explanation if it could only be found. After enough study, an explanation will doubtless turn up for the "breathing" phenomenon. Meteorologists may be the ones to solve the mystery.

There have been other unlikely exhibitions put on by air deep inside caves. One that was a mystery for a while has apparently been solved. The story is that a workman, digging in the hope of reaching a new chamber in Skyline Caverns, had his hat sucked off his head when he finally broke through into the chamber. A very great difference in air pressure obviously existed between the inside of the chamber and the rest of the cave. What could explain this? E. P. Henderson of the United States National Museum has a theory. Apparently the room at one time filled up with water and sediments. The sediments settled and dammed all the openings to the outside. This meant that for a time the air pocketed at the top of the room was probably at a pressure above normal. But as the sediment settled and water seeped out through pores in the limestone, the volume of the room expanded and air pressure was therefore lowered. Then, when the workman forced an opening to the sealed chamber, air from outside it rushed in, pulling his hat along with it.

It is part of folklore in some quarters that cave air is dangerous—or that there may not be enough of it to breathe. Spelunkers know better. They know that caves for the most part are a paradise for sufferers from hay fever, since the underground air usually lacks pollen and is free of dust unless human beings stir it up. However, from time to time, there have come reports that a certain cave contained "bad" air—people complained of mysterious symptoms that seemed to indicate lack of oxygen. In almost every case where a scientific examination of the air has been made, the oxygen content in these caves has been normal. On the other hand, there are situations which can mean "bad" air. It can get mighty stuffy in a small dead-end chamber with only a small entrance if several spelunkers stay there using up the oxygen for any length of time. Similarly, a fire in a chamber that has poor circulation will use up oxygen very rapidly. But actual poisonous gases in caves are exceedingly infrequent. In this respect caves differ greatly from mines.

Nevertheless, Kiser Cave between Fredericksburg and Mason, Texas, pours out a steady stream of carbon dioxide from its mouth. No one has yet found the source of this gas. Only three men have made an attempt to explore it with oxygen masks and tanks, and they nearly perished in the attempt.

Explorers looking for answers to questions about the living things in caves have not often had to risk their lives, but they have found that each question seems to beget new ones. Though cave life, except for bats, is usually sparse, the unknown facts about it are many.

How, exactly, did blind white cave creatures evolve? By what process have whole species—whose ancestors apparently had eyes and color—lost these two features?

What *exactly* are the sense organs that render service to cave animals in lieu of their non-functioning eyes? Apparently little experimental work has yet been done on this, and nobody knows at all what blind snails use instead of eyes—if indeed they use anything.

Other creatures still have scientists looking for some of the simplest facts about their mode of existence. For instance, when and where do salamanders lay their eggs? Very little has been observed about this or about the rate of growth of certain cave salamanders, which reproduce in their larval stage and never reach maturity. What is the full story on the feeding habits of salamanders which live partly in water and partly in the air on moist cave walls?

The question that William Stephenson asked many years ago—why do some bats move from one place to another in a cave during their hibernation period?—still remains unanswered. Experts still do not know where certain species of bats spend the winter. To all intents and purposes, they vanish. And where does the species known as *Myotis sodalis* spend the *summer*? So far no observer has been able to report the exact date on which migrating colonies of bats departed from a cave, nor has the date of their return been established. Nor do scientists know much about the causes of mortality in bats. It is believed that they have very few predatory enemies. At the mouth of Ney Cave in Texas duck hawks do plunge each evening into the thick column of emerging bats and make off with victims. But their kill is infinitesimal compared to the millions that issue from the cave. Other predators find it virtually impossible to reach the animals as they hang high on walls or from ceilings in pitch-dark caverns. And bats do not seem to die in any large numbers from natural causes in caves. They seem to have few diseases. Where, then, do they perish and why?

Why do Mexican Free-tailed bats fly in a counterclockwise spiral when they leave some caves, such as Carlsbad, but why do they come straight out—like bats out of hell—when they leave others? Ney Cave is an example. Here they rush from the entrance in a column about fifteen feet in diameter, flying in extremely close formation. Once out, the bat-column rises steeply, then levels off as it disappears into the distance. If, as some observers have suggested, the spiral flight-pattern helps to fix the location of such caves as Carlsbad in bats' memories, what brings the inhabitants of Ney Cave safely home?

Since these active and numerous cave mammals are surrounded with mystery, it should be no surprise that exceedingly little is known about the bacteria in cave earth. Do, as some investigators think, some cave bacteria act in a nitrogen-fixing capacity? So far as I know, petre-dirt is unique in that it can be mined over and over again. Miners found long ago that they could dig it up, leach out the nitrate, return the dirt to the cave floor, then—after the passage of three or four years—obtain more nitrate from the same dirt. Are bacteria the agency that works in the earth to produce a perennial supply of calcium nitrate?

At least one researcher has investigated cave earth with another thought in mind. Does it contain organisms that may be the source of new antibiotics?

What kind of bacteria or fungus or virus in the dust of some very dry caves causes a disease called "cave sickness" or "cave pneumonia"? Doctors have had very few cases of this disease to study. It broke out once among a group of treasure-seekers who stirred up a lot of dust from the floor of an Arkansas cavern. Medical authorities are satisfied that the origin of the sickness lay in the cave. But researchers have not yet been able to isolate the guilty organism.

On the other hand, is there a total absence of the bacteria of decay in certain dry caves? If so, this might explain why mummies (desiccated bodies) are preserved there.

Although it is most unlikely that "mummified" bodies of the very earliest men on this continent will ever be found, the search for at least some bones of Sandia Man and Folsom Man goes on. It is very logical to assume that these may be dug up in caves. But the question is, which caves contain the much desired trophies? The man or woman who finds the answer will create a major scientific sensation.

Indians who were much more recent than Sandia or Folsom Man had funerary practices of various sorts which are fairly well known, and those tribes about which we have data were usually far from casual about their dead. Some tribes bound up bodies in special ways and suspended them in trees; others practiced cremation. Some of the mounds of the Mound Builders were enormous cemeteries. And so on. But what explains the multitude of human skeletons that were found on the floor of Moaning Cave in the Sierra-Nevada foothills, at the bottom of a long vertical shaft? In the light of information about burial customs of Indians who lived in the area during historic times, this underground charnel house is most perplexing. Was the cave a place for human sacrifice to some god? What explains a large collection of Indian bones recently found in Falling Waters Cave in West Virginia, which was merely a hunting ground where no tribes lived in historic times? Were these skeletons remains of the prehistoric Mound Builders who practiced a cult of death?

It is interesting to speculate that archeologists, working in caves of the United States, may one day complete a chapter in the history of the Aztecs of Mexico. These amazing people, who ruled much of Mexico in Columbus' day, believed that the ancient and original home of their tribe was in seven caves far to the north. There is ample evidence that Aztecs did, in fact, move southward from the area of the United States into the high valley of Mexico. It would be an Indian feather in some speleologist's cap if he could solve the mystery of the longitude and latitude of caverns which the Aztecs *did* use in their migration southward. Archeologists may rise up in careful academic wrath and say that no such find can ever be made, but scholars were not impressed when Heinrich Schliemann set out to find the city of Troy with not much more than Homer to go by. Amazing things *have* turned up in American caves, among them a mysterious gold medallion, the story of which begins a long time ago and in another land.

Cro-Magnon Cave near the Spanish border in southwestern France was the home, perhaps eighteen thousand years ago, of one of the early examples of that extraordinary animal—modern man. And there is a story, part fancy but also part fact, that links a dweller in Cro-Magnon Cave to American Indians who used a cave far across the barrier of the Atlantic Ocean near the town of Ticonderoga in the northern part of New York State.

Pieced together out of possibilities and certainties, the story goes like this: One day a Cro-Magnon craftsman found a nugget of pure gold, as many men in many places have done since. He knew nothing about working in metal, nor did any of his fellows, but he found by hammering this reddish-yellow stone—as he hammered other stones he wished to shape into tools—that it was soft and could be flattened out. Pounding on, the craftsman shaped the nugget into a round disk about an inch in diameter. The novel color made it attractive as an ornament, and the soft metal invited more than just flattening. The Cro-Magnon innovator decided his disk or medallion would look better with a drawing on it, so he scratched one with a sharp-edged tool of flint. A natural subject to choose would be something at once familiar and perennially interesting—something to do with the hunt and food.

The craftsman traced the outline of the biggest, most majestic source of food he knew—a mastodon. Thereafter the medallion presumably served as a decoration or a charm that brought good luck in mastodon hunts, until its maker died, when it may have gone to his grave with him. At any rate, many thousands of years passed before a Spaniard chanced on the medallion and pocketed it as a curiosity. How many times it was traded or passed from hand to hand after that, no one knows.

When Columbus brought news to Spain that lands rich in gold existed across the Atlantic, many Spaniards began crossing the ocean in search of the precious metal. One who did so was the then-owner of the little medallion, and he took it along with him on his voyage as a good luck piece or as a way of showing Indians the kind of yellow metal he sought.

In the first generations after Columbus, Spaniards penetrated deep into the Great Smoky Mountains and crossed them. In this area they met the far-ranging Cherokees. The Spanish owner of the medallion may have gone along on this exploration. The story has it that an Indian acquired the golden disk at about this time, and in the course of normal Indian trades and raids it moved northward until it became the property of a member of the Iroquois nation. This man on occasion used a cave on Pharaoh Mountain near Ticonderoga as shelter. In a careless moment the Iroquois left the medallion in the cave and never returned to claim it. If others visited the cave, they overlooked the small round object.

Three centuries later, sometime about 1840, two children in the family of a farmer named Johnson, who lived nearby, went hunting on Pharaoh Mountain, and with them was an Indian boy. When a storm blew up, the Indian boy led the Johnson boys to a cave he knew about on the mountain. While they waited for the storm to blow over, the youngsters all looked curiously at the white walls of the cave on which there were carvings of birds and animals. And one of the Johnsons spied the little round disk and picked it up.

When he and his brother reached home and told of their adventure, the elder Johnsons grew worried. Who knew what dangers a cave might hold? They ordered the two boys to stay away from the place, and the boys obeyed—if for no other reason because their Indian guide was drowned soon after their expedition. Since the cave was to be out of bounds, the disk-finder wanted to make sure that he at least kept the interesting thing he had picked up. He dropped it into a barrel in which he kept various treasures safe from the eyes of scornful adults and the grasping fingers of other boys. But no sooner did he hide the medallion in the barrel than he forgot it.

Two generations passed, and the boy was now old Mr. Johnson— a grandfather. One day he was telling Richard, his grandson, some of his boyhood adventures. The story of entering the Pharaoh cave came to mind and with it the disk he had forgotten after he stowed it in his treasure barrel. Young Richard was understandably curious. What ever became of the barrel that held the disk?

Grandpa hadn't thought of it in a great many years, but he found it was still around. He fished among the meaningless junk the barrel contained—and there in the bottom lay the small round reminder of his day in the cave.

Richard now became owner of the medallion, and like his grandfather, he hid it for safekeeping, but not in a barrel. He found a place for his little age-darkened treasure on a high beam in the big old barn.

A long time passed before Richard thought of the medallion again, and when he did, he couldn't remember where he had put it. Search as he would, he couldn't find it, and search as he would for the entrance to the Pharaoh cave about which his grandfather had told him, he couldn't find that either. Possibly some of his scrambles over the mountain led young Richard to an interest in rocks. Whatever the cause, Richard Johnson became a geologist.

One day, long after he was a grown man, workmen tore down the old barn on the family farm—and there on the beam, just where he had left it, was the medallion. Johnson's eye as a geologist, supplemented by tests, told him what he had not known before—that his medallion was of pure gold. But it did not have the yellow color of gold found in the western hemisphere. A reddish tint revealed that it must have come from Europe or Asia. Then there was the drawing on it to be explained. It looked like other primitive drawings of mastodons.

Johnson sent the medallion to archeologists, who were greatly interested. It was definitely very ancient, they all agreed, and they agreed it was definitely not the work of American Indians. What men did live at the same time as mastodons and made drawings of them? Cro-Magnon men—but they were not known to have worked in metal. And how did a Cro-Magnon artifact get to Ticonderoga, New York, presumably in prehistoric times? On these points the experts disagreed. The story I have told grows out of one theory. But Richard Johnson is no romancer. He wanted the facts about his medallion, and the possibility existed that the Pharaoh cave would reveal them, so he set out in earnest to locate the cave.

Johnson knew from his geology that Grenville limestone underlay the area where the cave was supposed to be. In this limestone there could be just such a cave as his grandfather had described. Johnson hunted long and hard, but before he found the elusive entrance, ill health overtook him and he had to leave the search to others.

The best he could do was to lend the medallion for a while to the local museum, and in 1949 to let a newspaper reporter print the story of the mysterious disk—and to hope that someone's curiosity

Speleologists and spelunkers explored together for years, reaching ever farther into the unknown in Higgenbotham Cave, now called Cumberland Caverns, McMinnville, Tennessee. Here Donald Egbert studies the giant stalagmite named the Christmas Tree. *Courtesy: Cumberland Caverns*
Photo by Roy Davis

Kenneth Bunting, David Westmoreland and Roy Davis, all students from David Lipscomb College, pause beside a gypsum outcrop in the Great Extension of Higgenbotham Cave on the day in 1953 when they discovered this large new area. *Courtesy: Cumberland Caverns*

Among the sights that greeted explorers when they discovered the Great Extension in Higgenbotham Cave was this group of gypsum flowers known as the Tiger Lily. *Courtesy: Cumberland Caverns*
Photo by Roy Davis

Almost all supplies needed by explorers on the week-long 1954 expedition of the National Speleological Society in Floyd Collins' Crystal Cave had to be dragged through a thirteen-hundred-foot crawlway in containers like the one shown here. This Gurnee can has taken a terrific beating. Note the knee pads and the rappel patch across the right thigh of this member of the supply team. *Courtesy: National Speleological Society*
Photo by John L. Spence

Recent intensive exploration has gone on in the cavern system under Flint Ridge near Mammoth Cave. These explorers are walking through a virgin passage they have just discovered there. *Courtesy: Floyd Collins' Crystal Cave   Photo by W. T. Austin*

Nancy Rogers, Philip Harsham, William Burke ("Skeets") Miller, Donald N. Cournoyer enjoy a meal at Camp #1, far underground, during the week-long expedition in Floyd Collins' Crystal Cave in 1954. *Courtesy: National Speleological Society*

A few moments before this picture was taken, the man on the right nearly joined Floyd Collins as a martyr to the exploration of the cavern system under Flint Ridge. Roger Brucker, director of exploration which has gone on continuously since the 1954 expedition, slipped on mud and fell through a narrow opening into an underground stream. Here he has dragged himself out and clings precariously to the mud as W. T. Austin, cave manager, comes to his rescue. The fog is caused by body heat of the explorers in the cool cave air. *Courtesy:* Sports Illustrated *Photo by Robert Halmi*

Exploring has its welcome periods of ease. Here cavers stroll through an area called the Lost Passage. Floyd Collins, years ago, reported its existence, but with his death knowledge of the route to it disappeared. Finally it was rediscovered, and in it explorers camped for a week in 1954. *Courtesy: Floyd Collins' Crystal Cave*

Photo by W. T. Austin

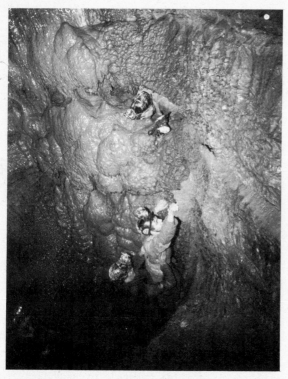

After wriggling sixty feet in a knobbly crawlway only ten inches high, an explorer looks out over a twelve-foot drop-off. One of his companions has made the descent, and the second is partway down the slick mud-covered side of the pit. Note the telephone line which has been strung from the entrance of Floyd Collins' Crystal Cave, three miles away. *Courtesy:* Sports Illustrated

Photo by Robert Halmi

To the left of Roger Brucker is a 90-foot drop-off. A little way ahead the ledge grows too narrow for crawling. Brucker will stand up, lean across the chasm, brace his hands against the opposite wall and keep on inching forward for some distance. In spite of the steel cable, which he can grasp as he stands up, it is a nerve-wracking experience to cross this Bottomless Pit in Floyd Collins' Crystal Cave. *Courtesy:* Sports Illustrated

Photo by Robert Halmi

The display of caves to the public is a big business, and operators, whether private or governmental, protect caves from vandals so they may be enjoyed by future generations. Here is the gateway to Crystal Cave in Sequoia National Park, California. *Courtesy: National Park Service*

Many commercial caves encourage wedding ceremonies and Easter and other religious services. Niagara Cave has a specially designed chapel. *Courtesy: Niagara Cave   Photo by S. W. Lock.*

Caves are important recreation areas.
Here tourists visit Diamond Cave, Jasper, Arkansas.
Courtesy: Arkansas Publicity and Information Department

Scientists have found caves of great value as places in which to conduct research.
Deep in Floyd Collins' Crystal Cave, a speleologist studies a stream to see if blind fish
or crayfish or other forms of life are there. *Courtesy:* Sports Illustrated

Photo by Robert Halmi

A part of the cave system known as Florida Caverns, in which these speleothems can
be seen, was discovered when a hurricane blew over a tree and exposed an entrance
hitherto unknown. *Courtesy: Florida State News Bureau*

Fishermen casting for trout in Sequoia National Park, California, looked up and saw the entrance to Crystal Cave, which is now one of the popular features of the Park. *Courtesy: National Park Service*

The horse which Absalom Lehman was riding one day in the 1870's as he looked after his cattle stumbled into the entrance of this cave. Lehman Caves National Monument in Nevada is now a part of the federal park system. *Courtesy: National Park Service Photo by Nevada Photo Service*

Railroad workers, cutting ties high in the Utah mountains, discovered one entrance to Timpanogos Cave where this picture was taken. A man out hunting deer found another entrance. *Courtesy: National Park Service*

After cave-hunting for a month, three men found in a limestone ledge a small hole which they enlarged and which led to this and other spectacular chambers in the cave called Luray Caverns. *Courtesy: Luray Caverns*

The body of Floyd Collins rests in this tomb in the cave which he discovered and which bears his name. He died in Sand Cave not far away. *Courtesy: Floyd Collins' Crystal Cave*
Photo by W. T. Austin

In 1804 Bernard Weyer discovered what is now Grand Caverns, one of the few caves in the United States known to have formations called shields or palettes. Weyer, determined to retrieve a trap which a woodchuck had dragged into a small hole, dug his way in after the animal and shortly thereafter found himself the first successful cave operator in the country. *Courtesy: Grand Caverns of Virginia*

In order to make an easy route to a gallery decorated with beautiful helictites, Floyd Collins chopped his way through 1,500 feet of clay, using a broad axe. The axe and Floyd's wheelbarrow are still to be seen in the cave. His father carved the head at the left out of clay from the passageway. *Courtesy: Floyd Collins' Crystal Cave*

Photo by W. T. Austin

One ever-present danger to cavers is fatigue. David Jones, who has just finished twenty-six hours of grueling activity in Floyd Collins' Crystal Cave, wearily reports to expedition leader Roger Brucker. *Courtesy: Floyd Collins' Crystal Cave*

Photo by W. T. Austin

Telephone communication from deep inside Floyd Collins' Crystal Cave to headquarters at the cave entrance provides a quick way of rendering reports— and of summoning help if necessary. *Courtesy: Sports Illustrated Photo by Robert Halmi*

Some cavers specialize in surveying and mapping. Here Roger Brucker and "Red" Watson use a Brunton compass and steel tape to help determine the exact extent of Floyd Collins' Crystal Cave, which the National Speleological Society believes to be the nucleus of the largest known cavern system in the United States. *Courtesy: Floyd Collins' Crystal Cave Photo by W. T. Austin*

Cavers must become skilled in various techniques used by alpinists. Here an underground mountaineer ascends a chimney by using the pressure of hands, feet and back on opposing rock faces. *Courtesy: National Speleological Society* *Photo by Ann Meuer*

Photographers in wild caves lack the elaborate equipment used by these movie makers who find the rich colors and great concentration of speleothems in Luray Caverns an interesting subject. *Courtesy: Luray Caverns*
Photo by Michael Lackovitch

Camera fans will be interested to know that this photograph was taken on Tri-X film with only the light of carbide lamps. *Courtesy: Floyd Collins' Crystal Cave*
Photo by W. T. Austin

There may be more cave above and beyond. Explorers probe everywhere in their effort to reach farther into the unknown. *Courtesy:* Sports Illustrated

Photo by Robert Halmi

would be sufficiently aroused to search the Mt. Pharaoh area inch by inch.

Such an explorer turned up in the person of Russell H. Gurnee, an active member of the National Speleological Society, who would much rather crawl through caves than follow his profession as a sheet-metal contractor. Gurnee tramped over the area where all evidence indicated the cave must lie—that is, a half-mile east of Mt. Pharaoh, a quarter-mile inside the Town of Ticonderoga. But the underbrush thereabouts is incredibly thick. Gurnee reports that a careful searcher could pass a few feet from a cave entrance and never see it. He also reports that he has not found the cave, but he has by no means given up hope that he may one day solve a tantalizing mystery and make possible a much more factual account of what appears to be at least a tenuous link between cave men in the Old World and a cave in the Adirondacks.

Meanwhile the mysterious medallion remains in the possession of Richard Johnson of Ticonderoga, and the Pharaoh cave is one of a long list of caves that await rediscovery and may reveal fascinating secrets of the past.

Another cavern that holds such secrets is Spanish Cave, also known as La Caverna del Oro, Marble Mountain Cave, Crystal Falls Cave and Music Pass Cave. Its names are almost as numerous as the spelunkers who have gone very far down through its 38° temperature into its depths. Very few people have, in recent years, climbed up to its entrance, which is nearly 12,000 feet above sea level on Marble Mountain in the magnificent Sangre de Cristo Range in southern Colorado. But at one time traffic was heavy there. The facts agreed on by different observers of Spanish Cave are these: Near the cavern entrance stands a stone building which appears to be the ruins of a fort. On the rock outside the entrance is painted a Maltese cross. Not far inside, crumbling wooden ladders lead down through a shaft. Beyond that are remnants of a wooden winch and large quantities of rotted rope. At times strong blasts of air issue from the cave; at other times the draft is inward. Agreement stops here, perhaps because different exploring parties visited different areas of the cave.

The mountaineer who seems to have gone deepest into it, Elwyn Arps, reports a two-hundred-foot passageway which looked to him as if it had been a mine tunnel but which was choked off at the end with mud, except for a space about five inches in diameter. Air pouring through this hole indicated that more of the cavern lay beyond. Arps also reports finding an old shovel. Old-timers in Wet Mountain Valley below the cave have their own reports, based on "reliable" second- or third-hand sources, they say. A suit of Spanish armor was found in or near the cave. Quantities of Indian arrowheads have been picked up in the vicinity. The Spaniards built the fort and, using Indian slave labor, mined the cave for gold.

Unanswered questions about this extraordinary place should tempt archeologist and spelunker alike. Why does Spanish Cave breathe? Do the remains of ladder and winch really give evidence that places them in the Spanish period or centuries later when other miners worked in the Sangre de Cristos? Are the remnants of rope of ancient or of modern manufacture? And why should such obviously vast labor have been put into defending and entering a hole in the ground in such a high, difficult, cold spot? How extensive is the cave, and what lies beyond the mud bank in the tunnel that seems to have been mined? Was there ever gold here?

The list of cave mysteries is endless, but in a sense the most obvious and provocative speleological problem is this: where, exactly, are all the thousands of caves that surely exist but whose whereabouts are not yet known?

CHAPTER FIFTEEN

How to Find a Cave

How does a spelunker go about finding a cave?

The chances are good that anyone who has persistence can do it. Luck will be a great help in shortening the process, and so will detective work based on at least a smattering of scientific knowledge. But it is not necessary to be an expert. The biggest and best caverns have been found by amateurs.

Those in the know guess that anywhere from thirty to fifty thousand caves in the United States are waiting to be located. That's a lot of caves. Many of them have never been entered by man. Others are "lost"—that is, they were once known to local farmers, adventurous youngsters or hunters, but are not mentioned in any list compiled by state or federal geologists, by speleological societies or other scientific agencies.

Historically speaking, the best way to find a cave is to be looking for something else. That's how it has often happened in the past. The pioneer who discovered Wind Cave in South Dakota was hunting for game. Another pioneer, Absalom Lehman, was thinking only of the stupid, ornery cattle he had to drive among the piñon and juniper trees of the Snake Range in eastern Nevada in the 1870's when his horse suddenly fell out from under him. His mount had stumbled into a natural opening to the vast cavern system which bears Lehman's name to this day and has become a National Monument.

Two farm boys near New Market, Virginia, went rabbit-hunting in 1879 on their day off, and their dogs chased a cottontail under a boulder. Determined to get the animal, the boys shifted the rock and saw below them a deep shaft. They forgot the rabbit, went for ropes and candles, and made the first entrance into what is now

187

known as Endless Caverns, one of the beautiful commercial caves of the Shenandoah Valley.

Grand Caverns nearby in Grottoes, Virginia, was discovered by Bernard Weyer in 1804 when he followed the trail of a groundhog into tangled underbrush. And a groundhog led Floyd Collins to the opening of his Crystal Cave in Kentucky. Hunters discovered the caves in two far-western areas now set aside as National Monuments—Oregon Caves, and Timpanogos Cave in Utah. Boys looking for three lost pigs followed the animals' trail into Niagara Cave, now a commercial cavern near Harmony, Minnesota.

The list of accidental discoveries could go on and on, and it suggests a time-tested technique which modern spelunkers are still able to use—on purpose. A patient cave-hunter, minus a gun or a trap, can follow clues in the form of groundhogs, rabbits, raccoons. For example, in the spring of 1955 two experienced cavers, Bernard Smeltzer and Palmer Tome, went for an outing in well-spelunked Pennsylvania, where it would seem all caverns should have been discovered by now. At one point they sat down to rest, and idly watched a woodchuck loafing on a ledge. Suddenly the animal disappeared. A glance at the ledge revealed a small telltale crack, and a stone that the men dropped into the hole fell a long way before landing. Smeltzer and Tome struggled for two hours, heaving away rocks and dirt until they had an opening large enough to enter. At the bottom of a corkscrew shaft lay a cave no one had ever seen before. That is always sufficient reward in itself, but Woodchuck Cave held a rich display of stalactites as well.

Fishermen, too, should keep their eyes open. Witness the experience of C. M. Webster and A. L. Medley, employees of Sequoia National Park, when they were casting for trout in Cascade Creek in April, 1918. They happened to notice an outcropping of white crystalline marble and thought they saw an opening in the rock. Webster and Medley abandoned their rods to explore, and they found Crystal Cave, now one of the most popular features of the park.

Prospectors roaming in search of gold and other minerals, miners and quarry-workers have accounted for many caves, some of them famous. Lewis and Clark Cave in Montana, Crystal Cave and Baker Caverns in Pennsylvania, Crystal Grottoes of Maryland, are spectacular by-products of rock-hammer and drill. Nor is this accidental discovery of caves by prospectors, miners and other diggers in the earth just a matter of ancient history. Almost a hundred years after the Gold Rush in California, men were still looking for the main gold vein of the famous Mother Lode. One of them, Ernie Byers, set off six charges of dynamite in a prospect hole. The next morning he heard his partner, Zeke Goodman, yell out: "Hey, something's wrong! There's a hell of a hole down here! I just rolled a rock in, and it takes half an hour to hear where it goes." Another large cavern system had been discovered.

Men excavating for a gas company inside the city limits of Louisville, Kentucky, suddenly burst into a cave. Young boys in Louisville are no different from boys elsewhere: They had been doing a thorough job of sidewalk-superintending, and now, when they saw the cave, they entered as soon as the workmen's backs were turned. Fear for the safety of the children led to the destruction of the cave. Under scientific guidance it was systematically mined of all its gypsum and calcite speleothems, which have been preserved in a museum. Then the entrance was closed.

The atomic age accounts for at least one accidental discovery of a cave. Following a test blast in Nevada, Adolf Schleicher found that Bat Cave, which he owned, was a lot bigger than he had suspected. The atom blast had started an earth slide in the cavern and opened up a chamber which early estimates indicated contained much more than half a million dollars' worth of bat guano.

Other forces as old as the world have recently led men to caves. A hurricane did the job in Florida, where a surveyor employed by the Florida Caverns State Park noticed a small opening under a tree that had been blown down by the violent wind. He enlarged the hole, crawled in and found a magnificent cave that apparently had never been known even to the Indians, who had used other underground chambers in the park.

At the moment I write this, word comes from King's Canyon National Park in California that a great forest fire has led two Rangers to discover three new caves. Actually the caves were new only to white men. Three Indian brothers, employed as fire fighters in a rugged and dangerous ravine, paused long enough in their labor to point out cave entrances. After the fire had been conquered, the

Rangers wanted to return and investigate. So they added a new twist to spelunking. To reach the almost inaccessible area they flew in by helicopter and made what may prove to be a rich archeological discovery. On the cave walls are Indian paintings, including pictures of human beings drawn in red and white and orange; and many artifacts indicate that the caves had long been used by the original Americans who discovered them.

All of which points to a second principle of cave hunting: go out into the countryside and talk to a lot of ordinary folks. They know about hundreds—perhaps thousands—of caves with which experts have not yet caught up. Moreover, a good deal has been written about some of these "unknown" caves. Local historians can dig up many leads out of their prodigious memories or their heaps of clippings. References appear in obscure local histories, diaries, small-town newspapers, country weeklies. Small-town librarians and newspaper editors are often good sources of information. Historical societies—county, regional or state—may be helpful. But whether the clues are in written or in oral form, the best originate with farmers, miners, hunters, youngsters who like the out-of-doors, and old people of all sorts who were once adventurous kids themselves. A practical hint: make a double check when an informant ends an involved set of directions with "You can't miss it." And don't be surprised if you find a cave referred to by several different names in the same neighborhood.

One devotee of this fascinating type of research, Clay Perry, has dug up enough literary riches from America's underground to fill two lively books, with more a-coming. A glance into his *New England's Buried Treasure* and his *Underground Empire* is all that is needed to show how much can be found out about "unknown" or "lost" caves and how to go about locating them.

Another time-honored formula is still good: hunt for mysterious cool drafts of air issuing from the ground and listen for whistling or moaning sounds that come from rocks. That is the way Lester Howe found his famous Howe Caverns; prospectors in South Dakota located Jewel Cave by the noise it made. A young girl, Martha Woodson, who was picking berries in Kentucky back in 1799 followed a breeze into a hole in the rock. With the help of her two younger brothers and a fallen tree trunk, she managed to slide down

into what is now called Mammoth Onyx Cave. Mt. Aetna Cave in
Maryland gave itself away, volcano-like, by blowing plumes of fog
out into the air. For Floyd Collins, professional cave hunter in
Kentucky, it was routine to walk over the ridges near his home in
winter, looking for telltale blow-holes in the snow.

There haven't been many men who, like Collins, got paid for cave
hunting, but a few investigators have hired others to aid them in
collecting information. One such was Dr. Henry C. Mercer, an early
eminent speleologist. At the turn of the century he employed
William H. Witte to locate and look into caves and sinkholes of the
Susquehanna Valley. Another Pennsylvanian, William Mines, hired
coal miners to dig into sinkholes in search of a cavern that was
suspected but had no opening to the surface. The result of this unusual mining operation was the discovery in 1930 of Kooken Cave—
the best area for underground mountaineering in the state. More
recently, active—not arm-chair—spelunkers have offered cash for information. The following advertisement appeared in the Blacksburg, Virginia, newspaper:

> The Virginia Polytechnic Institute Cave Club will pay $5.00
> per mile of cave to the first person who sends us the exact loca-
> tion of any cave we have not visited within 25 miles of Blacks-
> burg. Minimum payment $2.50. Length will be determined by
> survey. Send exact information on how to find the cave to Box
> 943, Va. Tech. Sta., Blacksburg, Va. All replies will be num-
> bered and considered in the order in which they are received.
> Include return address.

The Cave Club's financial flier produced no results that are
blazoned forth in speleological history. Replies to the advertisement
poured in, according to Albert C. Mueller, Vice-President of the
NSS, but unfortunately this novel—and sensible—way of locating
caves did not produce any *new* ones the first time it was tried.

All the foregoing methods of discovery are well and good, but
there is another which can give a different kind of delight—one
which offers real advantages, if you have an observant eye and a
little interest in rocks. You start, of course, by looking in country
where caves can exist—that is, first of all in areas where there is
soluble rock: limestone or dolomite or marble or gypsum. Don't

waste time looking in granite, gneiss, shale or a dozen other kinds of rock. The caves in sandstone are almost always shallow because they are usually merely wind-worn or water-washed. Long tunnels do exist in lava. But lava beds are few and far between, and they are a separate story, as are sea caves.

For the best luck go where there is limestone. But avoid most of the areas which glaciers of the Ice Age once covered. The glaciers either crushed or covered or filled up with debris almost all the underground hollows in Canada and in much of the northern part of the United States. Most of the known caves that survived the icy bull-dozing in glaciated regions are small, although there *are* hardy survivors in surprising numbers in the Berkshires and in south-central New York State. And farther west the glaciers by-passed certain areas, leaving caves intact.

The map on the end papers shows where the major limestone and cave areas lie. In some of these places the topography itself is a dead giveaway. You can tell by a glance at the surface that cavernous rock lies beneath. The first clue is the absence of small streams. Instead of the usual pattern of little brooks flowing into creeks and creeks flowing into a river, the brooks scarcely get started before they disappear underground. In a whole large area there may be only one good-sized creek or river, with no obvious system of tributaries. This means that rain water must be draining off beneath the surface.

Other clues are depressions in the land—sinkholes. They may be very small or very large, very shallow or very deep. Water can flow into them, but its only way out is through the bottom of the depression, either by seepage or through an actual opening. In other words, this is karst country, as geologists call it. And caves go with karst.

Recently I traveled through just such country north of Roswell in New Mexico. Geologists, of course, have long known that this karst area exists, but my inquiries among experts had failed to produce evidence of any caves thereabouts. So, as I headed southeast from Santa Fe for a revisit to Carlsbad Caverns, I was thinking a good deal more of making time over the high, almost featureless plateau north of Roswell than I was of caves.

But one thing about the vast cattle ranges on either side of the road caught my attention. Small depressions appeared here and there. In some, touches of new green grass stood out in startling contrast to the gray-brown plants that struggled for life on the semi-arid plain. This meant that water had collected in the depressions following a thundershower not too long ago. And there were no stream beds to carry the run-off of rainwater—the road had crossed not a single bridge, for mile after mile. I knew from experience the kind of deluge that can tear away at the surface of the dry New Mexico land. A flash flood is an ever present possibility in seemingly waterless areas of the Southwest. But here I saw no arroyos or washes betraying the violent erosion characteristic in other parts of the state. Obviously this plateau was a sort of giant stone sieve, and water ran off underneath the surface rather than on top.

I slowed my furious get-there speed and asked my wife and children to keep a sharp lookout for sinks, particularly those in which ledges of rock appeared. In no time we spotted one, not two hundred yards to the right. Nothing would do but that we should all pile out, crawl through the barbed-wire fence and have a look. My eleven-year-old, Rachel, was delayed a little en route while she stopped to examine a horned toad and admire cactus flowers. But she was up with us when we reached the edge of the sink. It wasn't a deep affair. Standing in the bottom of it, we could just see the top of our old car on the highway. Nevertheless there was a small hole at the base of the ledge of pink rock.

Seventeen-year-old Michael scratched professionally at the rock with his fingernail. "It's gypsum," he announced, and he was right.

There *had* to be a cave here. But the hole in the ledge was so tiny and so clogged with broken rock that it would be a day's work to dig our way in, and we lacked the tools and the time for such a large-scale operation. More than a little disappointed, we shuffled along the ledge, which jutted out at one point. Mike was in the lead. Suddenly he gave an excited shout: "Hey, Dad! Another hole!" There at his feet was a straight drop-off—an entrance to the cave.

The brilliant sunlight revealed easy handholds in the pink gypsum, and at the bottom of the shaft lay a mud bank which sloped off into darkness. Mud under an almost desert plain!

Mike ran back for spelunking gear—work shoes, carbide lamps and a length of rope that we always carry in the car. Then my wife and Rachel stood watch in the burning dry air at the entrance while

Mike and I roped down onto the slippery, incredibly sticky mud bank. A very few steps took us into total darkness, for the passage turned once, then again, shutting off any rays of sunlight. The muddy floor in the tortuous passage continued to slope, and its snakelike turns made it impossible for our carbide lamps to give us more than three or four feet of advance notice that there was a drop-off ahead—if indeed there was. I was glad for the rope around me which Mike, with feet braced against corrugations in the passage wall, belayed from above and behind me.

Before long the perpendicular cave walls took care of any remaining worry I had about tobogganing off into space. They drew closer and closer together and held me firmly wedged. Mike could go only a bit farther than I. It was frustrating to know that a smaller person or someone more adept at the spelunker's trick of angleworming might have gone on into an area where this drainage channel linked up with others into what must be a large interconnecting system. The best we could do was back up, explore a side channel that also grew too tight for us, and then emerge muddy and blinking and happy into the hundred-degree heat of the New Mexico afternoon.

Once outside, there was time to pause and wonder. At our first look in a small depression in this barren land, we had found a cave! We hadn't seen half a hundred cattle grazing in the last twenty miles. We hadn't seen a tree or a single human habitation, but the map showed the town of Mesa ahead of us about four miles. After changing our muddy clothes, we drove on. Mesa proved to be a filling station and snack bar all in one building. That was the town. The proprietor, an ex-cowboy, was more than a little interested in my discovery. Neither he nor any cowpoke of his acquaintance had ever noticed my cave in twenty years of range riding. But he did know of other caves nearby—lots of them. He had been in more than a dozen and had been amazed by the beautiful formations he saw. Some of the caves were large, and he offered to take us to the nearest one, into which we could walk and then walk on for more than an hour before reaching what seemed to be the end. In some of its side channels friends of his had got lost. And outlaw treasure, he *knew*, had been hidden in one of the caverns of the neighborhood. (He could have been right, too. Billy the Kid was only one of the "bad men" who roamed this particular country in the early days.) We made a date to come back and let him guide us.

Here was proof that an amateur with a little knowledge of geology can find a cave even when he isn't looking for one, and that talk with old-timers can lead to further caves not yet in the record books. (As a matter of practical advice, I should like to suggest that beginners should not wander into gypsum caves as I did, because gypsum can be very brittle, making footholds, handholds and even cave ceilings unsound.)

Not all caverns lie under a landscape that is typically karst in nature. New Mexico's Carlsbad, for example, does not betray its existence by karst features in the surface of the land above.

Fortunately there are other geologic clues to caves. Maps that show in some detail where beds of limestone, dolomite, marble or gypsum lie are a great help. Topographic maps that reveal the drainage pattern of an area can give important clues. Where water seeps or flows out of limestone formations there must be caves in the background. Two of the most famous explorers of Grand Canyon, the Kolb brothers, located many caverns in the area by the simple process of looking for springs and waterfalls that emerge high up on the steep canyon walls. (Although the method is simple, its application is incredibly difficult in the Grand Canyon, which seems to explorers to be nature's supreme effort at keeping man from getting where he wants to go.)

With more than just a smattering of geological knowledge, a cave-hunter can set out in cold blood, using more refined clues. A scientist looking at the dip of limestone beds, or at the known pattern of water drainage, and relying not at all on local legend, can say, "There simply has to be a cave at X spot on the map." Such was the story behind the discovery of Skyline Caverns near Front Royal in Virginia. Officials of this commercial cavern report:

. . . Mr. Walter Amos of Winchester, a caverns geologist, was sure there lay a great cavern somewhere in the vicinity of Front Royal, Virginia, due to the odd lay of the terrain along the foothills of the Skyline Drive. He and his party of men started exploring every small opening in the jagged limestone ledges that dotted the area. They had noticed that surface streams were disappearing into the side of the mountain, and after much searching could not find any springs or small streams where the water was escaping. They knew then it was emptying into some underground river or streams.

After searching for six months and seventeen days, the party broke through a small opening from which cool air was escaping and stood in a room that was just the beginning of one of the most beautiful caverns in the world. They explored all that day with electric lamps, and found that they were not retracing one step. . . .

Kooken Cave in Pennsylvania was discovered in this same way. A geologist looked over Robert Kooken's farm and said there had to be underground chambers beneath. It was on the strength of this scientific statement that miners were put to work digging, and they found the cave. Similar scientific deduction produced really startling results in Pennsylvania not long ago. William Devitt III studied available data and predicted that there must be caves in a certain area. Then, with a team of assistants who followed his directions, he found thirty-four in two days.

One of the most surprising scientific ways of locating a cavity under the earth calls for getting far above the earth in an airplane. From that vantage point, not only sinkholes but also ridges, which are often the dwelling places of caverns, can be seen, together with the whole drainage pattern. And anyone who has a fortune to spend —or who is trained as a geologist, chemist *and* physicist—might really make a thing out of prospecting for caves with the aid of electricity. The equipment consists of metal probes that can be thrust into the earth, wire to connect the probes, a battery and a sensitive galvanometer. An electric current sent into the earth from the battery is conducted through the rock, and the nature of the rock can be roughly determined by its resistance, which is indicated by the galvanometer. Current passes more readily through rock than through air. Thus the existence of air—that is, a cavern—may be detected. Its location may be pin-pointed if the probes are shifted around over a wide area. This may take a good deal of time, and the bill presented by the geophysicist may amount to $5,000 a month.

But when all is said and done, shanks' mare, plus a sharp eye and an alert ear, plus persistence and luck, are the most practical equipment. Happy caving!

CHAPTER SIXTEEN

"Stygian Caves Forlorn"

After the observant eye of a pioneer had found a cave in the old days, what could have been more natural than the wish to show it off to his family? Such was the feeling of a man by the name of Baker in Madison County, Kentucky, about the year 1800. He came home one day with news for his wife and three children. He had gone into a hole in the ground and had seen marvels there. Nothing would do but that the whole Baker family should go and have a look together. The expedition was pleasant enough for a while, and the wonders they beheld drew them farther and farther underground. Then suddenly Baker came to the terrifying realization that he was lost. Look as he would, he could find no way out. As time went on, fear grew to frenzy. His primitive light failed, and the family was not only lost, but lost in darkness. Father, mother and children clung together in terror and helplessness. No one knew where they had gone, nor would anyone even suspect where to look. Forty-eight long hours passed before they managed literally to feel their way out.

The similar and not altogether fictional ordeal of Tom Sawyer and Becky Thatcher is known to millions throughout the world. The cave near Hannibal, Missouri, in which they endured perfectly credible suffering from hunger and terror is a very real place, now commercialized as the Mark Twain Cave. There is no doubt that the young people of Hannibal—Mark Twain among them—did explore its intricate network by candlelight—and no cave-master stood at the entrance counting kids to make sure that all got out safely. It has taken a long time for safety procedures to become an established part of caving.

Aggressive as the early guides at Mammoth Cave were, their courage outran their caution and they often explored alone. Once while Matt Bransford was off poking into the unknown, his crude lantern burned out. Although he was experienced and bold, he suddenly grew panic-stricken. Then gradually he pulled himself together and began the slow process of crawling and feeling. Only after many hours did he reach a well-traveled route that he "recognized."

Light failure also plagued a now-famous pair of lovers who went on an expedition to Penn's Cave just before Christmas in the year 1848, and whose story is told in Henry W. Shoemaker's book about the cave. Romantic the couple may have been, but they showed singular good sense when their last match failed to light a new pitch-pine torch and left them helpless in a place they did not know. After some groping about in an effort to escape, they reasoned that the horses they had left outside would certainly be noticed and rescuers would come in. This logic proved correct, but it was Christmas time, and passers-by at the mouth of the cave were few. The young man and woman had to wait three full days in the chilly cave before a farmer saw the horses and guessed that somebody underground must be just as hungry as the animals obviously were.

It is almost impossible to imagine the emotion of people lost without lights in caves, when no one knows their whereabouts. The feelings are bad enough, cavers report, when they find themselves lightless in caverns with which they are familiar and when a rescue party will know where to look for them. A group of spelunkers, each of whom knew the need for three sources of light, went into the vast Nickajack Cave in 1946. Actually the party had a gasoline lantern in addition to the usual carbide lamps, flashlights and candles. First the lantern petered out and was abandoned. Then, after the spelunkers had labored through a 170-foot crawlway with a ceiling only about 12 inches high, all sat down to rest and refill their carbide lamps. But where was the large can of carbide they had had when they entered the cave? Every member of the party thought some other member had assumed responsibility for lugging it along. The fact was, the can had been left several "cave miles" away, near the entrance. The men then fell back on their personal supplies of extra carbide. One by one, most of them realized that they had forgotten to fill the little containers they carried in their pockets. A few even confessed they had expected to borrow from others. However, there was enough for a general re-fill, and the explorers pushed on deeper into the cave, since they all had flashlights and candles.

At the end of the journey inward, the carbide lamps guttered out one after another, and flashlights came into play. But all of these had seen heavy use, it appeared, and nobody had thought to bring extra batteries. On the return trip, one spelunker, then another, searched his pockets for candles as the flashlights failed. Stubs of candles there were. But the group had been doing heavy caving, and every man of them had neglected to replenish his candle supply. With only a flickering flame or two left, in stubs so short that they almost roasted their bearers' fingers, the party reached the entrance. To their credit, it must be reported, these cavers sent to the NSS *Bulletin* an anonymous cautionary account of all the sins they had committed. It was one thing for them to make fun of themselves after the event, but quite another to live through the experience of coming closer and closer to the point at which the darkness of a very large cave might close in completely.

Troubles with lights only begin the list of narrow escapes—and worse—in caves. A flood, following a sudden rain, is an ever present danger in some caverns. Once while Charles E. Mohr was studying the little-known and extraordinary animal life in Texas caves, he and his partner began to explore along an underground stream whose clear water held the promise of good collecting. The two scientists were wading up to their middles in the water through a passage whose smooth walls showed the result of long and powerful carving action by the stream, when suddenly a persistent, low noise pushed itself into their consciousness. Only one thought came to their minds—a flash flood. The sound drew closer, grew to a roar, and the two men expected that at any moment a wall of water would rush around a bend in the passage. Instead, there came a mass of flying bats, the whir of whose multitudinous wings was magnified by the cavern echoes. The ordeal of fear was there, but fortunately on this occasion the danger was not.

But then Texas is a place where the unusual is routine. Robert Hudson, one of two young men who discovered forty new Texas caves in a twenty-seven-day period, also has the distinction of exploring Kiser Cave, mentioned earlier in this book, which pours out carbon dioxide gas. He and two other spelunkers on duty as aviation cadets attempted to investigate this forbidding cavern with the aid of Air Force oxygen masks and tanks. The three men soon encountered crawlways and tight passages that were difficult to negotiate with their cumbersome gear, but there could be no thought of abandoning the equipment because they would suffocate in the gas that filled the cave. A ghastly sensation that they were trapped oppressed them, and the anxiety of claustrophobia became a new burden beyond the physical.

Then, Hudson reports, "Just before half of the oxygen was gone, I noticed the first symptoms of hypoxia, or oxygen starvation. In hypoxia, the fingernails become blue, peripheral vision fades, and gradually the eyesight is lost completely. Finally complete unconsciousness results, and then death. The first sign of hypoxia I noticed was gun-barrel vision. This is the effect of the fading of the peripheral vision, or the nerves that enable one to see objects and movement off to one side. I could see only when I looked directly at an object, and then there were big white spots just as though I had looked into a bright light and then tried to look into a dark room."

Now time was an enemy. The men had to get out. One of Hudson's companions started to crawl back toward fresh air. But the other refused to leave. Even with his own mind befogged, Hudson knew that his friend was "drunk" with hypoxia and did not know what he was doing. The man insisted on going ahead to see where the next passage led.

"I told him," Hudson says, "he had hypoxia and that if he did not come out, we would have a heck of a time getting his body out. That seemed to sober him up somewhat, and he turned around in the crawlway and started to crawl toward me."

With hardly a whiff of oxygen left in their tanks, the three men made it, into the breathable air of the outside world, all very weak, all suffering from terrific headaches.

Hudson is an experienced and careful caver. The three men in the party had been trained in the use of an artificial supply of oxygen. But these combined skills were not enough to lick Kiser Cave. And even though knowledge was gained on the first expedition, the cave is still likely to be an ordeal to those who finally penetrate to the mysterious source of the carbon dioxide gas.

Fortunately most cave air contains adequate oxygen, and spe-

lunkers need not carry in their own supply. But cave divers exploring underground waters do depend on the little tanks that they
carry on their backs. Jon Lindbergh, working as a diver with a party
from the Western Speleological Institute, had terrifying moments
in Bower Cave near Yosemite National Park. It was not his Aqua-
lung, however, that went bad. Young Lindbergh had volunteered to
swim under water for an unknown distance in the hope of finding
out whether cavern chambers lay beyond what seemed to be a
possible entrance. Wearing a frogman's rubber suit, he probed
around under water on two successive days, peering through his
goggles for signs of passages that might lead somewhere. On the
third day, something suddenly happened to the safety line which
connected him to his companions far behind him and, of course,
above water. Lindbergh could not swim ahead, nor could he tell
why he was stuck. Luckily quick action on the part of his support
crew freed the line and ended his brief but intense moments of
suspense and fear.

Because the air in all commercial caves is perfectly safe, no ventilation arrangements are necessary. However, one commercial cave
has installed a huge fan, and a horrifying story lies behind this really
unnecessary precaution.

Early one morning a number of years ago, two guides at Howe
Caverns descended in the elevator to do some work before the day's
tourist parties began to enter. After an hour had passed, the head
guide, Mr. Van Otten, noticed that the two men had not reappeared.
He wondered why, and went down in the elevator to have a look.
On the way a mysterious fit of coughing came over him. At the
bottom he opened the elevator door and saw ahead of him, writhing
on the floor, one of the missing guides who was almost literally
coughing his lungs out. Van Otten, now gasping terribly himself, ran
forward to look for the other man. Van Otten was only half-conscious
when he came upon the second man, who seemed dead. Completely
unaware of what he was doing and how he did it, Van Otten somehow struggled back to the elevator and leaned on the handle to
start it up. Time and again he lost his grip on the handle and the
car stopped, but at last he reached the surface and was rushed to a
hospital, from which he did not emerge for a very long time. He

survived, but the other two guides did not. All were victims of a poison gas that had mysteriously filled the beautiful cavern.

Investigation soon showed that the origin of the gas was a curious accident that had happened as part of normal quarrying operations conducted near the distant, uncommercialized part of Howe Caverns. There, as was their custom, quarrymen had drilled the day before to prepare for blasting, which was always done at night when the cavern was empty of tourists. They had dropped sticks of dynamite down a drill-hole, but when they tried to tamp the sticks into place, they discovered a very odd thing—the dynamite had disappeared. The hole, they concluded, had no bottom, and the dynamite had fallen through into some underground passageway. The quarrymen thought they knew what to do in a case like this. They stuffed cotton into the hole, put dynamite above it, and in due course exploded the charge. But they had not calculated on what might happen later. The explosion blew the cotton wad down into the cavern chamber below—and the cotton, which had caught fire, in turn ignited the dynamite sticks. Dynamite, when burned rather than exploded, gives off deadly poisonous fumes. It was these fumes which killed two Howe Caverns guides and made a lifelong invalid of a third. The horror-stricken management of the caverns was determined that no such accident would ever happen again, and they installed an enormous fan to clear the air of the cave, whether it needed clearing or not.

Accidents do happen in caves—there is no doubt about it. And they have happened to competent rock-climbing spelunkers who take every precaution. For example, in 1953 Carroll Slemaker, one of six NSS members exploring Church Cave in California, suddenly felt a rock roll out from under his foot when he was climbing a heap of breakdown 550 feet below the surface. Slemaker, thrown off balance but still on his feet, stepped downhill. Another rock, following the first one, banged against his leg and broke it. It was all too clear to his companions that he needed a doctor—right where he lay. The bone would have to be set before he could move, and he would have to move himself through a number of crawlways where the use of a stretcher was impossible. For hours Slemaker waited. A doctor who had never been in a cave before proved himself a real hero by conquering the difficult pitches and crawlways that lay between him and his patient. The accident happened at eight o'clock in the evening. At eight-thirty the next morning, the weary doctor, the weary spelunkers and the tortured Slemaker began their climb back to daylight. Only during part of the way were Slemaker's companions able to give him assistance. He had to make the crawlways under his own power, dragging his broken leg. Finally, at four in the afternoon, twenty hours after the accident, he was out and headed for a hospital.

No stupidity was involved here, no lack of careful planning. In fact, all careful plans for cave expeditions take into consideration the chance that there will be mishaps, and there are times when it cannot be far from a spelunker's mind that an underground accident is much worse than an accident topside. Such thoughts must have occurred to those who conducted the recent week-long exploration in Floyd Collins' Crystal Cave and who had very vivid firsthand knowledge of the ten-inch-high squeeze and the long crawlway that any casualty would have to face. They knew well the joys of exploring. They were masters of all the skills that were needed. They planned well, and no accidents happened. But every member of the party suffered from tension that must have had part of its origin in the knowledge that even a small, slipping rock can mean death or long-drawn-out suffering. They had all passed by the tomb of Floyd Collins in the commercialized part of Crystal Cave, which is not far from Sand Cave where a rock that moved only a few inches had caused Collins' death nearly thirty years before.

The story of Collins' death cannot begin with that rock. He was a phenomenon of his time—a professional cave-hunter. One day in 1917, when he was nearly thirty years old, he discovered the Crystal Cave which now bears his name. Then he promptly availed himself of local custom—he dickered with his father and brothers for half-ownership of commercial rights to the cavern which lay under family land. The Collins men did a lot of hard work to prepare their show place for visitors, but tourists were slow in coming. Crystal Cave in those days was a long way from any main road. The elder Collins and one of Floyd's brothers grew weary of waiting, and they listened with interest when a neighbor offered to buy them out. But Floyd was adamant. He would not sell his share. There must be some way to make the cave a success. Perhaps further exploration would reveal another entrance more conveniently located for tourists.

Floyd probably had this thought in mind when three of his neighbors came to him early in January, 1925, and asked him to explore Sand Cave on the usual share basis. He had already discovered this cave and named it, but he had never gone very far inside. Now he was glad for a good excuse to look it over thoroughly. If Sand Cave and Crystal Cave were—as he halfway suspected—two parts of one great cavern, he would be sitting pretty. And if they weren't, he still might discover something profitable.

Lodging and eating "week about" with the three farmers under whose land Sand Cave might possibly run, Floyd set to work. He entered the cave alone, as usual. He was always secretive about his underground trips. A shrewd instinct told him not to reveal anything until he was sure he had his legal interest well protected. After he entered any cave, Floyd was likely to stay a long time if he found promising leads. His three new partners were unaware of this habit and had to learn by experience that he liked to be let alone to work on any kind of schedule that suited him. Once, when he had been in Sand Cave for thirty hours, they grew worried and went in after him. Floyd was perfectly all right and very much excited because he had discovered a possible route into a room he felt sure was of considerable size. After that, when he didn't come back on time for supper, his partners put their minds at rest.

Day after day Floyd lighted a kerosene lantern and entered the cave, wearing his customary hobnailed boots, overalls, and an old blue denim jacket. He had begun the very slow work of enlarging a long crawlway which he hoped would lead to a major discovery. For this a crowbar was his main tool.

By January 29, the job was almost finished. He needed only to blast out the end of the passage into the big room beyond, which he could dimly see and sense. Using dynamite would be risky, he knew. The roof of the crawlway was a jumble of loose rock and gravel, but he was determined to go ahead. He laid his fuse out behind him as he withdrew, then lit it and left the cave.

On the morning of January 30 he went in to clear away the debris. The dynamite had done its work and, equally important, it had not brought the unstable roof of the crawlway tumbling down. Now began the tedious process of pushing or dragging shattered stone, piece by piece, out of the long crawlway, which was still only just high enough and wide enough for his body to squeeze through. At last he had most of the debris cleaned up. One rock, he noticed, seemed dangerously poised in the low roof, probably loosened by the blast. There would be time enough later to remove it. Now he merely avoided touching it and wriggled over sharp bits of freshly broken stone to see what lay beyond. The room he expected to find was there.

He lifted his lantern and peered. A huge chamber! More than that, it was beautiful. A rich display of speleothems sparkled in all directions as far as the dim light of his lantern could pierce the blackness. Collins knew enough about caves to realize that a room like this quite likely led to others. Sand Cave might really be worth something.

It would do no harm to let his partners know now that their prospects were good—very good. He had a binding contract with them. Excitedly he started to crawl back through the low, tight passage, and in his excitement he forgot the poised rock he had been so careful about on his trip in. A boot touched the rock after his body had passed under it. Suddenly it fell, pinioning his left leg over his right leg so that he could not move. One arm was caught under him in such a position that he could not use it. With his free hand he reached his crowbar, but there was no space in which to maneuver it and dislodge the not very big stone that held him prisoner.

As Collins rested, he calculated the time—early afternoon. The farmer with whom he was boarding this week would probably not start to worry until the next day because of Collins' own fierce insistence that he knew what he was doing in caves and that people shouldn't crawl in after him to see if he was all right. He realized he was going to have a long, cold wait before help came, and an exceedingly painful one. His leg didn't seem broken, but he couldn't move either it or his body to ease himself, and he'd taken off his jacket when he started to work in the crawlway. The kerosene lantern, which he had been thrusting ahead of him as he inched along, would soon burn out. In the darkness there would be still another torture—seepage water, drop by slow drop, kept falling on his tense face.

The farmer obeyed Collins' instructions and did not come to look for him when he failed to show up for supper. He did not even start searching when Collins was still absent at breakfast. But as Saturday, January 31, wore on, he and one of the other partners decided it was time to go into the cave and see if everything was all right.

Near the entrance they noticed the blue jacket. That meant Collins was still inside and hadn't gone off somewhere without leaving word. The son of one of the two farmers worked up courage enough to squirm into the crawlway. There the helpless Collins and the almost equally helpless rescuer faced each other in the rough stone tube.

A light and a human voice at last! After more than twenty-four hours that would have driven most men mad, Collins bluntly told what had happened and even reported that Sand Cave might amount to something. Now, how about getting him out of here?

The young farmer boy left his light and, sweating with fear, wriggled out feet first. He had no idea what to do, nor had his father. But at least they could notify the Collins family, so they sent word the fastest way possible—by a rider on a mule. Only one of Floyd's brothers was at home. He came immediately. The other took the first train from Louisville when word reached him.

The news passed quickly from farm to farm, then out over telegraph wires, that Floyd Collins was trapped alive in Sand Cave. Neighbors arrived and very soon after them, reporters. The crowd at the cave entrance grew rapidly—and kept growing. First there was only a handful, including Floyd's aging parents; then dozens, then hundreds—and finally thousands. People came to help or to stare, and many of them began to drink moonshine. At the mouth of Sand Cave a wild carnival was developing.

Among those who turned up was the particular neighbor who not long ago had tried unsuccessfully to buy Floyd's half-interest in Crystal Cave. As many others had been doing, he crawled in, but when he came back out he began issuing orders. Floyd, he said, wanted him to conduct the rescue. No one else was to enter the cave. Apparently the man labored long and hard in the crawlway in some kind of effort to free Floyd's foot, but there were ugly mutterings that here was one fellow who would rather see Floyd dead than alive. Still, who could prove that the solitary rescuer wasn't doing his level best? At any rate, the man's physical powers could last only so long. He finally joined Floyd's brothers and others who had so exhausted themselves in the struggle against unyielding stone that they could not re-enter the crawlway.

Reporters and photographers were part of the ever-growing crowd outside the cave. Before all visitors were excluded, the sufficiently hardy among the newspaper men crawled in to interview the trapped explorer and then rushed out to file sensational stories. The press and radio throughout the nation—and the world—carried frequent bulletins about the mounting tragedy in Sand Cave.

One among the newspapermen had done much more than scramble in for a story, then scramble out. He was a very young and very small cub reporter for the Louisville *Courier-Journal*, William Burke ("Skeets") Miller. Skeets made many trips back and forth, bringing hot coffee and hot soup to the chilly, hungry, desperate man in the crawlway. He dragged in electric wire and put a light on Collins' chest where it would warm him a little, while it held back the darkness.

Skeets even tried to use some of the jacks that had been sent to the scene with the thought that the right kind of pressure on the rock that held Collins down would do the trick of releasing him. The jacks proved useless. Skeets fumed and had to withdraw, exhausted.

Meanwhile nobody else did anything practical to save Floyd Collins. To be sure, there were ideas about what should be done. Schemes were almost as numerous as the rumors that kept sweeping over the unruly crowd outside the cave. Someone made a harness to fix around Floyd's shoulders. Perhaps rescuers pulling on the harness could yank him loose—even it it meant breaking and maiming his pinioned foot. Men volunteered for the job, among them one of Floyd's brothers, who soon collapsed because he could not endure the torture he was inflicting. Probably no team of men could have succeeded in exerting the kind of pull in this grim tug of war that would have made flesh and bone give way.

Someone else proposed that a doctor enter the crawlway and amputate Floyd's leg. But no doctor could have got himself and his instruments in position to do the grisly chore.

Into this nightmare of disorder and aimlessness came a quiet man, Henry Carmichael, who ran an asphalt company, and with him a crew of his workmen. Supported by the National Guard, Carmichael took charge of the rescue efforts. By now more of the roof of the crawlway had caved in. It was impossible to reach Floyd, although his low moans could still be heard. Carmichael reasoned that his men would have to dig a shaft down from the surface, but before digging could begin, an accurate survey had to be made. Precious time was lost in calculating the exact spot for the shaft. Meanwhile more volunteer laborers assembled. Among them were experienced miners who, because of their skill and persistence, were an inspiration to the others. College athletes appeared, including a whole football team, and they swung picks and shovels with a will. So did a young college president.

But Floyd Collins could not endure his agonizing imprisonment forever. Exactly two weeks after he was trapped—that is, on February 13—his moans were heard for the last time by a miner who went into the crawlway to tap the rock so that the crew digging in the shaft could tell how close they were to their objective. It was known to the few who could get near him that he had been delirious for days, but as long as he breathed, the rescuers had hope. Now, amid rubble that continually caved in upon them as they dug, the crew had to work on, knowing they would find only a body instead of a man. Three days after his death they reached Floyd Collins.

The crowds disappeared, and with them the hot-dog vendors they had attracted. Cars no longer lined up bumper to bumper for miles on the road to the cave. The hawker who had appeared with "Sand Cave" printed on balloons vanished into whatever kind of place such people come from. Aviators who had been holding their little biplanes in readiness to rush film to distant newspapers went elsewhere looking for work—among them, young Charles Lindbergh whose son Jon later on became a cave-diver.

The tragic ordeal of Floyd Collins was over. From the vantage point of today's accumulated experience, it is possible to say that his suffering and death were unnecessary and avoidable. If he had had companions when he went caving, they might have been able to free him at once from the fallen rock. If he had given his host a deadline after which search for him should begin, he might have been saved. If scientific rescue operations had been conducted in the crawlway, and if no time had been wasted in sinking the shaft, Floyd Collins might have lived to witness the scientific exploration of the cave system about which he knew so much.

As Roger W. Brucker has been careful to add in his account of Collins' death contained in the recently published *Celebrated American Caves*, the NSS today maintains trained rescue groups to prevent a repetition of what happened in Sand Cave. The knowledge of how to avoid or to handle efficiently the accidents which are inherent in caving, as in any sport, has enormously increased.

CHAPTER SEVENTEEN

Etiquette in the Underworld, and Other Keys to Survival

The know-how of caving has advanced a good deal since the day less than seventy-five years ago when lady spelunkers entered caverns wearing veils to keep bats out of their hair. Cavers today certainly haven't learned all there is to know about how to deport themselves underground, but their collective wisdom on the subject is well worth passing along.

If you plan to make a visit to a wild cave (except in certain portions of the West where the word "trespass" has not yet entered the lexicon), begin with an act of common courtesy. Get permission in advance from the owner of the property, and then behave like a good guest. There is an almost irresistible impulse to feel that *you* own a cave you have explored—and that this gives you the right to make yourself at home in its vicinity. Rid yourself of this pleasant illusion at once.

Very often caves lie under farms. To reach an entrance you may have to cross some fields and open some gates—in which case, close the gates behind you. If you don't, cattle may trample a cornfield or pigs may get into a garden patch. But when you find a gate open, don't succumb to a sudden urge to do the farmer a good turn. Leave it as it is. The owner has probably fixed it that way so his cows can come back to the barn at milking time, and he won't thank you if he has to hike because of your helpfulness. Park your car where he asks you to park it, so that it will be out of his way. If your trip calls for camping or outdoor picnicking, leave the area neat. That means burying every bit of litter—or possibly taking your garbage home with you. The owner who needs to clean up after you, or to mend fences, will have less reason to be cordial toward later spelunking parties. He is certain to be furious with the whole kit and caboodle of cavers if he finds anywhere on the landscape little telltale gray heaps of spent carbide that have been emptied from lamps. Cattle aren't the brightest critters in the world, and they go for the stuff, which isn't proper cow-food. So dig a hole, dump in your carbide and cover it up. Also, after you have made sure that your host has no objection to a campfire, be careful to put yours out. Better still, use a gasoline stove, which does not damage the farmer's pasture.

For the cave-owner's peace of mind, and for your own safety, tell him—or someone outside—that you are going into the cave and that you expect to be back by a certain hour. *This is an absolute must.* (In stating the hour you expect to leave the cave, give yourself plenty of time. Otherwise a rescue party may come after you when it's totally unnecessary, and the rescuers will be justifiably peeved.) After you get back from a trip, report.

Never enter a cave alone. This is another must, and it goes not only for novices but for the most experienced spelunkers. A party of four is better than a party of three, and three are a minimum because, if one person is injured or trapped, he should have company while help is being sought.

From the moment you enter a cave, there are certain standard procedures. The first is to look where you are going, and the second is to look where you have just been. In other words, make mental notes of landmarks from both fore and aft, as a precaution against getting lost. Shadows play strange tricks on you. A flowstone formation can be like Hamlet's cloud—it may resemble a camel as you come in, look like a weasel when you're halfway around it,

> Or like a whale?
> Very like a whale—

after you have passed by. Also, since a cave roof has distinguishing features that can be used as landmarks, it is well to look up from time to time.

In addition to observing carefully the features of the underground landscape, you can leave for yourself some simple clues pointing toward the all-important exit. Wherever passages turn off from the one you are following, make some kind of arrow mark, with the tip of the arrow pointing *back* toward the outer world. Make the arrow, if humanly possible, in some way that will not permanently deface the cave. Draw it in a mud bank, for example, or with chalk if the cave wall is dry. Or outline it on the floor with small loose stones. Or pile up a small cairn of stones with the top one arranged as a pointer. The flame of your carbide lamp will leave a black smudge if you hold it close to a wall, and you can draw an arrow with it, but don't resort to this unless you have to. A smudged-up cave is not attractive. Never point arrows toward fascinating speleothems or, egotistically, in the direction in which you may be found, way in yonder. You may get yourself, or some later spelunker, lost unless you observe the underground rule of the road which experienced cavers always abide by—point all arrows toward the exit.

You can also leave markers along your route in the form of burning candles or drippings from a candle. If you are lucky enough to have a map of the cave, consult it. A compass will also help you to keep your bearings, provided there are no iron deposits in the surrounding rock. The old device of unrolling string behind you is a great nuisance. One expert makes the point that in a small cave you don't need string, and in a large one you can't carry enough of it. However, little squares of Scotchlite may prove helpful. You leave them one by one in strategic places where they will reflect the light of your lamp. Then you can recover them as you retrace your steps.

If you keep your wits about you, there's no need to get lost in a cave. But there's no need to have auto accidents either, and they do happen. The minute you think you're lost, the first thing to do is *do nothing*. Sit down, keep calm, and reconstruct in your mind the route you have been following. Don't go rapidly off in all directions at once looking for a way out. Probably, with care, you can follow your own tracks—footprints in mud or dust, or scars made by boot-nails on rock. If these clues fail, you can start a careful process of elimination. Be systematic—explore through one opening, then another. If the first leads to nothing that is familiar, withdraw to your starting point, mark the opening to show it has been eliminated, then try the next one to the right, and so on.

Panic is your worst enemy. More than one scared amateur has started to run idiotically. Others, frozen in their tracks, have tried to yell their way out of a cave, or have turned on flashlights in addition to carbide lamps, as if light would magically dissolve rock walls. Aside from providing assorted cuts and bruises, and possibly breaks, frantic running exhausts you. There's no hurry. The cave isn't going any place. You won't starve in a few hours or freeze to death. So, unless you have absolute command of yourself and can make a cool search for your back trail, the best rule is to stay put, right where you are. If you entered with an organized party, your leader will see that you are found. If your whole party is lost, the person outside with whom you left word of your trip will start a search, and sooner or later you'll be located.

Since you don't know how long you'll have to wait, be a miser with your light supply. It can last for a long time if you use it carefully. A new eight-inch plumber's candle alone is good for about eight hours. A carbide lamp will burn for additional hours, depending on your supply of carbide and water, and your flashlight can extend the period of reassurance that comes from having some light.

Whatever you do, avoid wearing yourself out. A rescue party will thank you for staying in good enough condition to walk out of the cave under your own power. Your chances of being a stretcher case are much greater if exhaustion overcomes you—first, because you may literally collapse from weariness, and second, because the accident rate goes up as people approach the limits of their physical endurance.

In view of all the spelunking that goes on in this country, it is amazing how few cavers have been lost underground. Most veterans will admit that at some time or other they have been more than a wee mite puzzled as to their subterranean longitude and latitude. But without exception every member of every *organized* NSS party has found his way back to daylight—and almost always in fairly good shape. The publicized stories about people lost in caves usually deal with rank amateurs who entered alone or broke some other tenet of the safety code.

One of the great sources of trouble is that novices, out of a false sense of pride, attempt to push on beyond their own physical limits or try feats beyond their skills. The wise thing is to practice rock climbing and rope work *before* entering a cave—practice it under the guidance of an expert, and then have an experienced caver with you until you yourself attain this status.

Here are ten of the commandments of caving which good spelunkers observe. A few who didn't have found themselves ostracized from caving society.

Thou shalt not enter a cave alone.

Thou shalt not enter a cave if suffering from assorted ailments that may create burdens for others (heart trouble, epilepsy, etc.).

Thou shalt not enter a cave under the influence of John Barleycorn.

Thou shalt wear a hard hat on thy head—and use thy head at all times.

Thou shalt carry into a cave three sources of light, and matches in a waterproof container.

Thou shalt always leave word outside the cave as to thy whereabouts and expected time of return.

Honor thy leader and obey his instructions.

Thou shalt sit down at once and wait patiently on the spot if thy lights all fail, thus avoiding injury and making a minimum of trouble for rescuers who will surely come.

Thou shalt never jump. Thou shalt walk or crawl or wade or climb.

Thou shalt not kick down rocks on thy fellow cavers, considering their welfare in this as in all other matters.

Freak hazards *can* exist in and around caves, and no set of rules will anticipate all of them. For instance, one man built a fire in the mouth of a guano-filled cave in Texas. That was the last anybody ever saw of him. The fire set off a tremendous explosion in the decomposing, combustible guano, and the cave burned for two years thereafter. Another man allowed a fire to burn inside a small cave that had only one entrance. The fire used up all the oxygen; its builder lost consciousness and fell to his death.

Abandoned mines, in contrast to caves, often have "bad air," and mine tunnels are much more subject to collapse than are caves. Only in a small minority of caves does breakdown (the falling of rocks from the ceiling) take place these days. It is most unusual for a spelunker to be in a cave when a section of the roof falls. But it *can* happen. Several hundred years ago a huge boulder dropped on an Indian who was mining gypsum in Mammoth Cave, and his body was only recently discovered. The paleontologist John Dyas Parker, who is also National Safety Chairman of the NSS, might have had to wait for some future archeologist to exhume him when a big rock fell out of a cave roof without warning and almost buried him and a companion. Actually Parker had arranged in advance to short-change the scientists of the future. He had taken the routine precaution of leaving word outside the cave as to his whereabouts. And when he came out, he promptly posted notice that the cave was unsafe. Some other caves are known to be unsafe, and the local caving clubs, which should always be consulted, will warn you away from them. Most people aren't likely to chase a bear into a cave these days, but in the not too distant past a man in California did. His bones and the bear's were found side by side. (In Alaska where bears still abound spelunkers do enter caves with gun in hand.)

There are also hazards for spelunkers just outside caves. Some blithering idiots camped once at the very foot of a limestone cliff in which lay the cave they wanted to explore. Either they thought that the normal processes of nature would suspend themselves in their honor—or they didn't think at all. A piece of rock above them broke off as a result of frost action, and nearly killed one of the members of the party. Other spelunkers tested fate unnecessarily by building a fire against a limestone ledge in cold weather. The opposing forces of heat and cold split the ledge in a violent explosion. It was only luck that all members of the party were able to return, shamefaced, to suggest that other campers should not do likewise.

One problem in caves has to do with the quirks of human personality. Some individuals just can't stand tight places. They are unhappy sufferers from claustrophobia. Usually they know this and don't go in for spelunking, but sometimes they may not discover that they will go to pieces emotionally in a dark, confined area deep underground until they actually get into one. The symptoms are pallor, excessive perspiration, weakness, trembling, even collapse, and a sure cure is the sight of the sky overhead; but sometimes a spelunker can talk himself out of a spell of jitters; sometimes his companions can bring him around. Experienced cavers are considerate when they see a case of claustrophobia—they know, after all, that even an old salt can get seasick—but they wish they didn't have the trouble of evacuating the victim.

All these mishaps, hazards and safety rules may make it seem that caves are deathtraps, and that cavers take a mystical joy in risking their lives, half-hoping that they may lose them. The fact is that spelunkers love life and have no interest whatsoever in converting America's caverns into catacombs. No NSS member has ever been killed in a cave, and not many have been injured. The casualty rate is probably lower than in other strenuous sports such as football, baseball, skiing or mountaineering. Those accidents which have occurred belong to two main categories: falling objects have hurt people in caves; jumps have produced sprained ankles and broken bones. By far the most hazardous part of caving is the automobile trip to and from a cave entrance, a danger spelunkers share with all Americans. NSS members like to report with wry glee what they call the "most serious" accident that ever befell one of their number. A young lady caver broke her back, they allege, while crawling— not in a corkscrew passage—but into her girdle after an expedition was over!

In addition to the safety code, there is a basic rule of etiquette observed by all good cavers: *Leave everything in a cave exactly as you find it.* Don't litter the place with scraps of paper, burnt-out flashbulbs, leftover lunch or heaps of used carbide. Not only is the carbide unsightly, it may also be harmful to cave life if left where it can be washed down into pools or streams. Don't give way to the feeling that future generations will suffer if they don't find your name scrawled somewhere. Most important, the beauties and curiosities of caves are irreplaceable. One careless or covetous visitor can rob all future visitors of wonders built up over thousands and tens of thousands of years. Vandals have done just that in more caves than it is a pleasure to record. Some underground chambers once lovely are now barren because thoughtless individuals have stripped them. For protection against vandals, cave organizations have actually built gates in some places, and they have agreements with the owners that only parties known to be responsible will be given keys. They have also avoided publicizing many beautiful wild caves, believing that this was the best way to save them for future generations. Honoring this policy, I have given in this book directions to very few wild caves. About these the reader can get full information—and guidance—from cave organizations which are listed in the appendix.

Far from being selfish or sentimental, these conservation measures guarantee the survival of underground recreation areas and natural scientific laboratories as well. When speleology, now a young science, reaches maturity, there will be plenty of interesting caves to study, if the conservation policy is generally observed. If not, such things as gypsum flowers, salamanders, bats and blind fish will go the way of the buffalo. Perhaps the stricture against collecting sounds like a blue law. Actually, carefully planned collection is constantly going on in caves, and novices are invited to take part in it, when they work under scientific direction. A paleontologist may very well need your strong arm on a shovel or your patience with a sieve. Biologists often use volunteer help in bat-banding or in gathering laboratory specimens, and they welcome all observations made of the habits of living creatures. If they are satisfied that you know what you are doing, they will prescribe collecting equipment. Archeologists are delighted to receive reports of new evidence of early man's occupancy of caves. They will let you dig under their direction and will even name important finds after you. Remember that archeologists want the evidence left *in situ*. By disturbing a site even a little, you can make gobbledygook of the story that lies waiting to be revealed.

One kind of collecting in caves is ardently encouraged. Take away anything you like—on film. You and others will be the richer for it, and the cave will be no poorer.

CHAPTER EIGHTEEN

"Spelunk Junk"

Like all pioneers, spelunkers on the underground frontier have shown remarkable ingenuity. Old-time trappers and mountain men borrowed what they could use of Indian crafts and tools, added a few items from the white man's world of metal and machinery, then proceeded to innovate with the materials at hand. Spelunkers have had to do the same. If trading posts were few and far between for Daniel Boone or Jim Bridger, they are even scarcer for the caving fraternity. None at all can be found in caves, of course, and only two supply houses in the entire United States cater specially to spelunking needs. Cavers can—and do—rummage through sporting goods shops and army surplus outlets for the gadgets of their avocation, and many a home workshop has produced inventions for comfort, safety or efficiency. A gadget invented by the Indians and now sometimes manufactured at home by spelunkers has made it possible for mothers with young babies to go caving. This ingenious device—also useful in supermarkets—is a cradleboard or packboard to which junior is snugly wrapped in an upright position so that he can ride on mother's or father's back. Since he is upright, he can see whatever is to be seen, and a frame over his head protects him from bumps. Our national habit of tinkering, our mechanophile culture, our love of gadgetry, flourish with a special quality among the energetic people who delight in cave-crawling.

Spelunkers have borrowed devices from the older sport of mountaineering and from the still older trades of the miner and the seaman. The result is a costume and a set of tools which, taken all together, are something new under the sun. Modern troglodytes appear to be a shapeless and shabby lot when fully equipped to do battle against the hazards underground. The basic dress is a suit of coveralls that more than likely has a crude leather patch going in a generally southwesterly direction across one buttock, with another patch looking thoroughly misplaced on the opposite shoulder. The coveralls are sure to be a size too big, and their never very slim-looking waist may well be circled by a Huck Finn-ish hunk of rope that appears to be a belt but isn't. Around the knees may be strapped heavy rubber pads—the kind that miners or scrub women use to keep from getting housemaid's knee. Or the coveralls may simply have, patched on over each knee, a pocket into which rubber bath sponges have been stuffed. The headgear is most conspicuous of all, and above the drab costume it stands out in some glaring color. Red and orange are favorites. Most likely it is the narrow-brimmed type of hard hat worn by a miner, but possibly a football helmet has been converted in its owner's workshop to hold the carbide lamp which shines forth above the forehead like a great cyclopean eye. Possibly strips of Scotchlite tape on the hat reflect beams of light in the darkness, revealing the owner's nickname or some pertinent, or impertinent, decoration. A whistle, manufactured for a kid or a cop, may be secured by a lanyard around the neck and tucked inside the clothing so that it won't snag on anything and choke the wearer. Perhaps a shiny lump of what looks like snarled wire hangs from the rope around the waist. This is no tangle at all, but a remarkably efficient thirty-foot ladder that weighs only two pounds—and it may be homemade. A cigar-shaped object in a lady caver's breast pocket is no sign she imitates Amy Lowell. It is a first-aid kit, so shaped to take up the minimum space in her voluminous costume. A hip pocket may bulge a little with what seems to be a tobacco can—a water-tight container for carbide. And somewhere about a caver's person is sure to be a canteen for water.

Thoroughly pacific-looking cavers often carry ammunition cases slung over their shoulders. The only shots they are going to make are photographic. The cases are water-tight and lined with sponge rubber. Into them go delicate cameras and flashbulb equipment. A voice-powered telephone set, or a small rubber bundle that can be inflated into a boat may be included in the equipment. And somebody is sure to have a lot of strange-looking hardware—for use in rock climbing—that jangles around his waist.

On the ground nearby may sit a peculiar bullet-shaped metal

object with a rope attached to a ring at the small end. This is a Gurnee can, invented as we have seen by cavers for cavers, who had to have some way to snake extra supplies through tight places and around corners where anything not cone-shaped would jam.

All of this leads to the question: What sort of equipment *should* a spelunker have before going into a cave? The real answer is: It depends. One thing is sure—no spelunker can ever face an absolutely unknown cave with all the equipment he or she may need. A corps of porters couldn't carry it all. And even if they tried, they couldn't manage the keyholes, fat man's miseries, jumping-off places, and "bottomless" pits they might encounter. The fact is, a beginner should enter his first cave in the company of someone who knows the place, and therefore knows what equipment should be brought along. But it is wise in any case to have the following minimum gear:

1. *Footwear*. Good heavy work shoes or low-topped hiking boots are musts. The shoes should be large enough to accommodate two pairs of socks—one heavy pair and one light pair. Many spelunkers wear shoes with heavy composition soles. Others prefer cleated soles made of rubber or composition material. Still others choose to drive special climbing-nails into leather soles. Shoes with either cleats or nails are excellent for rock climbing underground, but they can be a great nuisance in certain wet caves where the uneven soles act as magnets to heavy loads of mud.

This, at least, is certain: except for easy trips where conditions are known in advance to be suitable, you should not wear oxfords or smooth-soled sneakers. Rubber soles and plain leather soles slip on wet rock, and they are better skids than brakes on steep mud banks. Basketball shoes are all right for a dry cave. But low shoes of any kind may stick in mud and stay there, leaving the spelunker at least temporarily barefoot. Moreover, low shoes give no support to ankles where the footing is uneven—as it usually is in wild caves. Shoes that come up over the ankles have prevented many a sprain.

High-top leather boots, however, are not necessary. Most people find them a nuisance. They are heavy and they may cramp the leg muscles.

2. *Socks*. Hikers' experience aboveground is a good guide to spelunkers underground. Two pairs of heavy athletic or woolen socks—with no holes or darns—are ideal, provided, of course, the

shoes are large enough. Otherwise wear a light pair under a heavy pair. Avoid very thin socks and short socks.

3. *Underclothes.* Most caves are cool or even chilly, and a great many are very humid. You may have to crawl in mud; you may have to wade; you may even have to swim, or you may get doused by a waterfall. Spelunkers do a lot of exercise, and if they are prone to sweat a great deal, a cave is a place where they will break all records. You can get wet, very wet, in a cave, and sometimes you have to make long waits while you're soaked. Choose your underwear with these facts in mind. Swimmers and athletes who sweat a lot usually wear wool; likewise some spelunkers put on long woolen undies to meet the conditions they face. But many wear just any old underwear that is comfortable. Only experience will tell you what you need.

4. *Outer garments.* Coveralls are ideal, but any tough clothes that are expendable will do. Spelunkers' garments take a terrific beating, so there can't be any thought of natty-looking outfits underground. More than likely a caver will end a day's work with assorted frays, rips and tears in whatever he has on, and will be well smeared with mud in addition. Coveralls are made to take rough treatment, and if they are bought large enough, they will not bind or constrict the wearer. However, if they fit too loosely they will bunch up and snag. A one-piece garment can't be caught on as many projections as can separate trousers and jacket. In going through a crawlway, nobody likes to have a clawlike finger of rock grab his pants and hold them firmly while he proceeds without them. In backing out of a tight place, it's a nuisance to have your jacket pulled up around your ears, and this can be downright dangerous when you are descending a steep rock face.

Many cavers like to wear wool shirts under their coveralls. Others wear sweaters or sweatshirts; some wear only T-shirts. *De gustibus non est disputandum*, but it must be remembered that caves are cool.

Here is a pointer if you *don't* wear coveralls. Try to avoid garments with zippers. They can be ornery gadgets under the best of conditions, but it takes only a little cave mud to make them impossible.

Whatever you wear, it is useful to have garments that can be tightened around the ankles and wrists to keep out sand and mud. Loose cuffs may also catch on projections and cause falls.

One more thing: If you are going to carry small objects in coverall pockets, see that each pocket is equipped with at least one button and buttonhole to keep the stuff from falling out—which it assuredly will do if it gets a chance. *Don't* use safety pins as fasteners. You will be pressing against the pins time and time again. They may snap open and give you a painful poke when you least need one.

5. *Gloves.* Ordinary cotton work gloves can be a great comfort and even a help. You can remove them if bare hands or clean hands are needed. A photographer gets into real trouble when he tries to use his camera with muddy fingers. Wool gloves are often preferred in wet caves.

6. *Headgear.* Wear a brimless hard hat that is rigged to carry a carbide lamp. Or rig a football helmet to hold a lamp. In any case, wear something stiff to protect your head from painful bangs against stalactites and low ceilings, from rocks that may be kicked down by spelunkers above you, or flashlights that may be dropped— or even cameras. See that the hat has a strap which passes under your chin. It's no good to lean forward—and see your hat, with lamp, drop down into space. The best kind of strap is one that has a snap-fastening under the chin. Should your hard hat get stuck in a tight place, you can choke yourself if you don't have a strap that can be opened easily.

On many organized caving trips, hard hats are mandatory equipment. Expedition leaders are not just humanitarian—casualties can cause them a lot of trouble.

7. *Light.* Every caver has to carry all the light he or she will be likely to need. Each individual must be self-sufficient. But what kind of light? First of all, a carbide lamp that can be fitted into the slot on a hard hat. Note that not every style of lamp fits every hat, and the mouth of a cave is no place to discover that you have a hat and lamp not meant for each other.

Extra carbide is a necessity. (One charge—equal to a couple of tablespoonfuls—will last only two or three hours.) Likewise, you must take along water in a container, since the lamp will not run without water and it is quite likely to need recharging at some point where there is no underground spring or stream.

A tiny repair kit for a carbide lamp is also a must. This consists of a spare tip (the little nozzle through which acetylene gas shoots out), a little bundle of wires called a tip cleaner or a tickler, and assorted other parts—all of which can fit into a small plastic vial.

Some cavers attach electric headlights instead of carbide lamps to their hard hats. These give a superior light but are expensive and cumbersome, since they require batteries, and wires passing from the batteries to the lamp. But an ordinary flashlight is another question. Every caver should carry one. A watertight flashlight with an unbreakable plastic lens is best. You should have an extra bulb and batteries. Attach the flashlight to your person with a lanyard—first, because a loose flashlight may slip out of your pocket or your hand and you'll be without a light; more important, you don't want to bean one of your fellow spelunkers if you drop it on him from above.

If you are a bear-cat on efficiency and want to reduce the bulk and weight of your gear (by a few ounces), you can obtain an imported flashlight that operates without batteries. You squeeze a lever which activates a generator in the little contrivance. This is more tiring than it sounds, but as long as you can keep on squeezing, you have light.

Also, a spelunker should carry matches (in a waterproof container) and a candle. Some old hands prefer to cut one large plumber's candle into several inch-long pieces, being careful to fix the wicks so they can be lighted easily. These small sections have two advantages: They stow away easily, and if a spelunker needs to, he can light a section, leave it, and still have some candle for later use.

Three sources of light are a common-sense safety precaution. A carbide lamp can and sometimes does go completely out of commission. It can also be dropped in a careless moment into some place from which it cannot be retrieved. A flashlight is then necessary. But it is a useful supplement to a carbide lamp anyway. You can see many things with its focused beam that you will miss with the more diffuse light that comes from a carbide lamp. And a spelunker without either a lamp or a flashlight is a great burden to himself and to others in his party unless he has a candle to fall back on, and with only a candle he will still be something of a nuisance.

Candles have at least one other use in a cave. The flames of four or five of them will heat water for soup or coffee. There are times when something hot is mighty welcome.

8. *Canteen.* An ordinary army or Boy Scout canteen is a nuisance to carry, but thirst can be worse than a nuisance. Water in caves should always be considered unsafe for drinking unless it has been scientifically tested. (There's no telling what barnyard or outhouse may drain into a rimstone pool that looks crystal clear.) Some cavers carry halozone tablets which, when dropped into a container of water, will purify it in half an hour. Others avoid the inconvenience of a full-sized canteen by carrying a smaller and lighter plastic water container. A spelunker may even carry two of these—one for drinking water and the other to use in filling his carbide lamp. The second may be refilled with impure water and no harm done.

9. *Waterproof containers.* A variety of match-containers are available on the market, as are plastic bottles and boxes that will keep carbide and small articles dry. Army surplus stores sometimes have pocket-sized metal boxes that are reasonably waterproof. You can also protect articles by wrapping them carefully in plastic sheets. Whatever you do, don't carry glass containers in your pockets. These are too likely to break.

From here on, personal equipment can vary a great deal. A watch is desirable. Without it, you have absolutely no way of knowing the time in the perpetual darkness of a cave—and the hours have a way of passing more quickly than you would suspect. A compass may prove practical or it may not, depending on whether there is iron ore in the vicinity which will deflect the needle. A whistle can be useful for giving signals. The type of plastic reflecting tape known commercially as Scotchlite has its uses. It reflects light and can be left along trails as markers. (It's better than string, which has long since gone out of style.) Stuck onto a hard hat, the tape tells others who you are and where you are. You will want a map of a cave, if one is available, and it can be kept dry in a plastic wrapping. A first-aid kit is highly desirable. A small knife for cutting rope or food may come in handy. Also, you may want a spoon and a folding army-type can opener.

Another popular item of personal equipment is a twenty-foot length of nylon cord, wrapped belt-fashion around the waist and fastened in front with a snaplink or karabiner. A light bag with a shoulder strap has advantages. Things that otherwise would have to go into pockets can be carried in it; you can push it ahead of you or drag it behind you in a crawlway, or hand it to someone else to hold while you climb a difficult pitch; you can carry it over your shoulder when the going is easy.

If a party is going to face difficult rock climbing, there must be other equipment. A coil, or coils, of rope, for instance. The best, because it is light and resilient and does not rot or fray easily, is stabilized filament nylon. A cheaper rope—excellent when in good condition—is Manila. But comparison between the best grade Manila and the best nylon—each dry and each capable of holding the same strain before breaking—reveals one important fact: the Manila weighs roughly twice as much. And when the same ropes are wet, the relative weight of Manila is still greater. Regardless of whether Manila or nylon is used, the rope should be examined and tested each time before it is taken into a cave. If a rope is going to be used as a safety line, it must be capable of taking sudden, terrific strains. (For further information about rope, see Chapter 19.)

Cavers differ from mountaineers in one important respect—when it comes to rock climbing. Cavers thoroughly enjoy climbing problems, but they climb in order to get some place underground— usually to explore. A mountaineer often climbs just for the fun of it. This difference in attitude leads cavers to one item of equipment which alpinists scorn—the ladder.

Far and away the strongest and lightest ladder is made of thin steel cables with hollow aluminum-alloy rungs. A thirty-foot length of it, five inches wide, weighs only two pounds and rolls into a neat little bundle. Though this type of ladder is ideal, spelunkers often can't afford it. Instead they use cheaper, more cumbersome rope ladders with wooden rungs.

Assorted mountaineering hardware may also be part of the gear of a caving party. (Items such as pitons, piton hammers, expansion bolts and karabiners are described in Chapter 19.)

Most of the equipment mentioned so far—from shoes to hard hats to hardware—can be easily obtained even if your local sporting goods store doesn't have it. You need only to write away for a catalogue to Gerry, Ward, Colorado. This extraordinary mail-order house is run by a dedicated lover of mountaineering—a veteran of the Army's alpine troops—who built his own shop and storeroom 9,500 feet above sea level, 5 miles outside the ghost town of Ward (population 25). Gerry Cunningham and his wife spend the snowy winters designing and making much of the equipment they sell. The Cunninghams' twins have even led them into a unique side line of what is already a highly specialized business—kid-sized mountaineering gear.

Don't set your heart on driving to Ward in the summertime and buying over the counter. There are no billboards directing you to Gerry's. If you do find the place, as likely as not the Cunninghams will be off making good use of their own wares on some sheer mountain face. But if you order by mail what Gerry advertises as "spelunk junk," you'll get it by return mail, in spite of the fact that Ward is twenty-five miles from the nearest railroad.

Among the man-made mountains and caves of Manhattan, you can climb a rickety flight of stairs at 112 Chambers Street to the premises of Ben Seminof's Camp and Trail Outfitters. There, amid a welter of the kind of gadgets dear to hikers, Seminof has for sale the special things that cavers need. As you examine a piton or a carbide lamp, wisps of goosedown may float over a low partition from the place where sleeping bags are being made. Camp and Trail sends a mail-order catalogue on request, as does Gerry.

Other firms offer the mountaineering and camping equipment that fill part of a spelunker's requirements. For exact descriptions of the gear, and for the names of many places where it can be obtained, send fifty cents to the Potomac Appalachian Club, 1916 Sunderland Place, N. W., Washington, D. C., and ask for their forty-six–page booklet, *Hiking, Camping, Mountaineering and Trail Clearing Equipment.*

Of course, those who go into caves for scientific purposes often have very elaborate gear, but that is not a part of this particular story. Nor is the equipment used by the surprisingly large number of serious photographers who find the beauties of the underworld irresistible.

Finally, you will do well to give some thought to food before you enter a cave. Spelunking can be very hard work. Don't make it harder by carrying a bulky lunch. You will want compact food that will satisfy your hunger and provide quick energy. Chocolate and fruit-flavored hard candy meet this demand. So do raisins or other dried fruits, peanuts and cheese. Small cans of army-type rations are also popular—G.I.'s will please excuse the expression. Remember, exhaustion is the worst enemy of cavers, and proper food is an enemy of exhaustion.

CHAPTER NINETEEN

Spelunking Specialties

İ

If this book has at all served its purpose as an invitation to caving, it has made clear that there is a rich variety of interesting things in and around caves to be understood or lazily enjoyed or actively done. And no matter what your special interest, once you have graduated from the high-heels or walk-in caves that have been commercialized, you will face a question that confronts all who venture very far underground: how does one surmount the difficulties of this extraordinary terrain?

  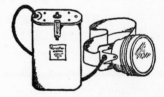

Hard hat - Carbide lamp - Headlight. *Courtesy: Gerry, Ward, Col.*

Whole books have been written on mountaineering techniques. Until a full-scale handbook of spelunking appears, two of these—Kenneth A. Henderson's *Handbook of American Mountaineering*, and the War Department's field manual, *Mountain Operations*—are in the library of every serious cave-crawler. Even these detailed volumes, or the anticipated speleologist's handbook which the NSS has announced it is preparing, will serve only a limited purpose for those who want to learn the tricks of traveling underground.

The only way to master the art of caving is by handling the actual materials used in the sport, by facing the actual problems in caves—and most important—by learning in the company of those who already know. It would be irresponsible to offer this chapter without serious words of warning. The reader should not glance at them and then go out and try the techniques mentioned. I have outlined a few of the many mountaineering problems and solutions primarily to give the armchair caver a means of understanding terms and practices referred to elsewhere in this book—and to give anyone interested a sound basis for the belief that even the most difficult underground problems *can* be solved.

I repeat: don't read this and then dash off into a cave unless you are in the company of experienced cavers.

The most important single tool of the rock-climber is rope. But what kind of rope should a caver have and how much of it? The best kind, from almost every point of view except price, is stabilized filament nylon. New Manila is also excellent. A minimum set of ropes will include:

1. At least 120 feet of either nylon or Manila, 7/16″ in diameter. This thickness is dictated because hands cannot readily hold onto ropes of smaller diameter.

2. A waist line—a length of 5/16″ rope spliced so as to form an endless loop which can go around the wearer's body. It is held by a karabiner (see page 237) which acts as a kind of belt buckle. Its length is roughly twice the waist measure of the wearer. This rope can be, among other things, a useful safety device. For instance, the karabiner can be snapped around the rung of a ladder when the climber needs a rest. Then he can relax without fear of falling.

An organized party will be equipped with more ropes, among them the following:

1. An additional 200 feet of 5/16″ nylon, or an equal length of Manila that is 3/8″ in diameter, which may be used as a rappel or descent line or for safety or other purposes.

2. Several pieces of 5/16″ Manila 10 to 12 feet long, which may be used as slings—that is, when doubled around a support, they will hold other ropes. For safety reasons, these are considered expendable and are not re-used because they are often passed around rocks with sharp edges. The bending and possible fraying can greatly weaken them.

3. Experienced mountaineers will carry 3 endless loops of 5/16″-line which can be used in ascending a perpendicular rope.

Since a caver's life often depends on rope, he should take good care of it. This means coiling it clockwise when it is not in use; freeing it of all kinks before it is used; fixing the ends so they don't fray (the easiest and quickest way to do this is to wrap the ends with adhesive tape, but the best way is to whip them, and this process is described in easily available books which deal with rope knots); drying a Manila rope as soon as possible after it has been wet; never storing a Manila rope in a place where it can get wet; never storing a rope by hanging it over an object with sharp edges, or an object that is very thin, such as a nail, or where it is hot and dry; washing the mud and grit off a rope in plain water; and never using a Manila rope that is frozen.

Despite every precaution taken, a rope should always be tested before it is lugged into a cave. First, look at it for obvious signs of cuts and breaks. Then tie it about waist-high to a tree and get a crew of spelunkers to pull on it, tug-of-war fashion. The problem is to put half as much strain on the rope as it is supposed to stand. (Dealers can tell you the breaking strength of rope—that is, the number of pounds it will hold before breaking—and both the Sierra Club and the American Alpine Club have published the results of independent tests made on ropes of different kinds). When three-quarters of the total weight of your tug-of-war crew equals half the breaking strength of the rope, and when the rope doesn't break when they all pull, then you know your rope is safe.

You cannot climb safely with a rope unless you know how to tie a few basic knots—and unless you know the uses and limitations of the knots. Instructions for making them can be found in the *Boy Scout Handbook, the American Merchant Seaman's Manual,* or *Ashley Book of Knots.* The minimum knots are:

1. *Bowline*—used when a safety line is to be tied around a climber. The loop of the bowline goes around the chest of the person to whom the safety line is attached. A bowline is also used for securing a rope to some stationary object, and for other purposes.

2. *Half-hitch*—a single half-hitch should *never* be used alone. The main purpose of a single half-hitch in caving is to give extra security to some other knot.

3. *Fisherman's knot*—used for tying the ends of two ropes together.

4. *Prusik knot*—a knot which spelunkers use in ascending a rope.

Warning: Never use a square knot when human life depends on it. Even when properly made—which it too often is not—it has been a cause of serious accidents in mountain climbing.

Sitting belay.

With the proper technique, a caver can negotiate steep or perpendicular rock faces—he can go up, down or sideways. The first necessity in any rock climbing is a safety line attached to the climber; second, the safety line must be belayed—that is, it must be secured in some way so that it can bear his full weight and, if he falls, will also yield somewhat to the added load that will come from a sudden jerk. A fellow-climber may serve as the belay point, standing or sitting well braced with the rope passed around his shoulders or hips and held with a hand on either side. The rope may also be belayed around a rock that does not have knife-edged corners, or from a rope sling or from a karabiner snapped to a piton (see page 237); and there are other combinations of these methods depending on the situation.

For a descent where there are adequate handholds and footholds, no rope in addition to the safety line is necessary. Otherwise, the descent can be made by rappel. First, the rappel rope, usually doubled, must be firmly supported by a solid rock, or a karabiner (also called a snaplink) suspended from the eye of a small steel spike called a piton that has been driven into the rock. Other variations are possible.

From the belay point, the rope is dropped down over the rock which is to be descended. The climber then stands astride the rope, reaches behind him, lifts the rope around one hip and up over the head and onto the opposite shoulder, and lets it fall across his chest and down beside the original hip. This winds the rope around him. With one hand he grasps the part of the rope that is in front of him for balance; with the other he grasps the part that dangles behind him in order to control the rate of descent. Now he walks backward, leaning out till he is nearly perpendicular to the face of the rock. He slackens the grip of both hands, and gravity pulls him down. But the friction of the rope around his body acts as a brake, and he can stop himself at any time simply by tightening his grip on the rope behind him.

As he descends, he keeps his legs stretched wide apart providing two support points for good balance on the rock. Pads or leather patches on the shoulder and on buttock and hip of his spelunking clothes help to insulate his skin against the heat of friction produced by the rope. An experienced rappeler descends in a series of bounds, rather than in a steady slide along the rope. With each bound he literally jumps away from the rock face, lets himself slip down, then brakes his fall with pressure of his downhill hand as he swings in again toward the rock. A rappel, when it can be fully seen—something not always possible in a cave—is as spectacular as a circus stunt, but is remarkably safe, after a climber has had sufficient practice.

There are a number of variations on the basic rappel technique, but no rappeling should be attempted except under expert guidance.

The rappel can also be used to descend vertically where there is no contact with a rock face—for example, from an overhanging ledge into a pit. As a rule, if a steel-cable ladder or a rope ladder is available, spelunkers use this in making a descent into a pit, principally because the return trip up a ladder is quicker and easier than the ascent of a rope. Nevertheless, there are important tricks to be

Rappeling.

learned about climbing on a flexible ladder. The rungs of the steel-cable type are only five inches wide. The climber puts one foot—toes forward—onto the first rung, swings the other foot around to the back side of the ladder and sets it heel-first onto the next rung. Thus one foot pushes the ladder in one direction while the other foot pushes in the opposite direction, helping to hold it vertical.

There is no way to rappel up, unfortunately, and no spelunker who values his life *ever* attempts to climb a rope hand-over-hand.

However, when a spelunker finds himself at the bottom of a vertical shaft with no ladder and only a free-swinging (standing) rope to climb, he has an ingenious but tedious technique at his disposal. By the use of a device called prusik knots he ascends in much the same fashion as a linesman ascends a telephone pole. His equipment consists of three rope loops, which the reader can easily understand by an experiment with a pencil and a rubber band. Lay the pencil across the rubber band at right angles to the long axis. There now appear to be two loops, one on either side of the pencil. Pick up the left-hand loop, pass it over and around the pencil twice, then through the right-hand loop. Finally, pull on the end that came

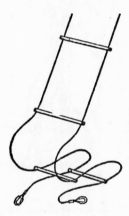

Cable ladder. *Courtesy: Gerry, Ward, Col.*

from the left side. You now have a prusik knot. It is non-skid and absolutely tight as long as you put pressure on it. But with pressure removed, it loosens easily and can be moved up or down the pencil.

The climber uses the standing rope the way you have used the pencil. He makes prusik knots with his three rope loops. The free end of the highest loop goes under his arms and across his back. He places one foot in the second loop and the other foot in the third. Now he is ready to climb.

He shifts all his weight to the foot which is higher, loosens the prusik knot which holds the other foot and slides the knot up the rope, then shifts his weight into that loop. Next he loosens and raises the knot in the loop that passes under his arms. Repeating this process, he goes up by slow stages.

There are other ways to get out of a hole. They require the use of pitons or expansion bolts and karabiners. A piton is a metal wedge with an eye in one end. It is designed to be driven into a crack in a

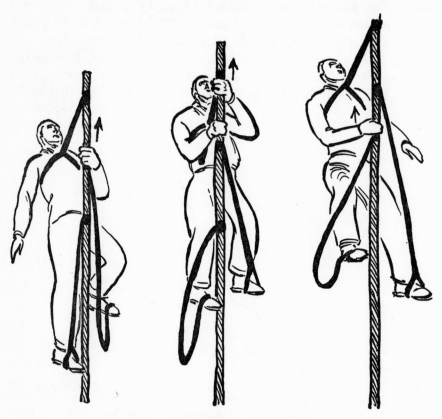

Ascending a rope with the use of prusik knots.

rock. After it is driven in, the eye becomes a fixed ring which is used as a belay point. A climber usually carries a special piton hammer to drive a piton into place. Pitons vary in design depending on whether they are meant for vertical or horizontal, or big or small cracks. In rock faces where there are no cracks, a climber can still make a belay point. He does this by using a star drill and piton hammer to make a hole in which he places an expansion bolt. The

Vertical piton - Horizontal piton. *Courtesy: Gerry, Ward, Col.*

eye in the expansion bolt then serves as a belay point. In the eye of a piton or an expansion bolt, the climber places a karabiner. This useful piece of hardware is made somewhat like a big safety

Piton and expansion bolt. *Courtesy: Gerry, Ward, Col.*

pin, except that the gate swings inward so that rope passing through it will not force it open. A karabiner is smooth and will not cut the rope. It is removable and can be used over and over, whereas pitons should be considered expendable.

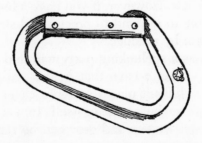

Karabiner. *Courtesy: Gerry, Ward, Col.*

To climb up or across a rock face, a spelunker drives a piton into a crack ahead of him, places a karabiner in the eye of the piton, then pushes his rope through the gate of the karabiner which opens inward. Immediately the gate snaps shut, and the climber has a belay point which can help hold his weight. One end of the rope he uses is tied around his body; the other is held by a partner below who is always ready to brake and stop a fall. By repeating the process, he can go upward or laterally as far as the length of the rope allows. Several variations on this technique are possible.

Rock piton hammer. *Courtesy: Gerry, Ward, Col.*

Two very simple tricks of the mountaineering craft can be used in some places without recourse to elaborate rope techniques. One climber can turn a companion into a ladder. This shoulder stand, or *courte echelle*, is good for short pitches. Another technique, sometimes usable for quite long ascents or descents, depends on having two rock faces fairly close together forming a sort of chute or chimney. The climber—by exerting pressure on the opposing walls with various combinations of hands, back and feet—can inch his way up or down. This is called chimneying.

There are more human fly techniques, but none of them can be learned in an arm chair. However, if you have a body that by nature or by training is able to respond to precise and strenuous demands, you can master them by practice.

On some occasions a spelunking party will find it efficient to use rigging in order to enter a cave that begins with a perpendicular shaft or to conquer difficult places within a cave. Rigging—derived from seamanship—is a whole craft in itself. In a cave it provides an elevator by which passengers and gear can be raised and lowered, or a means of transporting passengers and gear laterally across a

pit. Sometimes a structure has to be erected in order to permit a free
run of rope through a block suspended from it over the mouth of a
cave. At other times well-rooted trees provide the necessary support.
Like other mountaineering techniques, safe rigging depends on a
thorough knowledge of the subject, and amateurs must not attempt it.

Traverse.

II

Crucial though mountaineering techniques are, they cannot get
spelunkers to the end of every cave. Water often intervenes between
the explorer and his goal. Sometimes there is no way to find out
what lies beyond except by swimming under water—and, of course,
for an unknown distance. So cavers have applied what divers have
learned about the possibilities and hazards of working sometimes
at considerable depths out of reach of air.

A cave-diver dons a rubber suit with frog feet, an Aqua-lung
outfit (*not* picked up in a secondhand store or surplus outlet), plus
a spare tank of oxygen, a depth gauge, a waterproof watch, a
weight-belt, and a powerful electric headlight. Then, while a sup-

port diver stands ready to help out in case of emergency, he plunges in. Attached to his body is a safety line which serves two purposes. It provides a sure way of return to his starting point, and it is a means of sending signals, by a prearranged pattern of jerks, to the rest of his party on the bank of the underground lake or river. In addition to the support diver, the minimum party includes an assistant who pays out the safety line, and a log-keeper who keeps track of time and records all reports signaled on the safety line.

An underwater spelunker has a most complex set of problems to keep constantly in mind while he does the arduous and daring labor of exploration. He must be sure that his oxygen tank is functioning properly, and he must know from his own physical reactions whether he is getting too much oxygen (which produces oxygen poisoning) or too little. In either case he could become helpless and an attempted rescue might be too late. He must be careful that his safety line does not get fouled or stuck in a crack. Sometimes he may assume the additional responsibility of making notes on the spot—under water. For this he uses a sheet of celluloid and a grease crayon. Or he may take waterproof photographic equipment along. It is worth noting that the diver's task is so difficult that the others in his party do everything possible to save his energy. They lug every ounce of equipment to the point at which the dive is to begin.

Speleologists both on the West Coast and in the East have made interesting underwater discoveries, and they have a perfect safety record in spite of the hazards, although an American who was a professional diver did lose his life in an English cave. Some cavers have considered the field sufficiently important to set up an Underwater Speleological Research Group. Although this group is an independent organization, it requires that all members belong to both the NSS and a skin-diving club. It goes without saying that no diving enthusiast should attempt any work in a cave without having availed himself of the full experience of this group.

III

Rock climbing and diving by no means exhaust the specialized activities in which cavers can participate. Athletic or not, amateurs can respond to the many requests from biologists for information about cave life. A typical plea went out to spelunkers not too long ago from the scientist Brother G. Nicholas, who was engaged in research on the small, colorless flatworms that inhabit some cave waters. Any caver who saw such flatworms was asked to communicate their precise location to Brother Nicholas, who would then investigate. A similar request came from Dr. W. J. Gertsch of the American Museum of Natural History, who wanted information about tiny cave spiders of the genus *Nesticus*, which can be recognized by their pale gray color and fragile-looking legs.

Chiropterists have asked spelunkers to examine any dead bat they find underground, or above. If it has a band, the caver should note the number and time and place of discovery, and send the information to the Fish and Wildlife Service in Washington. The scientists also want to receive reports of any large concentrations of bats in caves. They still have not been able to cover all of the possible bat dwelling places. Although they are eager for this kind of assistance, they urge amateurs not to handle or otherwise disturb the little animals they find hanging in caves. It's too likely to be a case of curiosity killed the bat.

And so it is with the handling of any kind of cave creature. None should ever be collected except under explicit scientific direction. A past president of the NSS, Charles E. Mohr, even goes so far as to say that "most cave populations are too small to justify *any* collecting."

IV

An important arm of the speleological sciences is photography. A photograph can show, and no argument about it, exactly how an Indian artifact lies in relation to the bone of a prehistorical animal. It can show the full glistening splendor of delicate anthodites in their natural setting. Pictures can preserve as nothing else can the sinuous and varied movements and forms of spindle-legged salamanders or fish and planarians in the water. Often, valuable data about the levels of water or the courses of underground streams can be gathered by the study of photographs. It is possible in looking at prints—without ever entering a cave—to determine whether a passageway has been created solely by solution or by some other process. Each science has a long list of things its practitioners want to know from the study of carefully taken pictures.

But for most spelunkers, photography begins, at least, as an act of sheer delight. A glance at a party of cavers is enough to convince anyone that there must be something underground worth photographing. Spelunkers carry a wide assortment of cameras and their lighting equipment in specially designed bags. Rarely, however, do they take movie cameras into caves. The problem of getting adequate light for movies is almost insurmountable. Flares can't be used, except in the largest rooms where there is plenty of air movement, because they make too much smoke; and it is a superhuman task to transport far into most caves batteries to provide a source of light. On one expedition a group of NSS members did succeed in making a cave film. They set up at the cave entrance a generator driven by gasoline motor, and laid many hundreds of feet of electric cable, plus a telephone line, to the various scenes of operation.

When the question is asked: "How do you take pictures in a cave?" the presumption must be that one knows how to take pictures *outside* a cave. The answer can only lie in pointing out special conditions that the spelunking photographer has to face.

The first is total and absolute darkness, except for the little flickering lights of carbide lamps and the whiter beams of flashlights. Neither of these is an adequate source of light, even for very long time exposures. All the *portable* lighting devices used by photographers topside can be used underground, and only experience will tell an individual how much he wants to lug with him. As a rule, the longer a photographer has worked in caves, the more compact his gear has become. He uses midget flashbulbs instead of the normal-sized ones. Although flash powder is much more easily transportable than bulbs, it has a number of disadvantages. The smoke produced spoils even a large chamber for further shots for some time, since the circulation of air in caves is usually slow. Flash powder is dangerous, and only after many practice shots made aboveground should one attempt its use in a cave. Never use flash powder in any cave that contains bats during the hibernating season.

A photographer discovers very soon that a great deal more light is required for shots in a cave than he had ever guessed would be necessary. The dark surroundings seem to sop up the puny rays sent out by flashbulbs. However, old hands have found they can cheat the darkness in ingenious ways. For example, a photographer will get his camera firmly settled, and focused on some object he wants to shoot. Then, with the aid of friends hidden in the dark at strategic points, he can have a series of flashes set off, all of which will register as simultaneous on his film, because the shutter can be left open between flashes with no harm done. Since their head lamps will register as spots or wavy lines, these assistants should keep their heads turned away from the camera when the lens shutter is open.

Photographers find it to their mutual advantage to help one another. They "ride" the flashes—that is, all those wishing to get a certain shot set their cameras on Time or Bulb. Whoever holds the flash gun intones "One!" as a signal that operations are about to begin. "Two!" is a warning to open shutters. On "Three!" the flash is fired. Any person included in the picture must be cautioned to remain absolutely still during the interval the shutter is open. If he moves, the flame of his light will appear as a wavy line in the photograph. This kind of cooperation means that each photographer can carry a smaller supply of bulbs—a very important consideration.

Seldom is there sufficient illumination to focus in the picture area. Therefore a little practice in estimating distances is very helpful. Where it is practical, place a flashlight or a head lamp at the spot you intend to photograph; focus, and then remove the lamp before shooting the picture. Pictures of speleothems can be very deceptive. A tiny stalactite and an enormous one may look exactly the same when they turn up on film unless some object of known size appears in the picture to set the scale—a human being or a piton hammer do very well.

The high humidity and the cool temperature of many caves may present a problem. Warm moist breath can fog the camera lens or send a miniature cloud between the camera and the object being filmed. The photographer soon learns to hold his breath and to make sure his lens is dry and clean. For this he may use a little camel's hair brush that he carries in a tiny container. He also approaches his camera with clean hands—quite a trick in muddy caves. Gloves are the answer, and he sometimes carries an extra pair.

To keep the camera itself clean and dry—and safe from shocks—

is still another problem. Experts are likely to wrap cameras first in a plastic bag, then in a piece of thick, soft cloth, then possibly in another bag. This whole bundle goes into a carrying case, which may be a surplus ammunition case that has been lined with foam rubber. Or it may be a padded canvas bag. To carry his equipment, John L. Spence, former president of the New York Camera Club, has designed a plywood box which fits inside a foam-rubber-padded bag. The box holds two cameras (one for black and white and one for color), and it opens in such a way that both remain inside the box while pictures are being taken. Flash equipment is also built in, together with batteries and a battery-powered light by which adjustments of cameras and equipment are easy to make. The whole assembly is a marvel of efficiency and ingenuity. The carrying bag can be held in the hand, suitcase fashion, or dragged at the end of a light nylon cord through very small and rough crawlways. Mud will not harm it; water cannot get into it. This device is Spence's special pleasure. Other cavers have solved the portage problem in different ways. One thing is sure: no two sets of cave photographer's equipment are identical. And if you want to start an argument that will last far into the night, you need only say among cavers that one type of camera or one type of film or your particular rig for lighting or for anything else is superior. It is not the function of this book to join such an argument. But it *is* part of the fun of caving for each individual to experiment and find the equipment and techniques that meet his or her particular needs. Scientists regret that most cave photography is done in color, for they find black and white shots far superior for their purposes. Nevertheless, cavers all agree that the underground world is so beautiful that only color photography can do it esthetic justice.

A Glossary of Speleological Terms

The following glossary is intended as a convenience to readers who encounter unfamiliar terms in this book and in other recent American books on caves and caving. It is also designed as an introduction to terms that will be found in more technical writing about caves. More complete glossaries, to which I am indebted, exist in *British Caving,* edited by C. H. D. Cullingford (1953), and in a compilation prepared by Dr. Martin H. and Katharine E. Muma which appeared in NSS *Bulletin* No. 6, July, 1944.

alabaster—massive gypsum. The word is also applied, on occasion, to calcite.

anthodite—a cluster of long crystals which radiate outward from a common base.

aragonite—a form of calcium carbonate having the same chemical nature as calcite but differing in crystalline structure, and probably formed under different conditions.

bacon—a thin, stalactitic sheet of calcite which has alternating dark and light bands giving it the appearance of a strip of bacon. The dark stain is usually caused by an iron oxide.

bedding plane—the meeting point of two different layers of sediment which have become hardened into rock.

belay—This is a tough one to define, but every seaman, mountaineer or spelunker knows what the word means. It is both a verb and a noun. It is used to describe the process of making a rope absolutely secure. It is also used to describe the process of paying out a rope gradually from a fixed point. The noun refers to the point at which a rope is made secure or from which it is paid out under control.

blowing cave—a cave out of which a current of air flows for extended periods. Air flows into blowing caves at other periods. Changes in barometric pressure cause this phenomenon.

botryoid—from the Greek meaning "a cluster of grapes." A term used to describe minerals, including calcium carbonate, deposited in a form resembling grapes.

boxwork—calcium carbonate deposits formed in a closely intersecting network of joints. Subsequent solution of limestone between the deposits leaves a speleothem resembling a honeycomb.

breakdown—heaps of rock on a cavern floor caused by collapse of part, at least, of the walls or ceiling.

breathing cave—a cave in which an air current changes the direction of its flow at frequent intervals. The cause of this phenomenon is unknown. In both Latin and Greek the word for cave meant "a breathing place."

calcite—a crystalline form of calcium carbonate, the stuff of which most stalactites, stalagmites, flowstone and other speleothems are formed.

calcite bubble—a rare form of calcite concretion which is hollow and rounded and can float on water.

carabiner—*See* karabiner.

cave coral—a type of calcite deposit in caves, so called because it resembles true coral, formed under water. Cave coral in some places is deposited on pre-existing speleothems, indicating that water has risen and at least partially filled an area that had earlier been drained.

cave ice—ordinary ice which is formed inside caves.

cave master—a man or woman who coordinates activities on a caving expedition.

cave onyx—a highly polished piece of calcite or aragonite, stained in bands with other minerals, which is sold commercially.

cave pearl—a roundish unattached concretion of calcium carbonate formed under water.

cave system—Where cavernous passages are numerous in a geological formation, all are grouped together under the term *cave system*, whether or not the passages connect with each other.

chimney—(*noun*) a narrow vertical shaft in rock. It may be a rough tube resembling the chimney of a house, or it may simply be a narrow cleft between two more or less parallel walls of rock. (*verb*) to ascend or descend a chimney in a series of inching motions with the back pressed against one wall, and one or both feet pressed against the opposite wall.

column—a speleothem formed by the growing together of a stalactite and a stalagmite.

concretion—a lump or nodule of mineral usually deposited from water. As a rule, concretions of one mineral exist within rock which is of different nature—thus, flint concretions occur in limestone.

corrasion—the mechanical wearing away of cave passages by the action of water-borne particles of rock.

crawlway—a passageway so low that you have to get down on your hands and knees or on your belly in order to get through.

dead cave—a cave into which seepage water no longer penetrates and in which speleothems have ceased to grow.

dip—the angle with the horizontal of a tilted sedimentary deposit.

dogtooth spar—a comparatively rare crystalline form of calcite which vaguely resembles a dog's tooth.

dolomite—a sedimentary rock, akin to limestone, which contains a large percentage of magnesium carbonate. Caves can occur in dolomite.

dome-pit—a large solution cavity in rock, the longest dimension of which is vertical. The upper portion is not to be confused with the dome-shaped ceilings caused by breakdown.

drapery—a hanging speleothem which takes the form of a curtain or drape.

dripstone—a calcite deposit left by dripping water.

expansion bolt—a device familiar to builders which has been adapted by rock climbers. When driven into a drilled hole in rock, it spreads out and holds fast. When fully assembled, a karabiner can hang from it through an eye and hold a rope.

fault—Pressures on a bed of rock can crack it, causing the two parts to shift in relation to each other, and the crack along which this shift takes place is called a fault. Some caves form along faults. A notable example is Timpanogos Cave in Utah.

fill—any rock, sand, clay, mud or other material on cave floors which is there because of breakdown of ceilings or walls, or which has been deposited by water flowing in from the surface.

flint—a silicaceous concretion that sometimes appears in limestone.

flowstone—calcite deposited by water running down a cave wall or over a cave floor.

formation—a term geologists use to describe a body of rock. It is also widely used to describe the calcite, aragonite and gypsum deposits in caves. To distinguish the latter, the word speleothem is preferable.

grape formation—See botryoid.

grotto—As used by American cavers, this word refers to a small cavity opening off a larger one. A grotto might be called "a cave within a cave."

guano—As far as caves are concerned, guano is bat dung. It has commercial value as fertilizer because of its high nitrogen content.

guide rope—an auxiliary rope used in connection with another rope which bears a spelunker's full weight when he descends a shaft or a rock wall. It literally guides him past difficulties or to a proper landing place.

gypsum—calcium sulphate with a high water content. Where massive formations of gypsum appear, there can be caves, because gypsum is soluble. Gypsum speleothems also exist in caves in limestone beds. The term "gypsum cave" may refer to a cave in gypsum, or it may refer to a cave in limestone decorated with gypsum speleothems.

gypsum flower—Crystalline gypsum in a curved or twisted form often resembles flowers. Oulopholite is the "long-hair" word for this type of speleothem.

helictite—a variant form of stalactite which does not hang vertically or which has side growths resembling branches or twisted roots of plants.

hydrology—the science that deals with surface water and underground water.

ice cave—a cave within which ice forms. Sometimes the ice takes on the form of stalactites, stalagmites, curtains or flowstone. It often persists throughout the entire year.

joint—a crack, which in limestone forms at an angle to a bedding plane. A series of joints often intersect each other in a four-sided pattern.

karabiner—a steel link, oval or ovaloid in shape, with a gate on one side which can be opened inward and which is normally held shut by a spring. Used by rock climbers as a quick, convenient means for holding a rope. Sometimes called a snaplink.

karst—a term used to describe terrain marked by sinkholes and underground drainage.

keyhole—a small passage or opening in a cave, so named because it resembles a keyhole in shape.

lava tube—a long cavity formed within lava as it cools.

lead—a side passage in a cave.

live cave—a cave that is being actively affected by water, such as a flowing stream that enlarges its passages, seepage water that enlarges cavities, or seepage water that leaves deposits.

lost river—a river which runs underground throughout part of its length.

meteorology—the scientific study of the atmosphere and related phenomena. Meteorologists have found many fascinating problems connected with the atmosphere in caves.

moon milk—a rare form of calcium carbonate which is semi-liquid.

niche cave—See shelter cave.

one-cycle theory—an explanation of the origin of caves which holds that they were created by acid-bearing vadose water at or above the water table.

oölitic limestone—a variety of limestone composed of tiny spherical grains of calcium carbonate.

oulopholite—See gypsum flower.

palette—See shield.

phreatic water—See phreatic zone.

phreatic zone—the region, below the water table, in which rock is saturated with water. The water in this zone is called phreatic, from the Greek word meaning "well."

pisolite—See cave pearl.

pitch—a climber's word to describe a very steep or vertical descent or ascent.

piton—a metal wedge, with an eye in one end, which is driven into cracks in rock in order to form a belay point (see belay). Pitons come in different shapes for vertical and horizontal cracks. There are also special pitons for use in ice and mud.

rappel—to slide down a rope, with a turn of the rope passing around the body to provide friction and thus to serve as a brake. The word is also used as a noun. For example, a climber may say he "got into rappel."

rimstone—a calcium carbonate deposit around the edge of a pool of water.

safety—a verb used to describe a process by which one climber belays the safety rope attached to another climber. (*See* belay.)

safety rope—a rope which is tied to a rock climber and which serves to prevent a serious fall—for example, when a climber slips.

sea cave—a cavity in rock produced by the pounding action of waves.

selenite—gypsum crystals, often in the form of blades.

shelter cave—a depression in the face of any kind of rock, in which it is possible to take shelter.

shield—a speleothem that has formed in the shape of a disk and that usually projects out from a cave wall at a sharp angle. Also called a palette.

sink—a depression in the landscape caused by collapse of the roof of a cavity beneath the surface. *See also* sinkhole.

sinkhole—an opening that leads steeply downward from the surface to a cavernous area. Such holes may appear in the bottoms of sinks, or their mouths may be flush with the surface of the surrounding terrain.

siphon—a passage in rock, shaped like an inverted U, through which water flows under pressure.

snaplink—*See* karabiner.

soda straw—a small, hollow stalactite inside which drops of water descend.

speleology—the scientific study of caves in all their aspects.

speleothem—a general term used to describe the deposits, in caves, of calcite, aragonite and gypsum. The word is more and more frequently used instead of the word "formation" which geologists use to describe large bodies of rock. Thus, a cave may be said to be in a certain limestone formation.

spelunker—one who explores caves as a sportsman or as an amateur speleologist.

squeeze—a passageway in a cave that is very tight from a human point of view.

stalactite—a calcium carbonate speleothem which grows downward, icicle-fashion, as a result of deposits left by dripping water.

stalagmite—a deposite of calcium carbonate which is built upward from a cave floor by dripping water.

strike—the compass direction of a line at right angles to the dip in a sedimentary deposit. (*See* dip.)

traverse—to cross a rock wall laterally. Also used as a noun.

travertine—a term loosely applied to several forms of calcium carbonate deposits.

two-cycle theory—an explanation of the origin of caves which holds that they were created by acid-bearing phreatic water below the water table; and that then, in a later stage, when the cave was drained of water and lay above the water table, calcium-bearing vadose water deposited the speleothems.

vadose water—*See* vadose zone.

vadose zone—the region lying between the surface of the earth and the water table. Water which seeps or flows through this region under the pull of gravity is called vadose water.

water table—the meeting place of the phreatic and the vadose zones. Below it, the rock is saturated with water; above it, water under the pull of gravity is continuously flowing downward.

wild cave—a cave in its natural state. The term is used in contrast to commercial caves in which paths, lights, or other conveniences for the public have been installed.

A Directory of Caves Open to the Public

The following directory attempts to list all caves operated either privately or by federal, state or local agencies. Every effort has been made to include all solution caves (those which have been formed in limestone, gypsum, dolomite or marble). Sea caves, lava tubes and two caverns under granite boulders are also listed. Other underground recesses are not.

It may well be that some caves deserving mention have been omitted. If so, diligent search has failed to discover them, and the author will be grateful for information which will make revision possible in later editions of this book.

In most cases, cave managers have confirmed the information given here. In a few cases, information about caves known to be open had to come from other sources, such as *Palaces Under the Earth, a Directory of Commercially Operated Caves,* published by the National Speleological Society in 1951. In other cases, up-to-date information about caves believed to be open was not forthcoming from any source.

The listings are arranged by states and alphabetically within states. The mail address of each cave appears directly after the cave name, and is given for the convenience of those wishing to write for further information. Most operators will answer specific questions and will also send a printed folder.

Unless otherwise stated, caves about which detailed information is given are open all year.

Where the time of day is listed, the first entry refers to the hour at which the first tour begins; the second refers to the hour at which the last daily tour begins. The length of each tour is indicated in hours or minutes.

In some caves tours are not regularly scheduled. Usually as soon as a party of four or more is ready to enter, the tour begins. This is indicated in the listing by the words *on demand.*

The entrance fees (always subject to change without notice) are indicated in dollars and cents, with the adult fee given first and the fee for children under twelve given second. Some caves have different fees for children of various ages. These variations are *not* given. Most caves offer reduced rates for organized groups, and information about such rates can be obtained by writing to the manager. In most cases, but not all, the entrance fee given includes tax.

Some caves are located in parks for which there is an admission fee per car or per person. These fees are *not* listed.

Where facilities for meals exist on the cave premises, this is indicated by the words *snack bar, lunch room* or *restaurant.* Overnight accommodations on the premises are indicated by the words *hotel, lodge, cabins, cottages, motel.* Where the management has facilities for trailers or tent camping, this is indicated by the words *trailers* or *camping.* Where no such listing appears, no such facilities are known to exist. Frequently, but not always, meals and overnight accommodations may be obtained somewhere near the cave.

ALABAMA

CRYSTAL CAVERNS, Trussville, Ala. 21 miles E of Birmingham Court House, on US 11. Snack bar.

ARIZONA

COLOSSAL CAVE, Vail, Ariz. 8 miles NE of Vail, off US 80. 8 A.M., 5 P.M. 1 hr. $1.10; $.50. Camping.

ARKANSAS

BIG HURRICANE CAVERN, Rt. 1, Everton, Ark. 17 miles S of Harrison, off US 65. 7 A.M., 6 P.M. 1 hr. $1.15; $.65. Restaurant. Trailers. Camping.

DIAMOND CAVERNS, Jasper, Ark. 4 miles SW of Jasper, off US 7. 7 A.M., 7 P.M. 1¾ hr. $1.22; $.61. Restaurant. Cabins. Camping.

MYSTIC CAVERN, Marble Falls, Ark. 7 miles S of Harrison, on Ark. 7. 7 A.M., 8 P.M. 40 min. $1.00; $.50. Restaurant. Camping.

ONYX CAVE, Eureka Springs, Ark. 7 miles E of Eureka Springs, on US 62. 8 A.M., 5 P.M. 30 min. $1; $.60.

WONDERLAND CAVE, Bella Vista, Ark. In Bella Vista, off Ark. 100. 8 A.M., 5 P.M. 30 min. $.90; $.50.

CALIFORNIA

BEAR GULCH CAVES, Pinnacles National Monument, Paicines, Calif. 35 miles S of Hollister, off Calif. 25. Self-guided tours. Trailers. Camping. *Lava tubes.*

BOYDEN CAVE, Box 217, Kings Canyon National Park, Calif. 80 miles E of Fresno, on Calif. 180, inside Sequoia National Forest. June 15-Labor Day. 9 or 10 A.M., 4 P.M. 45 min. $.35; $.15. Snack bar. Camping.

CRYSTAL CAVE, Sequoia National Park, Three Rivers, Calif. 9 miles from Giant Forest in Sequoia National Park. June 25-Labor Day. Closed Mondays except when Monday is a holiday. 9 A.M., 3 P.M. 50 min. $.50; free. Lodges. Cabins. Camping.

LA JOLLA CAVES, 1325 Coast Blvd., La Jolla, Calif. Same address. 9:30 A.M., 4:45 P.M. 20 min. $.30; $.10. *Sea caves.*

Lava Beds Caves, Lava Beds National Monument, Tulelake, Calif. S from Merrill, Ore., on Ore. 39; or from Tulelake, Calif., on Calif. 139; or NW from Alturas, on Calif. 139; or on road leading off US 97, NE of Dorris, Calif. Self-guided tours. Free. Camping. *More than 30 lava tubes.*

Mercer Caverns, Murphys, Calif. 1 mile N of Murphys, on Calif. 4. Daily except in winter, when weekends only. On demand. 40 min. $1.10; $.50. Snack bar.

Mitchell's Caverns, Mitchell's Caverns State Park, Box 1, Essex, Calif. 22 miles NW of Essex, Calif., off US 66. Write to manager before visiting. Cave is being prepared for public as this book goes to press. Will be open at unknown future date.

Moaning Cave, Vallecito, Calif. 2 miles SW of Vallecito off Calif. 49.

COLORADO

Cave of the Winds, Manitou Springs, Colo. 2 miles N of Manitou Springs, off US 24. (Summer) 8 a.m., 6 p.m.; (Winter) 9 a.m., 5 p.m. 40 min. $1.20; $.60.

FLORIDA

Florida Caverns State Park, Florida Caverns State Park, Box 678, Marianna, Fla. 3 miles N of Marianna, off Fla. 167. 8 a.m., 4:30 p.m. 45 min. $.78; $.25. Trailers. Camping.

GEORGIA

Cave Springs Cave, Cedartown, Floyd County, Ga. 9 miles NW of Cedartown, on Ga. 161. 8 a.m., 5 p.m. 10 min. $.25; $.15.

White River Cave, Rockmart, Polk County, Ga. 3 miles from Rockmart, off Ga. 113. 8 a.m., 8 p.m. $.20; $.20. Trailers. Camping.

IDAHO

Craters of the Moon Caves, Craters of the Moon National Monument, Arco, Idaho. 20 miles SW of Arco, on US 93A. May 15-Nov. 1. Self-guided tours. Lunchroom. Cabins. Camping. *Lava tubes.*

Minnetonka Cave, Paris, Idaho. 8 miles W of St. Charles, off US 89. June 1-Sept. 1. 9 a.m., 3 p.m. 2 hrs. $.50; $.25.

ILLINOIS

Burksville Cave, Burksville, Ill.

Cave-in-Rock, Cave-in-Rock State Park, Cave-in-Rock, Ill. At southern end of Ill. 1. (Summer) 8 a.m., midnight; (Winter) 8 a.m., 8 p.m. Self-guided tours. Camping.

INDIANA

Donaldson Cave, Spring Mill State Park, Mitchell, Ind. 3 miles E of Mitchell, on Ind. 60. Apr. 1-Nov. 1. 9 a.m., 4:50 p.m. 10 min. Boat trip, $.10. Restaurant. Hotel. Camping.

ENDLESS CAVERN, Campbellsburg, Ind. 2 miles N of Campbellsburg, off Ind. 60, in Cave River Valley Park. May 1-Sept. 30. On demand. Free. Snack bar. Cabins. Camping.

MARENGO CAVE, Marengo, Ind. ½ mile N of Marengo, off Ind. 64. 9 A.M., 4 P.M. 1 hr. $1.10; $.50. Camping.

RIVER CAVE, Campbellsburg, Ind. 2 miles N of Campbellsburg, off Ind. 60, in Cave River Valley Park. May 1-Sept. 30. On demand. Boat ride $.50. Snack bar. Cabins. Camping.

TWIN CAVE, Spring Mill State Park, Mitchell, Ind. 3 miles E of Mitchell, on Ind. 60. Apr. 1-Nov. 1. 9 A.M., 4:45 P.M. 15 min. Boat trip $.15. Restaurant. Hotel. Camping.

WYANDOTTE CAVES, Wyandotte, Ind. ¼ mile off US 460. May 1-Dec. 1. 8 A.M., 5 P.M. 45 min.—$1.20, $.50. Or 2 hrs.—$1.65, $.85. Or 8 hrs.— $3.30, $1.65. Lunchroom. Cabins. Camping.

IOWA

CRYSTAL LAKE CAVE, RR 3, Dubuque, Ia. 6 miles S of Dubuque, off US 52. May 1-Nov. 1. 7:20 A.M., 5:45 P.M. 30 min. $.90; $.45. Snack bar. Camping.

MAQUOKETA CAVE, Maquoketa Caves State Monument, Maquoketa, Ia. 7 miles NW of Maquoketa, on Ia. 130. Self-guided tours. Free. Snack bar (June-Sept.). Camping.

WONDER CAVE, 210 West St., Decorah, Ia. 2½ miles NE of Decorah, off US 52. May 1-Nov. 1. 8 A.M., 6 P.M. 30 min. Guide fee charged.

KENTUCKY

CARTER CAVES, Carter Caves State Park, Olive Hill, Ky. 6 miles E of Olive Hill, off US 60. Apr. 1-Nov. 1. 8:45 A.M., 4:15 P.M. Salt Petre Cave—45 min.; X Cave—30 min. Each $.60; $.25. Lunchroom. Cabins.

CASCADE CAVERNS, 931 - 5th Ave., Huntington, West Va. 5 miles E of Olive Hill, Ky., off US 60 on Ky. 209. On demand. 45 min. $1.25; $.64. Restaurant and hotel (May 1-Oct. 1). Camping.

DANIEL BOONE'S CAVE, RR 3, Nicholasville, Ky. 20 miles S of Lexington, on US 27. Apr. 15-Nov. 1. 8 A.M., 6 P.M. 45 min. $.55; $.35. Restaurant. Camping.

DIAMOND CAVERNS, Park City, Ky. 1½ miles from Park City, on Ky. 255. (Summer) 7:30 A.M., 6:30 P.M.; (Winter) 8 A.M., 5 P.M. 1½ hrs. $2; $1. Hotel. Restaurant. Lunchroom. Camping.

FLOYD COLLINS' CRYSTAL CAVE, Horse Cave, Ky. 14 miles NW of Cave City, off US 31W, on private property inside Mammoth Cave National Park. 7 A.M., 6 P.M. 1 hr. and 3 hrs. $2.34; $1.20. Snack bar. Camping.

GREAT ONYX CAVE, Mammoth Cave, Ky. On private property inside Mammoth Cave National Park. On demand. 30 min. to 2 hrs. $1.85; $.95. Restaurant. Hotel. Camping.

LOST RIVER CAVE, Rt. 4, Bowling Green, Ky. 2½ miles S of Bowling Green, off US 31W. Closed about 2 months in winter. 7 A.M., 6 P.M. 40 min. $.90; free. Underground night club restaurant.

MAMMOTH CAVE, Mammoth Cave National Park, Ky. 9 A.M., 4 P.M. 1½ hrs. to 7 hrs. $1.25 to $2.50; free. Underground lunchroom. Restaurant. Hotel. Cabins. Trailers. Camping.

MAMMOTH ONYX CAVE, Horse Cave, Ky. 2 miles W of Horse Cave, off US 31W. 7 A.M., 6 P.M. 1½ hrs. $2.34; $1.20. Snack bar.

SALT PETER CAVE, Mt. Vernon, Ky. 2 miles S of Mt. Vernon on local road. April 1-Nov. 1. 8:30 A.M., 4:30 P.M. 2 hrs. $.50; $.25. Camping.

MAINE

ANEMONE CAVE, Acadia National Park, Bar Harbor, Me. 3¼ miles S of Bar Harbor. May 1-Dec. 1. Self-guided tours. Free. Camping. *Sea Cave.*

MARYLAND

CRYSTAL GROTTOES, RD 1, Boonsboro, Md. 1 mile S of Boonsboro, off Md. 34. 9 A.M., 6 P.M. 40 min. $1; $.60. Camping.

MINNESOTA

MYSTERY CAVE, Spring Valley, Minn. 8 miles SE of Spring Valley, off US 16. Apr. 1-Dec. 1. (Summer) 7 A.M., 8 P.M.; (Spring and Fall) 8 A.M., 6 P.M. 1 hr. $1.10; $.50. Snack bar. Trailers. Camping.

NIAGARA CAVE, Harmony, Minn. 4 miles SW of Harmony, off US 52. (Summer) 7A.M., 8 P.M.; (Winter) 8 A.M., 5 P.M. 1¼ hrs. $1.20; $.50. Lunchroom. Trailers. Camping.

MISSOURI

BLUFF DWELLERS CAVE, Noel, Mo. 2 miles S of Noel, on US 71. 7 A.M., 5:30 P.M. 40 min. $1; free. Camping.

BRIDAL CAVE, Camdenton, Mo. 2 miles N of Camdenton, off US 54. 7:30 A.M., 7:30 P.M. 30 min. $1.25; $.50.

CAVE SPRING ONYX CAVERNS, Van Buren, Mo. 2 miles W of Van Buren, on US 60. 9 A.M., 5 P.M. 45 min. Free. Lunchroom. Cabins. Camping.

CHEROKEE CAVE, Technical Service Corp., St. Louis, Mo. Cherokee and 13th Streets, in St. Louis.

CRYSTAL CAVE, Box 950, Rt. 1, Springfield, Mo. 5 miles N of Springfield, off US 65. 7 A.M., 6 P.M. 1 hr. $1.25; $.65.

CRYSTAL CAVERNS, Cassville, Mo. 1 mile N of Cassville, off Mo. 37. 8 A.M., sundown. 25 min. $.71; $.71.

FAIRY CAVE, Reeds Spring, Mo. 5 miles S of Reeds Spring, off Mo. 13. 8 A.M., 6 P.M. 45 min. $1.10; $.50. Camping.

FANTASTIC CAVERNS, Springfield, Mo. 5 miles NW of Springfield, off US 66. 7:30 A.M., 7:30 P.M. 45 min. $1.12; $.51.

FISHERS CAVE, Meramec State Park, Sullivan, Mo. 1 mile E of Sullivan off US 66. 8 A.M., 6 P.M. 1 hr. $1.00; $.50. Lunchroom. Cabins. Hotel. Camping.

INCA CAVE, Laquey, Mo. 8 miles W of Waynesville, off US 66. 7:30 A.M., 7 P.M. 40 min. $1.00; $.50.

JACOB'S CAVE, Versailles, Mo. 6 miles S of Versailles, off Mo. 5. Apr. 1-Nov. 1. 8 A.M., 5:15 P.M. 45 min. $1; $.50. Camping.

KEENER CAVE, Williamsville, Mo. Near Williamsville, off US 67 on Mo. JJ. Open only to guests in cottages on premises. 1 tour weekly.

MARK TWAIN CAVE, Box 26, Hannibal, Mo. 2 miles S of Hannibal, off US 36. (Summer) 8 A.M., 8 P.M.; (Winter) 8 A.M., 5 P.M. 45 min. $1; $.50. Snack bar.

MARVEL CAVE, Reeds Spring, Mo. 9 miles W of Branson, on Mo. 148. (Summer) 8 A.M., 6 P.M.; (Winter) 8 A.M., 4 P.M. 1¼ hrs. $1.35; $.75. Camping.

MERAMEC CAVERNS, Stanton, Mo. 3 miles S of Stanton, off US 66. 8 A.M., dark. 1½ hrs. $1.22; $.66. Restaurant. Cabins. Camping.

MT. SHIRA CAVE, Noel, Mo.

OLD SPANISH CAVE, Reeds Spring, Mo. 2 miles N of Reeds Spring, on US 65. 7 A.M., 6:30 P.M. 40 min. $1.25; $.60.

ONONDAGA CAVE, Leasburg, Mo. 7 miles off US 66, between Bourbon and Cuba. (Summer) 6 A.M., 8 P.M.; (Winter) 6 A.M., 5 P.M. 45 min. $1.50; $.75. Restaurant. Cabins. Camping.

OZARK CAVERNS, Camdenton, Mo. 3 miles E of Camdenton, off US 54 on road A. Apr. 1-Nov. 1. 8 A.M., 6 P.M. 45 min. $1; $.50.

OZARK WONDER CAVE, Elk Springs, Mo. 4 miles N of Noel, off US 71. 7 A.M., 10 P.M. 45 min. $1; $.50. Cabins.

RIVER CAVE, 623 Finance Bldg., Kansas City, Mo. 2½ miles W of Camdenton, off US 54; then south on road K. Summer. 9 A.M., 5 P.M. 30 min. $1; free. Restaurant. Lodge.

ROUND SPRING CAVERNS, Round Spring, Mo. 14 miles N of Eminence, off Mo. 19. 6 A.M., 6 P.M. 1½ hrs. $1.25; $.65. Lunchroom. Lodge. Cabins. Camping.

SMITTLE CAVE, Grove Springs, Mo. Near Lebanon, on Mo. 5. On demand. $.75; $.50. Camping.

STARK CAVERNS, Eldon, Mo. 7¾ miles N of Bagnell Dam, off US 54. Mar. 1-Nov. 1. 7:30 A.M., 7 P.M. 40 min. $.75; $.35.

TRUITT'S CAVE, Lanagan, Mo. Near Lanagan, off US 71. Underground dining room.

WONDER CAVE, Reeds Spring, Mo.

MONTANA

LEWIS AND CLARK CAVERN, Lewis and Clark Cavern State Park, Whitehall, Mont. 18 miles E of Whitehall, off US 10. May 1-Oct. 1. 8 A.M.,

8 P.M. (June 15 to Labor Day); otherwise, 8 A.M., 5 P.M. 1½ hrs. $1; $.50. Restaurant. Camping.

NEVADA

LEHMAN CAVES, Lehman Caves National Monument, Baker, Nev. 5 miles W of Baker, off US 6. (Summer) 9 A.M., 5 P.M.; (Winter) 9 A.M., 4 P.M. 1 hr. $.50; free. Lunchroom. Cabins. Camping.

NEW HAMPSHIRE

LOST RIVER GLACIAL CAVERNS, North Woodstock, N. H. 5 miles W of North Woodstock, off NH 112. May 30-Oct. 15. 9 A.M., 5:30 P.M. 1 to 2 hrs. $.75; $.50. *Caves under heaps of granite boulders.*

POLAR CAVES, Rumney Depot, N. H. 5 miles W of Plymouth, on NH 25. May 15-Oct. 27. 8 A.M., 10 P.M. 45 min. $1; $.50. Restaurant. *Caves under heaps of granite boulders.*

NEW MEXICO

CARLSBAD CAVERNS, Carlsbad Caverns National Park, Carlsbad, N. M. 27 miles SW of Carlsbad, off US 62. (May 25-Labor Day) 7 A.M., 1:30 P.M.; (Labor Day-May 25) 8:30 A.M., 12:30 P.M. 4 hrs. Also a shorter tour on separate schedule. $1.50; free. Underground lunchroom. Snack bar.

PERPETUAL ICE CAVES, Star Route 2, Grants, N. M. 26 miles SW of Grants, off NM 53. On demand. $.51; $.25. Lunchroom. Cabins. Trailers. Camping. *Lava tube.*

NEW YORK

HOWE CAVERNS, Howe Cave, N. Y. 7 miles E of Cobleskill, off NY 7. 8 A.M., 8 P.M. 1 hr. $1.80; free. (With boat trip, 1¼ hrs. $2.40; free.) Restaurant. Camping.

SECRET CAVERNS, Howe Cave, N. Y. 3 miles W of Central Bridge, off NY 7. Apr. 1-Nov. 1. 8 A.M., 8 P.M. (May 1-Oct. 1); 9 A.M., 5 P.M. (April and Nov.). 45 min. $1.20. Camping.

STONE BRIDGE AND CAVES, Pottersville, N. Y. ½ mile N of Pottersville, then 2 miles W, off US 9. May 15-Oct. 15. 8 A.M., dark. $.80; $.40.

NORTH CAROLINA

LINVILLE CAVERNS, Ashford, N. C. 15 miles S of Linville, on US 221. 7 A.M., dark. 50 min. $1; $.50.

OHIO

CRYSTAL CAVE AND MAMMOTH CAVE, Put-in-Bay, Ohio. On South Bass Island, by ferry from Sandusky, Port Clinton or Catawba. Memorial Day-Labor Day. 9 A.M., 5 P.M. 30 min. $.25; $.15. Snack bar. Camping.

OHIO CAVERNS, West Liberty, Ohio. On Ohio 275, between US 68 and US 33. 8 A.M., 5 P.M. 45 min. $1.50; $.85. Camping.

PERRY'S CAVE, Put-in-Bay, Ohio. On South Bass Island, by ferry from Sandusky, Port Clinton or Catawba. Memorial Day-Labor Day. 30 min. $.25. Hotel.

SENECA CAVERNS, Bellevue, Ohio. 3 miles S of Bellevue, off Ohio 18. May 1-Oct. 1. 9 A.M., 7 P.M. 1 hr. $1.50; $.68.

SEVEN CAVES, Bainbridge, Ohio. 5 miles W of Bainbridge, off US 50. Mar. 15-Dec. 1. 2½ hrs. Self-guided. $1.20; $.50. Restaurant.

ZANE CAVERNS, Bellefontaine, Ohio. 7 miles E of Bellefontaine, off Ohio 540. 9 A.M., 6 P.M. 1 hr. $1.50; $.75. Camping.

OKLAHOMA

ALABASTER CAVERNS, Alabaster Caverns State Park, Freedom, Okla. 9 miles SE of Freedom, off Okla. 50. 8 A.M., 6 P.M. 1½ hrs. $1.25; free. Camping.

OREGON

LAVA RIVER CAVES, Lava River Caves State Park, Bend, Ore. 12 miles S of Bend, off US 97. May 1-Oct. 1. 9 A.M., 5 P.M. Self-guided. Free. *Lava tubes.*

OREGON CAVES NATIONAL MONUMENT, Supt., Crater Lake National Park, Crater Lake, Ore. 20 miles E of Cave Junction, on Ore. 46. 10 A.M., 5 P.M. (May 29-June 15; Sept. 10-Oct. 1). 9 A.M., 7 P.M. (June 15-Sept. 10). Special schedule in winter. 2 hrs. $.85; $.50. Children under 6 not admitted; nursery service available. Restaurant. Hotel. Cabins.

SEA LION CAVES, Florence, Ore. 11 miles N of Florence, on US 101. 8 A.M., ½ hr. before sunset, 45 min. $.50; $.25. Restaurant. *Sea cave.*

PENNSYLVANIA

CRYSTAL CAVE, Kutztown, Pa. 3 miles SW of Kutztown, off US 222. Mar. 1-Jan. 1. 8 A.M., 8 P.M. (May 1-Nov. 1); 9 A.M., 5 P.M. (Nov., Dec., Mar., April). 30 min. $1.30; $.75. Snack bar.

INDIAN CAVERNS, Spruce Creek, Pa. Between Water Street and State College, on Pa. 45. 9 A.M., 9 P.M. 1 hr. $1.50; $.75. Camping.

INDIAN ECHO CAVERNS, Hummelstown, Pa. ½ mile S of Hummelstown, on US 422 Bypass. 9 A.M., dark (Apr. 1-Nov. 1). Remainder of year, Saturdays and Sundays only. 45 min. $.90; $.45.

LINCOLN CAVERNS, Huntingdon, Pa. 3 miles W of Huntingdon, on US 22. Mar. 1-Dec. 1. 8 A.M., 8 P.M. (June 1-Oct. 1); 9 A.M., 5 P.M. (Mar., Apr., May, Oct., Nov.). 1 hr. $1.25; $.62. Lunch room.

LOST CAVE, Hellertown, Pa. 3 miles S of Bethlehem, off Pa. 412. 7 A.M., 11 P.M. 40 min. $1.10; $.55. Camping.

ONYX CAVE, RD 2, Box 308, Hamburg, Pa. 6 miles SE of Hamburg, off US 22. On demand. 30 min. $.75; $.35. Camping.

PENN'S CAVE, Centre Hall, Pa. 5 miles E of Centre Hall, on Pa. 95. 9 A.M., 9 P.M. (May 1-Oct. 1); 9 A.M., 6 P.M. (Oct. 1-May 1). 40 min. Entirely by motor boat. $1.50; $.75. Snack bar. Camping.

WONDERLAND CAVERNS, Manns Choice, Pa. S of Manns Choice, on US 31. May 15-Sept. 15. 9 A.M., 6 P.M. 30 min. $1.20; $.55. Camping.

WOODWARD CAVE, Woodward, Pa. 2 miles SW of Woodward, off Pa. 45. May 1-Nov. 1. 8 A.M., 5 P.M. 40 min. $1.20; $.60. Camping.

SOUTH DAKOTA

CRYSTAL CAVE, Tilford, S.D. 7½ miles SW of Tilford, off US 14. May 15-Nov. 1. 6 A.M., 9 P.M. $1.13; $.57. Lunchroom. Camping.

JEWEL CAVE, Jewel Cave National Monument, Wind Cave National Park, Hot Springs, S. D. 12 miles W of Custer, off US 16. Memorial Day-Labor Day. 8 A.M., 4 P.M. 45 min. $.60; free. Camping.

NAMELESS CAVE, Rt. 1, Box 89, Rapid City, S. D. 3½ miles W of Rapid City, off SD 40. May 1-Nov. 1. 6 A.M., 10 P.M. 45 min. $1.00; $.35. Camping.

RUSHMORE CAVE, Keystone, S.D. 5 miles E of Keystone off SD 16A. May 1-Nov. 15. Open 24 hrs. a day (June 1-Sept. 1); 7 A.M., 7 P.M. (May, Sept., Oct., Nov.). 1 hr. $1; $.50.

SITTING BULL CRYSTAL CAVERNS, Box 1649, Rapid City, S. D. 9 miles S of Rapid City, off US 16. 5 A.M., 9 P.M. 45 min. $1.25; $.75. Lunch stand. Camping.

STAGE BARN CRYSTAL CAVERNS, Piedmont, S. D. 12 miles NW of Rapid City, off US 14. Open 24 hrs. a day. On demand. $1.20; $.60.

WILDCAT CAVE, Rt. 1, Rapid City, S. D. 5 miles W of Rapid City, on SD 40. 6 A.M., 10 P.M. (June 1-Oct. 1); 9 A.M., 5 P.M. (Oct. 1-June 1). 1 hr. $1.00; $.35. Lunchroom.

WIND CAVE, Wind Cave National Park, Hot Springs, S. D. 10 miles N of Hot Springs, on US 85A. 8 A.M., 5 P.M. (June 1-Aug. 31); 8:30 A.M., 3 P.M. (Sept., Oct., Apr., May). Write or phone for guide service remainder of year. 1 hr. $.75; free. Lunchroom (summer). Camping.

WONDERLAND CAVE, Tilford, S. D. 12 miles S of Sturgis, off US 14. 6 A.M., 9 P.M. $1; $.50.

TENNESSEE

BRISTOL CAVERNS, Box 188, Bristol, Tenn.-Va. (on the state line). 5 miles SE of Bristol, off US 421. 9 A.M., 6 P.M. 1 hr. $1.50; $.75.

CRYSTAL CITY CAVES, Chattanooga, Tenn. Off US 41 North. 7 A.M., 8 P.M. 45 min. $1.50; $.75. Camping.

CUDJO'S CAVE, Cumberland Gap, Tenn.

CUMBERLAND CAVERNS (formerly HIGGENBOTHAM CAVE), Rt. 6, McMinnville, Tenn. 8 miles SE of McMinnville, off Tenn. 8. 6 A.M., 11 P.M. 1½ to 3 hrs. $1.50; $1.00. Camping. (Scheduled to open July, 1956.)

DUNBAR CAVE, Clarksville, Tenn. 3 miles N of Clarksville, off US 79. May 15-Sept. 15. 10 A.M., 5 P.M. 1 hr. $1; $.50. Snack bar. Lodge. Camping.

INDIAN CAVE, New Market, Tenn. 7 miles E of Blaine, off US 11 W. 1 hr. Snack bar. Camping.

JEWEL CAVE, Rt. 3, Dickson, Tenn. 12 miles W of Dickson, off US 70. 7 A.M., 6 P.M. 1 hr. $1.20; $.50. Snack bar. Camping.

RUBY FALLS CAVE, Chattanooga, Tenn. 1 mile S of Chattanooga, off US 11. 7 A.M., 10 P.M. 40 min. $1.50; $.75. Restaurant.

TUCKALEECHEE CAVERNS, Townsend, Tenn. 2 miles S of Townsend, off Tenn. 73. Apr. 1-Nov. 1. 7:30 A.M., 6:30 P.M. 1 hr. $1.50; $.50.

WONDER CAVE, Monteagle, Tenn. Near Monteagle, ½ mile E of US 41. 7 A.M., sundown. 1 hr. $1.50; $.85. Camping.

TEXAS

CASCADE CAVERNS, Boerne, Tex. 24 miles NW of San Antonio, off US 87. 8 A.M., 6 P.M. 1½ hrs. $1.20; $.48. Restaurant. Cabins. Camping.

CAVE-WITHOUT-A-NAME, Boerne, Tex. 11 miles NE of Boerne, off US 87. 8 A.M., 6 P.M. 45 min. $1.10; $.44. Camping.

TEXAS LONGHORN CAVERN, Texas Longhorn Cavern State Park, Burnet, Tex. 11 miles SW of Burnet, off US 281. 10 A.M., 5 P.M. 2 hrs. $1.20; free. Snack bar. Camping.

WONDER CAVE, San Marcos, Tex. Within city limits, off US 81. 8 A.M., 6 P.M. 1 hr. $1.00; $.50. Restaurant. Cabins. Camping.

UTAH

TIMPANOGOS CAVE, Timpanogos Cave National Monument, American Fork, Utah. 7 miles NE of American Fork, on Utah 80, then 1½ miles by foot up mountain trail. May 1-Oct. 31. 9 A.M., 4 P.M. (at cave mouth). Round-trip 3 hrs. from parking lot; 1 hr. in cave. $.50; free. Snack bar. Camping.

VIRGINIA

BATTLEFIELD CRYSTAL CAVERNS, Strasburg, Va. 1 mile N of Strasburg, off US 11. 7 A.M., 7 P.M. 45 min. $1.10. Camping.

DIXIE CAVERNS, RR 3, Box 394, Salem, Va. 7 miles W of Salem, off US 11. 8 A.M., 8 P.M. (June 1-Sept. 15); 8 A.M., 5:30 P.M. (Sept. 15-May 31). 45 min. $1.50; $.75. Snack bar. Restaurant. Camping.

ENDLESS CAVERNS, New Market, Va. 3 miles S of New Market, off US 11. On demand 24 hours a day. 1¼ hrs. $1.80; $.90. Restaurant. Trailers. Camping.

GRAND CAVERNS, Grottoes, Va. On US 340 between Elkton and Waynesboro. Closed Christmas Day. 7:30 A.M., 8 P.M. (Apr. 15-Oct. 15); 8 A.M., 5 P.M. (Oct. 16-Apr. 14). 1 hr. $1.65; $.75. Snack bar (summer).

LURAY CAVERNS, Luray, Va. Near Luray on US 211. 8 A.M., 8 P.M. (May 1-Nov. 1); 9 A.M., 7 P.M. (Nov. 1-May 1). 80 min. $1.80; $.90. Restaurant. Lunchroom. Trailers. Camping.

MASSANUTTEN CAVERNS, Keezletown, Va. 5 miles E of Harrisonburg, off US 33. 8 A.M., 8 P.M. 1 hr. $1.65; $.80. Cottages and camping by the week.

MELROSE CAVERNS, Harrisonburg, Va. 6 miles N of Harrisonburg, off US 11. 45 min. $1.25; $.63. Cabins. Trailers.

NATURAL TUNNEL AND CHASM, Natural Tunnel, Va. On US 23, US 58, US 421. Self-guided tours during daylight hours. Free. Restaurant. Motel.

SHENANDOAH CAVERNS, New Market, Va. 4 miles NW of New Market, off US 11. On demand. 1 hr. $1.50; $.75. Snack bar.

SKYLINE CAVERNS, Front Royal, Va. 2 miles S of Front Royal, on Va. 12. 7 A.M., 9 P.M. (May 15-Sept. 15); 8 A.M., 8 P.M. (Sept. 16-Oct. 30, and Mar. 1-May 14); 9 A.M., 5 P.M. (Nov. 1-Feb. 28). 1 hr. $1.80; $.90. Restaurant. Camping.

WASHINGTON

CHELAN ICE CAVES, Lake Chelan State Park, Chelan, Wash. 6 miles N of Chelan, off US 97. Self-guided tours. Free. Camping.

CRAWFORD CAVE, Riverside State Park, Spokane 14, Wash. 12 miles NW of Metaline on county road. June 1-Oct. 31. Self-guided tours. Free. Bring own lights.

WEST VIRGINIA

ORGAN CAVE, Ronceverte, West Va. 6 miles W of Caldwell, off US 60. 8 A.M., dark. 1 hr. $1.12; $.56. Camping.

SENECA CAVERNS, Riverton, West Va. 3½ miles E of Riverton, off US 33. Apr. 1-Dec. 1. 7 A.M., 9 P.M. 45 min. $1.10; $.50. Restaurant. Camping.

SMOKEHOLE CAVERNS, Moorefield, West Va. 8 miles W of Petersburg, on West Va. 4 & 28. June 1-Nov. 1. 9 A.M., 5:30 P.M. 45 min. $1.12; $.51. Camping.

WISCONSIN

CAVE OF THE MOUNDS, Blue Mounds, Wis. 25 miles W of Madison, off US 18 and 151. Apr. 15-Nov. 1. 9 A.M., 5 P.M. (Apr. 15-June 1, and Labor Day-Nov. 1); 8 A.M., 7:30 P.M. (June 1-Labor Day). 30 min. $.80; $.35. Snack bar.

CRYSTAL CAVE, Spring Valley, Wis. 1 mile W of Spring Valley, on Wis. 29. Mar. 15-Nov. 15. (Sundays only, Nov. 15-Mar. 15.) 8 A.M., 8 P.M. (Summer); 9 A.M., 6 P.M. (Fall); 2 P.M., 5 P.M. (Winter); 9 A.M., 7 P.M. (Spring). 1 hr. $1.25; $.50. Restaurant.

EAGLE CAVE, Muscoda, Wis. 8 miles NW of Muscoda. Apr. 15-Nov. 1. 8 A.M., 6 P.M. 45 min. $1.00; $.50. Trailers. Camping.

KICKAPOO CAVERNS, Wauzeka, Wis. 4 miles W of Wauzeka, off Wis. 60. May 15-Nov. 1. 8 A.M. 30 min. $.80; $.40. Camping.

Speleological Societies in the United States

General Speleological Organizations

The National Speleological Society, Inc.
Mrs. Mary McKenzie, Secretary
1407 Hickory Court
Broyhill Park
Falls Church, Va.

A wide range of literature of interest to cavers may be obtained from this office.

The Western Speleological Institute, Inc.
Phil C. Orr, Director
Museum of Natural History
Santa Barbara, Calif.

The Western Speleological Institute is a purely scientific organization, not a membership organization, and it does not conduct caving trips in which amateurs may participate. The speleologists associated with the Institute work on a professional basis, and the information they gain from surveys and excavations is exchanged with scientific institutions.

Grottoes of the National Speleological Society

Anyone interested in exploring wild caves should do so in the company of experienced cavers. Most such cavers are members of the National Speleological Society. The following list gives the addresses of all National Speleological Society Grottoes as of January 1, 1956.

ALABAMA

Alabama Polytechnic Institute
  Grotto (Student Grotto)
Dr. J. D. McClung, Faculty Sponsor
P. O. Box 322,
Auburn, Ala.

Huntsville Grotto
Paul Kane, Secretary
1209 Brandon St.,
Huntsville, Ala.

CALIFORNIA

San Joaquin Valley Grotto
Darrel Tomer, Secretary
Rt. 5, Box 254
Hanford, Calif.

Southern California Grotto
Carroll S. Slemaker, Secretary
1735 N. Orchid,
Hollywood, Calif.

COLORADO

Colorado Grotto
John Streich, Secretary
1132 Lima,
Aurora, Colo.

DISTRICT OF COLUMBIA

District of Columbia Grotto
Marilyn Bozeman, Secretary
4528 32nd St.,
Mt. Rainier, Md.

GEORGIA

Atlanta Grotto
J. Roy Chapman, Chairman
Box 701,
Atlanta, Ga.

INDIANA

Central Indiana Grotto
Kathryn McCartney, Secretary
5342 E. Tenth St.,
Indianapolis, Ind.

Scotto Grotto
Jack W. Dorsey, Chairman
RFD 3,
Scottsburgh, Ind.

Tarevac Grotto
T. L. Carr, Acting Chairman
1012 15th St.,
Tell City, Ind.

KENTUCKY

Kentucky-Indiana Grotto
Charles B. Fort, Secretary
1426 S. 3rd St.,
Louisville, Ky.

MARYLAND

Baltimore Grotto
James Holechek, Publicity Director
2903 Louise Ave.,
Baltimore 14, Md.

MASSACHUSETTS

Boston Grotto
Thomas Richardson, Chairman
53 Appleton St.,
Arlington, Mass.

MINNESOTA

Twin City Grotto
David S. Gebhard, Secretary
1665 Montreal Ave.,
St. Paul 5, Minn.

MISSOURI

Missouri School of Mines Grotto
   (Student Grotto)
Dr. J. P. Roston, Faculty Advisor
Mining Department,
Missouri School of Mines,
Rolla, Mo.

Western Missouri Grotto
Oscar Hawksley, Secretary
Central Missouri State College,
Warrensburg, Mo.

NEW JERSEY

Enterprise Dilettante Speleology
   Grotto
Alfred Hulstrunk, Co-chairman
139 Halsted St.,
East Orange, N. J.

Northern New Jersey Grotto
Peggy Mueller, Secretary
549 Jerusalem Rd.,
Scotch Plains, N. J.

NEW YORK

Cornell Grotto
T. L. Poulson, Treasurer
216 Park Ave.,
Manhasset, N. Y.

Metropolitan New York Grotto
Catherine Keane, Secretary
645 E. 232nd St.,
New York 66, N. Y.

NORTH CAROLINA

Piedmont Grotto
Samuel Phifer, Chairman
Box 258,
Monroe, N. C.

OHIO

Central Ohio Grotto
Bruce Schneider, Secretary
41 West Blake,
Columbus 2, Ohio

Cleveland Grotto
Julius Kerby, Secretary
12528 Griffing Ave.,
Cleveland, Ohio

OKLAHOMA

Tulsa Grotto
Richard Tenney, Secretary
1304 S. Yale,
Tulsa, Okla.

PENNSYLVANIA

Nittany Grotto (Student Grotto)
Dr. S. W. Frost, Faculty Advisor
465 E. Foster Ave.,
State College, Pa.

Philadelphia Grotto
Audrey Welsh, Secretary
161 Lakeside Blvd.,
Trenton 10, N. J.

Pittsburgh Grotto
Allen McCrady, Secretary
304 Ross St.,
Pittsburgh 19, Pa.

Shippensburg State Teachers College Grotto (Student Grotto)
Jack E. Harclerode, Chairman
No. 126 SSTC,
Shippensburg, Pa.

Standing Stone Grotto
Maurice A. Henry, Secretary
Apt. 5, The Village,
Huntingdon, Pa.

SOUTH DAKOTA

Black Hills Grotto
Lilace Taylor, Secretary
309 N. 4th St.,
Hot Springs, S. D.

TENNESSEE

Cumberland Grotto
Daniel E. Bloxsom, Secretary
Oak Park,
Tullahoma, Tenn.

Nashville Grotto
Standiford Gorin
General Shoe Corporation,
Nashville, Tenn.

TEXAS

Balcones Grotto
Joe C. Pearce, Secretary
5713 Avenue G,
Austin, Tex.

University of Texas Grotto
(Student Grotto)
Dr. Austin Phelps, Faculty Advisor
3115 Tom Green,
Austin, Tex.

UTAH

Salt Lake Grotto
J. Robert Kennedy, Secretary
5762 Lindon St.,
Salt Lake City, Utah

VIRGINIA

University of Virginia Grotto
(Student Grotto)
John A. Barnes, Secretary
6 Echols House,
The University,
Charlottesville, Va.

VPI Grotto (Student Grotto)
Dr. John W. Murray, Faculty
Advisor
Dept. of Chemistry,
Virginia Polytechnic Institute,
Blacksburg, Va.

Wytheville Grotto
Betty Sabatinos, Secretary
102 Faculty St.,
Blacksburg, Va.

WEST VIRGINIA

Charleston Grotto
Elizabeth Snowden, Secretary
708 Clinton Ave.,
Charleston, W. Va.

Morgantown Grotto
William D. Conner, Secretary
P. O. Box 72,
Morgantown, W. Va.

A Sample Cave Field Report Form

(Systematic cave exploration is by no means simple. The following form is used by members of the National Speleological Society in recording what they find out about the caves they investigate.)

(1) Prepare in duplicate; one for National Headquarters and one for local files.
(2) Leave no item *unmarked*. If data is not available, draw a line through item to indicate that fact.
(3) Describe location accurately. If needed, add an attached sheet.
(4) If cave has more than one entrance, mark pertinent data for each entrance with identifying figure; as (1), (3), etc. and indicate type of entrance, as Sinkhole, Hillside, etc.
(5) Indicate all measured data by letter M; estimated data by letter E; i.e.—100 ft. E, 300 ft. M.
(6) Indicate all slopes in degrees, as 25° (M or E).
(7) Where a series of items are indicated, check ( ) appropriate ones only, and mark E or M, if proper.
(8) Additional copies of this form can be obtained from National Speleological Society Headquarters.

Name _____ Date _____

Location _____
          State   County   Nearest Village

_____
    U.S. Geological Survey Quadrangle Map   Special Notes

Owner _____
              Name   Address

Exterior: (Check items which apply) Wooded_____ Open_____
    Cultivated_____ Flat_____ Hilly_____ Mountainous_____

Entrance: Hillside_____ Bottom ⅓_____ Middle ⅓_____ Top ⅓_____
    Sinkhole_____ Bottom_____ Side_____ Other_____
    Muddy_____ Dry_____ Size_____ X _____
                                    Height   Width
    Level_____ Slope up_____ Slope down_____

266

Rock: Solid____ Massive____ Slightly fractured____ Thick Bedded____
Broken____ Thin Bedded____ Strike____ Dip____ Limestone____
Sandstone____ Shale____ Other____ Geological Period____

General Course of Cave: Along strike____ Across strike____ Along
joints and seams____ No order____ Horizontal____
Sloping up____ ° Sloping down____ ° Vertical____ No order____
Number of levels 1____, 2____, 3____, 4____, 5____
Wells and Chimneys____ ____ Approximate number and size____
                   Yes   No

Direction of Cave: (As N.W. to S.E.) Main part____ Minor leads____
Vertical drops in passageway requiring ropes or ladders_____
Number of____ Maximum____ Minimum____ Average____

Size of Cave: (Mark only part explored. Mark E if estimated; M if measured.) Main Passageway____ 100′ or less____ 100′-300′____
300′-500′____ 500′-1000′____ 1000′ to ½ mile____ Over ½
mile____ Average width____ Maximum width____
Average height ____ Maximum height____ Percentage of
passageway requiring crawling____ Total length of passages____ft.

Rooms: Approximate number____ Average size ____ X ____ X ____
                                        Width   Length   Height
Maximum size____ X ____ X ____
           Width   Length   Height

Decoration: Flowstone: None____ Scarce____ Average____ Much____
Dripstone: None____ Scarce____ Average____ Much____
Other types of formations: None____ Scarce____ Average____ Much____
Outstanding large formations: None____ Few____ Many____
Other notes _____

Coloring: (Mark percentage) Pure White____ Black____ Brown____
Red____ Other____ Remarks: _____

Floors: Bedrock____ Mud____ Sand____ Broken Rock____ Gravel____

Streams: Number____ Size____ Velocity____ Direction of flow____

Lakes and Ponds: Under 5′ in diameter____ 25′-100′____ Over 100′____
Depth: Under 2 feet____ 2′-5′____ 5′-10′____ Over 10′____

Springs: _____

General Moisture Conditions: Extremely dry____ Dry____ Average____
Wet____ Extremely wet____ Trash____ Wood____

Photographic Opportunities: Bad____ Fair____ Good____ Excellent____

Fauna: Bats: None____ Few____ Many____ Large Colonies____
    Band Numbers Noted_____

_____

(List of band numbers should also be sent to Fish & Wildlife Service, Washington 25, D. C., including complete band number, date and location where bat was noted, and sex and species if determined. The Fish and Wildlife Service will notify you of the place and date of banding as well as giving you the bander's name.)

    Bat guano_____ Species (if identified)_____
            Depth of deposits
    Rats: None____ Evidences of____ Seen____
    Snails: No____ Evidences of____ Seen____
    Crickets: Yes____ No____
    Flies: Yes____ No____
    Spiders: Yes____ No____
    Mosquitoes: Yes____ No____
    Crayfish: Yes____ No____
    Salamanders: Yes____ No____
    Fish: Yes____ No____
    Other _____

Plant Life: Fungi_____
    Roots _____
    Other _____

Air: Temperature: ____ ° Outside____ Inside at end of daylight____
    Interior____ Of flowing streams____
    Circulation: Strong____ Fair____ None____ Evidence of lack of
    Oxygen____ Foul air____

General Cave Conditions: Good_____ Fair_____ Dangerous_____
    If dangerous, explain_____

Possibilities of becoming lost: None____ Slight____ Average____
    Great____

Data Collected: Mapped by_____
    Photographs by _____

_____
_____
_____

Members of Party:_____

_____

_____

_____

_____

Previous Cave History:_____

_____

_____

_____

Other Data:_____

_____

_____

Report Prepared by:_____
N. B. (Attach additional sheets if necessary to complete data on any item.)

Suggested Reading List on Caves and Caving

Since William E. Davies, President of the National Speleological Society, has prepared an exhaustive *Bibliography of North American Speleology* through 1950, which is scheduled for early publication, there is no need to attempt an extensive bibliography in these pages. Nor, considering the nature and aims of this book, has it been deemed necessary to provide the elaborate scholarly apparatus which is appropriate for books of a more technical nature.

It does seem useful, however, to list in one place some of the literature which is more or less readily obtainable and which provides detailed information on a variety of topics that could only be touched in these pages.

ANONYMOUS. *Hiking, Camping, Mountaineering and Trail-Clearing Equipment.* Washington, D. C.: Potomac Appalachian Trail Club, 1954. 49 pp. (A careful analysis of equipment useful to spelunkers, with information as to where it can be obtained.)

ANONYMOUS. *Jim White's Story of Carlsbad Caverns.* Carlsbad, N. M.: Charlie L. White and Jim White, Jr., 1951. (Biographical sketch of White and the story of his explorations.)

BRETZ, J HARLEN. "Vadose and Phreatic Features of Limestone Caverns," *Journal of Geology,* Vol. 50, No. 6, pp. 675-811. 1942. (A theory of cave origin.)

BRIDWELL, MARGARET M. *The Story of Mammoth Cave National Park.* Mammoth Cave, Ky.: Margaret M. Bridwell, 1952. 64 pp. (Brief history of the cave.)

Bulletin of the National Speleological Society. (Published intermittently, at least once a year. Contains a wealth of scientific information, as well as some material of particular interest to spelunkers.)

CASTERET, NORBERT. *The Darkness Under the Earth.* New York: Henry Holt, 1954. 174 pp. (A famous French speleologist tells of adventures and dangers in French caves.)

CLYMER, VIRGIL H. (ed.). *Story of Howe Caverns.* Howe Caverns, Inc., 1946. 72 pp. (History and description.)

Cullingford, C. H. D. (ed.). *British Caving, an Introduction to Speleology.* London: Routledge and Kegan Paul, Ltd., 1953. 468 pp. (Articles by fourteen experts on all aspects of the science and practice of caving in Britain.)

Davies, William E. *Caverns of West Virginia.* West Virginia Geological Survey, Vol. XIX, 1949. 353 pp. (Clear summary of all important information about West Virginia caves. Maps.)

——. *The Caves of Maryland.* Department of Geology, Mines and Water Resources; State of Maryland. Bulletin 7. 1950. 75 pp. (Clear summary of all important information about Maryland caves. Maps.)

Davis, W. M. "Origin of Limestone Caverns," *Bulletin of the Geological Society of America,* Vol. 41, No. 3, pp. 475-628. 1930. (A theory of cave origin.)

De Saussure, R. E.; Lange, A. L.; Mowat, G. D. *Report of the California-Nevada Speleological Survey.* Western Speleological Institute. 1954. 198 pp. mimeographed. (A detailed survey prepared under the auspices of the Western Speleological Institute and the National Speleological Society. Available only to qualified researchers.)

Explorer, The. Explorers Club of Pittsburgh, May, 1955. 8 pp. mimeographed. (Special issue devoted to Schoolhouse Cave. Map.)

Gardner, James H. "Origin and Development of Limestone Caverns," *Bulletin of the Geological Society of America,* Vol. 46, No. 8, pp. 1255-1274. 1935. (A theory of cave origin.)

Hartley, Howard W. *The Tragedy of Sand Cave.* Louisville, Ky.: Louisville Standard Printing Co., 1925. 145 pp. (A contemporary summary of events connected with the death of Floyd Collins.)

Henderson, Kenneth A. *Handbook of American Mountaineering.* Boston: Houghton Mifflin Co., 1942. 239 pp. (A practical guide to the mountaineering techniques used by spelunkers.)

Hendrix, Charles E. *The Cave Book.* Revere, Mass.: Earth Science Publishing Co., 1950. 66 pp. (Brief survey of cave geology and spelunking techniques.)

Hovey, Horace C. *Celebrated American Caverns.* Cincinnati: R. Clarke & Co., 1882. 228 pp. (This classic remained the only popular general book on American caves until 1955. Out of print, but available in many large libraries.)

Jackson, George F. *Wyandotte Cave.* Narberth, Pa.: Livingston Publishing Co., 1953. 66 pp. (History, description, archeology, geology. Map.)

Lawrence, Joe, Jr., and Brucker, Roger W. *The Caves Beyond.* New York: Funk & Wagnalls. 1955. 283 pp. (The story of exploration in Floyd Collins' Crystal Cave. Maps.)

Malott, Clyde A. "Invasion Theory of Cavern Development," *Proceedings of the Geological Society of America (Abstract),* p. 323. 1937. (A theory of cave origin.)

McGILL, WILLIAM M. *Caverns of Virginia.* Charlottesville: University of Virginia Press, 1933. 187 pp. (Out of print. Deals primarily with the geology of the commercial caverns of the Shenandoah Valley.)

MOHR, CHARLES E. (ed.). *The Caves of Texas.* Bulletin 10, National Speleological Society. 1948. 136 pp. (Articles on a variety of topics, plus information about all caves known in 1948. A few maps.)

MOHR, CHARLES E., and SLOANE, HOWARD N. (eds.). *Celebrated American Caves.* New Brunswick: Rutgers University Press, 1955. 339 pp. (Sixteen contributors cover many important aspects of caves and caving in the United States and Latin America. Maps.)

The News. National Speleological Society. Monthly. (Contains a wealth of information about spelunking and also some reports of scientific developments.)

Occasional Papers. National Speleological Society. No. 1, George W. Moore, "The Origin of Helictites"; No. 2, E. R. Pohl, "Vertical Shafts in Limestone Caves."

OWEN, LUELLA AGNES. *Cave Regions of the Ozarks and Black Hills.* Cincinnati: Editor Publishing Co., 1898. 228 pp. (This regional book, long out of print, is available in some libraries.)

PERRY, CLAY. *New England's Buried Treasure.* New York: Stephen Daye Press, 1946. 348 pp. (Spelunking, history and folklore in New England.)

———. *Underground Empire.* New York: Stephen Daye Press, 1948. 221 pp. (Spelunking, history and folklore in New York state.)

ROTHERT, OTTO A. *The Outlaws of Cave-in-Rock.* Cleveland: Arthur H. Clark Co., 1924. 364 pp. (A detailed chronicle of the pirates and murderers who used this cave.)

SHOEMAKER, HENRY W. *Pennsylvania's Grandest Cavern.* Harrisburg: Telegraph Press, 1950. 109 pp. (History, legends, description of Penn's Cave.)

STONE, RALPH W. (ed.). *Caves of Pennsylvania.* Bulletin 15, National Speleological Society. 1953. 143 pp. (Articles on a variety of topics, plus detailed information about all caves known in 1953. Maps.)

SWINNERTON, A. C. "Origin of Limestone Caverns," *Bulletin of the Geological Society of America,* Vol. 43, No. 3, pp. 663-694. 1932. (A theory of cave origin.)

TAZIEFF, HAROUN. *Caves of Adventure.* New York: Harper & Bros, 1953. 222 pp. (Stories of exploration in the caves of Pierre Saint-Martin in the Pyrenees.)

THRAILKILL, JOHN. *Introduction to Caving.* Ward, Colo.: Gerry Mountaineering Equipment Co., 1954. 28 pp. (Very brief guide to spelunking.)

Miscellaneous

Cave Surveys. In most cave areas about which books have not yet been published, Grottoes of the National Speleological Society are conducting surveys which attempt to include most important information about all known caves. NSS Grottoes will often make this unpublished information available to those interested. (For addresses of Grottoes, see pages 263-65.)

Films. *The News,* National Speleological Society, October, 1950, published a list of films about caves and caving.

"Limestone Caverns," 16 mm., 1 reel, color, may be obtained from the American Museum of Natural History. (Deals with formation of caves and speleothems.)

"Luray Caverns," 16 mm. and 8 mm., may be obtained from Luray Caverns, Luray, Va., or from the Virginia Department of Conservation.

The NSS Visual Aids Library has some black and white 35 mm. historical films.

Folders. Nearly every cave listed in the Commercial Cave Directory, pages 251-61, will supply a printed folder on request, and some operators can supply more detailed pamphlets as well.

Maps. In the above list of books, those which contain small-scale cave maps have been noted. Larger maps and unpublished maps are often obtainable through NSS Grottoes (see list on pages 263-65). The national office of the NSS has for sale maps of hundreds of American caves.

Slides. Color transparencies suitable for projection, and in some cases accompanied with a tape-recorded explanatory lecture, may be rented from the NSS through John D. Parker, 149 Trent Road, Philadelphia, Pa.

Index

(Figures in italics refer to illustrations. To find a photograph, look in the group of pictures following the text page given in italics. Since much of the material beginning with page 245 consists of alphabetized lists, such material is *not* listed in this index.)

Bunting, Kenneth, *184*
Byers, Ernie, 189

Cabot, John, 40
Cabot, Sebastian, 40
calcite, 20-23, *24*, 24, 25, 52, 54, 97, 177.
  See also calcium carbonate
calcite bubble, 22, *24*
calcium bicarbonate, 11, 14, 20
calcium carbonate, 11, 12, 13, 14, 15, 16,
  20, *152*
calcium nitrate, 180. *See also* saltpetre
  mining
calcium sulphate, 23. *See also* gypsum
Cambarus ayersii, 88
camel, 45
Camp and Trail Outfitters, 227
Campbell, Andrew, 82-84, 92, 93, *152*
Campbell, Dr. Charles A. R., 115
Campbell, William, 82-84
cancer, 31
carabiner. *See* karabiner
carbide, 212, 214
carbide lamp, 6-7, 214, 223, 229
carbon dioxide, 11, 13, 20, *179*, 199
Carbon 14 dating, 48
carbonic acid, 11, 12, 15
Carlsbad Caverns, 19, *24*, 88, 101-109,
  111-112, 117, 119, *152*, 160, 167, 171,
  176, 180, 192, 195
Carmichael, Henry, 208
cave(s): accidents in, 197-209, 215, 217;
  air in, 74; clothing in, 76, 79, 95, 96,
  112, 204, 221-223; cave coral, 22, *24*,
  152; commercial directory, 251-261;
  "dead," 24-25, *88*, *152*; diving, *24*, 130,
  201, 239-240; field report form, 266-
  269; how to find, 187-196; lighting in,
  76, 79, 80, 81, 146, *152*; "living," 19-
  24; "cave mile," 111; mysteries, 175-
  186; onyx, 22; origin of, 11-18, 91, 114,
  175-176; pearls, 22, *24*, 109, 148; photography, 241-244; reading list, 270-
  272; uses, 159-174. *See also* equipment,
  fauna, flora
Cave Carnival, 134
Cave-in-Rock, 66-67, 169, 175-176
Cave of the Winds, 90
"cave pneumonia," 180
*Cave Regions of the Ozarks and Black
  Hills*, 95
"cave sickness," 180
cave survey, model, 127-130, 273
Caverns of West Virginia, 127
Caves Beyond, The, 156
Caves of Maryland, The, 127
Caves of Pennsylvania, The, 127
Celebrated American Caverns, 90, 91, 93
Celebrated American Caves, 209
celestite, 160
Ceremonial Cave, 55-56, *88*

Chapman, J. Roy, 86
Cherokee Cave, 35-38
chimneying, *184*, 238
Christmas Tree (Cumberland Caverns),
  184
Church Cave, 202
Civil War, 85, 86, 93, 142, 151, 159, 161,
  166
claustrophobia, 216, 217
clay, 12, 114
Clymer, Virgil, 65
Cockrum, Dr. E. Lendell, 121
collecting, 88, 241
Collett, Prof. John, 51
Collins, Floyd, 155, 172, *184*, 188, 191,
  203-209
Colossal Cave, 88, 107-108, 112-113, 120,
  121, *152*, 157, 174, 176
column, 21, *24*, *88*, *152*, *184*
commercial caves, directory of, 251-261
conservation, 217, 218
Cope, Edward D., 99
corrasion, *24*, 35
Cosgrove, Mr. and Mrs. C. B., 54, 55
counterfeiters, 168, 169
Cournoyer, Donald N., *184*
courte echelle, 238
Cove Run Cave, 161
cradleboard, *152*, 219
Craighead Caverns, 38-40
Crane, 107
crayfish, 28, 29, 30, *88*, 91
cricket, 28
crinoids, 89, 129
Croghan, Dr. John, 74, 75, 84, *152*
Cro-Magnon Cave, 182
Crystal Cave (Calif.), *24*, *184*, 188
Crystal Cave (Penna.), 86, 188
Crystal Cave. *See also* Floyd Collins'
  Crystal Cave
Crystal Falls Cave, 185
Crystal Grottoes, 188
Crystal Palace (Cumberland Caverns),
  88
Cuddington, Bill, 137
Cullingford, C. H. D., 245
Cumberland Bone Cave, 41-44
Cumberland Caverns, *24*, *88*, *184*. *See
  also* Higgenbotham Cave
curtain, 21, *24*

Danz, Gordon, 136
Darwin, 91, 98
Davies, William E., 127, 270
Davis, Kenneth, 47
Davis, Roy A. *88*, 136-139, 148, 149,
  184
Davis, W. M., 114
"dead" cave, 24-25, *88*, *152*
Dead Dog Cave, 164
Denton, Bert, 143, 144, 145

depth, 176
de Saussure, Raymond, 56
De Soto, 62
Devil's Hole, 173
Devil's Quarry (Cumberland Caverns), 144
Devil's Sinkhole, 106-107
Devitt, William, III, 196
Diamond Cave, *184*
dip, 129
directory of caves open to the public, 251-261
dispersion, 30
dogtooth spar, 22
dolomite, 14, 191
dome, 16, *24*
drapes, 21, *24*
dripstone, 21
duck hawk, 179
Duden, Gottfried, 37
Durham Cave, 98

early man. *See* archeology, artifacts, Indians
echo-location, 118-119, 120
ecology, 142
Edwards Plateau, 106
Egbert, Donald, *152, 184*
eland, 41
elk, 39, 40
Elkhorn Cave, 130-133
Elks Lodge Room (Wind Cave), *152*
Endless Caverns (Va.), 85, 187-188
Epsom salts, 75, 76, 161
equipment: caving, 219-228; Colossal Cave expedition, 112-113; Floyd Collins' Crystal Cave expedition, 155; mountaineering, 239-240; oxygen, 200, 201, 240; photographic, 241-242
erosion, 12-13, 14, 16, 25, 27, 42
expansion bolt, 145, 151, 236, *237*

Fairy Cave, 96
Falling Waters Cave, 181
Farmer, Malcolm F., 56
fatigue, 153, *184*
fauna, 27-34, 35-44, 91, 179-180
Faust, Burton, 177-178
Fertig, Duane, 147
films, 273
fish, 28, 29. *See also* blind fish
Fisher, John, *24*
fisherman's knot, 232
flatworm, 28, 29, 241
flint, 53
flora, 27, 28
Florida Caverns State Park, *24, 61, 88, 184,* 189
flowstone, 22, *88*
Floyd Collins' Crystal Cave, *24, 88, 152,* 153-156, 158, 159, 176, *184,* 188, 203

fluorescein, 123, 128, 129, 164
Folsom Man, 46, 47, 181
formations, 19-25, 176-177. *See also* speleothems
Fort, Charles B., 143, 147
Fountain, Col. A. J., 170
French bowline, 131, 132
fried eggs (Luray Caverns), *88*
Frio Cave, 106, 160
fruit-eating bat, 120, 121
Fugitive Slave Act, 162
fungus, 28, 91
Furlong, 57-59

Gale, Bennett T., 157
galvanometer, 196
Garden of Eden, 80, 82
Gardner, Milford, 147
Garman, Samuel, 93, 94
Garvin, William, 73, 74
Gazin, C. Lewis, 43
General Land Office, 106, 111
geology. *See* cave, limestone, names of minerals, speleothems, etc.
Gerry, 226, 227
Gertsch, Dr. W. J., 241
Giant Totem Pole (Luray Caverns), *24*
Gidley, J. W., 43
glossary of speleological terms, 245-250
Goodman, Zeke, 189
Goodro, Harold, 152
Gorin, Franklin, 71, 74
Gorin, Standiford (Tank), 136, 147, 148, 149, *152*
Gouffre, 137-139
Grand Canyon, 18, 56, *88,* 124, 195
Grand Caverns, *24,* 78, *184,* 188. *See also* Weyer's Cave
Great Extension (Higgenbotham Cave), *88,* 148, *184*
Great Onyx Cave, *24, 88*
Griffin, Donald R., 116-120
Grotto(es) of the National Speleological Society, 126, 130, 133, 152, 263-265, 273
ground sloth, 49
Guadalupe Mountains, 101, 102
guano, 52, 104, 105, 160, 189, 215
Gurnee can, 155, 156, *184,* 221
Gurnee, Russell H., 155, 185
Gurnee, Mrs. Russell H., *152*
gypsum: 17, 23, 191, 193, 195; flowers, 23, *88,* 148, 149, 177, *184;* needles, 23; snow, 148; snowball, *88. See also* calcium sulphate

half-hitch, 231
halozone, 225
Handbook of American Mountaineering, 229
Hanson, Carl, 74

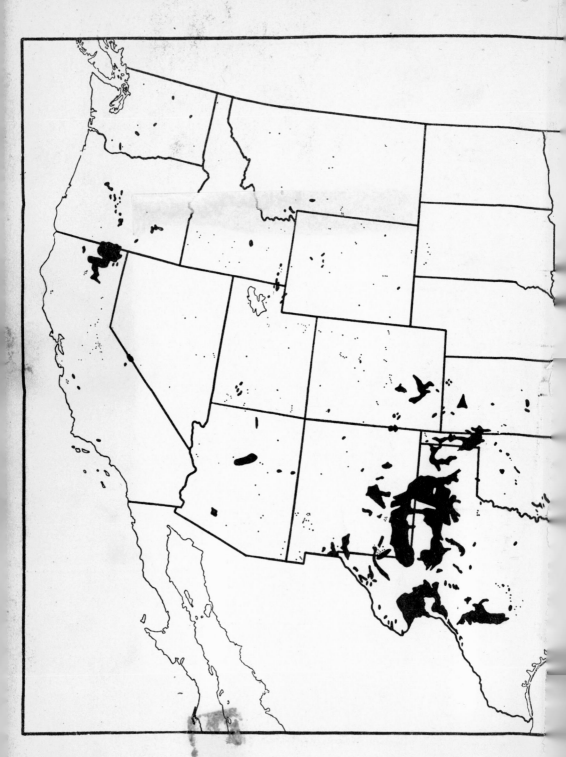